100 Years of the American Female from Harper's Bazaar

HARPER'S BAZAAR

100 years
of the
American
female
the sumptuous
the expensive
the precious
the moneyed
the luxe
the tasteful
the opulent
and the
amusing
woman
from Bazaar
edited by
Jane Trahey

Random House
New York

Acknowledgments

Literally dozens of people work on a book of this nature. For me, special acknowledgment and appreciation go to the following people who gave their valuable time and energies. To Jean Chiesa, Executive Editor of *Harper's Bazaar* and to Alice Morris, Literary Editor of *Harper's Bazaar*. To Richard Whittemore of Hearst for his companionable cooperation, and to Earl Butler, who helped me lift, tote, type, read, compile. To my editor at Random House, Paul Lapolla, and especially to Sally Kovalchick of Random House, whose bloodhound persistence won over every obstacle. To Robert Giusti, who designed the book, to Henry Wolf, who designed the jacket, and to Jo Gilberg, who saw the book through production. But there is no thank you grand enough for Nancy White, Editor of *Harper's Bazaar,* who gave me such large chunks of time in her busy schedule. For her good humor and for the pure joy of working with her, I am very grateful indeed.

FIRST PRINTING

© Copyright, 1913 through 1967, by Hearst Corporation

Library of Congress catalog card number: 67-22634

Designed by Robert Giusti

Contents

Introduction

If for a moment I had calculated mathematically, I doubt if I ever would have edited the 100 years of *Bazaar*. I just started reading a bit here and a bit there and found myself "hooked." Had I ever counted or multiplied or conjectured or even had a glimpse of the material in one room at one time, I should have quickly forgotten the whole project. For if you take a magazine that was a weekly, as *Bazaar* was for its first thirty years or so, and multiply an average of twenty pages per issue by fifty-two weeks and then by thirty years, you begin to get the picture. Then figure 150 pages monthly for the next twenty years, 175 pages for the next two decades and 200 pages per issue for the remainder. New or old math, you really do come up with considerable reading material.

Of course, no one told me I had to read *all* the articles on the Colonial Servant Problem or all about Mrs. Lincoln's highly irregular clothes budget, or *all* the advertising, but I defy anyone who likes to read, or to laugh, to skip a page called *What Lillian Russell Says About Fibre Chamois Cloth* or to miss a snobbish Jello advertisement of the Twenties that said: *Voyez comme il est facilement apprêté.*

The more I read, the more I envisioned Random House issuing a set of volumes pared down to 200,000 pages—each purchase delivered by truck right to one's door. For if I went for just the pure fashion, modes and mores, I was certain to be unfair to the literary heritage and splendor that *Bazaar* offered from its first issue to today. After all, it wasn't every weekly that ran a Charles Dickens–Wilkie Collins mystery with each author miming the style of the other, so that each Saturday readers placed wagers on who wrote what.

If I channeled in on Graphics (and most certainly I could not go wrong here as *Bazaar*'s leadership in Art and Art Direction from the days of Erté to Brodovitch, from Henry Wolf to Marvin Israel to Ruth Ansel and Bea Feitler are unparalleled), I would edit a book that included such photogenius names as Eugene Atget, Baron de Meyer, Munkacsi (the man who made fashion move), Cartier-Bresson, Man Ray, Hoyningen-Huene and Louise Dahl-Wolfe. My book could come up to date with the new school of Saul Leiter, Sokolsky, Hiro, Moore, and Sieff—the school Richard Avedon rules as undisputed leader. In fact, I could do a very handsome book of just Avedon photographs that ran in *Bazaar* for fifteen years. With this kind of book, I could throw in for encores such delights to the eye as Erté, Steinmetz, Luza, Vertès, Cocteau, Lichtenstein, Steinberg, Denziger, and Brunetta drawings.

But if I did this then I would most certainly have to give up Jane Bowles' *Camp Cataract* and Flannery O'Connor's *Good Country People* and Honor Tracy's *Blossom Viewing* and Sigrid Undset and Edith Sitwell and Mary McCarthy and Maria Dermoût and Susan Sontag—and pity then, no one but me and Henry Sell and Anita Loos would know that Lorelei of *Gentlemen Prefer Blondes* fame had a baby in *Bazaar* long after the story officially ended for the world.

I could make a delicious banquet on Diets—from 1870, when a diet called *Removing Flesh* ran (certainly the most honest "moniker" I have heard applied to the subject), to the famous *Nine Day Wonder Diet* that millions of women swear by. I could begin this diet book with a gem of a poem Ogden Nash did for *Bazaar's* beauty editor called *"I Can't Have a Martini Dear but You Take One . . . or . . . Are You Going to Sit There Guzzling All Night?"*

There could be a sizable book just on *The Beginning of American Fashion*. Certainly there could be a book on *The Movie-Star Influence on Fashion*. Also, a slim, handsome volume on *Famous Models of Our Time* could be edited. Any one of them was possible, as I winnowed and selected out the thousands of pages and pictures. For *Bazaar* was and is and will probably always be a marketplace for the discovery of the new and intriguing, a happy ambiance for the lunatic fringe, the unusual, the creative. For it was that special capacity of its editors all through its hundred years—the ability to scold female inebriates and still report on Carry Nation, to provide sewing instructions for an old lady's kerchief and report on the Inaugural Ball of President Hayes—that has always made *Bazaar* the magazine of restless women. For what *Bazaar* discovered that looked novel, strange, and different, usually became the byword, the accepted, the fashion, and eventually, the nostalgic and the remembered.

So the hardest part begins—how to get the "pot" and keep the "pourri." I know all too well that the fashion devotees will miss many things and the photo-buffs will find I'm shy here and there something they remember and the highly literates will most certainly wonder how I could skip all the gentlemen who wrote for *Bazaar,* including such illustrious names as Truman Capote, Ernest Hemingway, John Steinbeck, Thomas Hardy and a list too number-ous to mention. But the truth is that 320 pages is just that and no more.

What I picked from this torrent of evocative and provocative material is revealed in the title of the book: 100 Years of the sumptuous, the expensive, the precious, the moneyed, the luxe, the tasteful, the opulent, and the amusing American female from *Bazaar*.

It's about women. What they wrote. What they did. It includes snippets of their art, a sampling from their literature, a flash of photos, a cross section of fashions and the designers who made them happen. It is *Bazaar*. These 320 pages, then, are what the affluent female in America since 1867 saw, wrote, dreamed, devoured, dieted on, feasted on, lived in, fought for, and wore for a hundred years.

It was quite a century!

Jane Trahey
May 1967

bigger than ever. Spectacular lights burn brightly, like Judy Garland, Audrey Hepburn, Anna Magnani. Grace Kelly gives it all up for a Kingdom. Balenciaga, the master, better than ever. Bikinis hit the beach. Jacques Fath very much in. Topolski sketches Kay Kendall for *Bazaar*. Avedon creates the model of the Fifties, Suzy Parker. Cecil Beaton photographs Marilyn Monroe and writes about her. Marianne Moore, Merman and Grandma Moses make news. And right around the corner is a place called Canaveral.

Space and the Sixties | 260

The first human space traveler goes into orbit. President Kennedy is assassinated. It's at last the era of civil rights. Pop Art. Pop music, underground movies. The designers of the Sixties are still from France, Givenchy, Courrèges and Saint Laurent. Sassoon cuts hair as it hasn't been cut since the Twenties and pants come in as they haven't come in since the Twenties. Jacqueline Kennedy is the most familiar face of the decade. *Bazaar*'s April '65 space issue rocks the land, and begins the era of mods and moon clothes. Skirts shorter than the Twenties. The big dance, the Frug. The big song, "Winchester Cathedral." The big stars, Julie Christie, Barbra Streisand. What next, what's new?

Literary Supplement

VIII

Foreword

I cannot help but believe that the many distinguished, brilliant and powerful spirits that hover over the editor's chair, who are responsible for *Bazaar*'s heritage and its tradition, would not join in my delight in this volume.

I have long wished that Jane Trahey would become an editor of the magazine. Now, in part, my wish has come true—for in these pages she is editor-in-chief of the whole wild, wonderful, incredible first hundred years of *Harper's Bazaar*.

This book came into being because Jane, a devoted and lifelong friend of *Harper's Bazaar*, believed. She believed she could encompass the full century of our magazine. Jane believed and I doubted. Not because the task was prodigious—that was obvious. I doubted because I felt *Harper's Bazaar* could not be contained between the two covers of any single book, no matter the number of pages.

What should be remembered of *Harper's Bazaar*'s richness, its distinction, its flamboyance, its impertinence, its nostalgia, its daring, its whims and wisdom? What forgotten? How could any editor or group of editors who had lived such a small fraction of *Harper's Bazaar*'s history pull it off?

Well, Jane has. The countless hours and months, the more than three years she spent at her work, are only a portion of what has made this book possible. The larger portion of this effort I can only describe as true love. For without a real love for *Harper's Bazaar*, no one could have had the discernment, the analytic eye, the critical taste, the wit of juxtaposition to glean from ten decades of material not just what is the best of *Bazaar*, but what *Bazaar is*.

Although I had known Jane slightly before I joined *Harper's Bazaar*, it was the magazine that cemented our friendship. I had been trying to put into words, as any new editor always must, what I believed *Bazaar* really stood for. What sort of magazine was it? What made it great? Jane jogged my thoughts, goaded me, needled, prodded, until I had put down on paper what I considered the priceless ingredients of the magazine which I had that month come to edit. Those words, now some nine years old, are: authority, awareness, wit, spirit, surprise, curiosity, intelligence, timing, food for thought, vitality, balance and youth. They apply, as they ought, to this book.

Nancy White
Editor-in-Chief
Harper's Bazaar
April, 1967

Just what sort of reception the new weekly, Harper's Bazar, *would receive must have caused some speculation at* Harper's Weekly. *Fletcher Harper quietly took over the task of running the magazine and post-haste appointed Mary L. Booth as its first female editor. It was the very same year Maximilian was executed by Juárez and Canada was established and Alaska was sold to the United States for $7,000,000. Today a single perfume company might go on the market for far more.*

America had just finished the Civil War, a war that had plummeted women into many positions that had previously been taboo for them. The Bazar *aimed at the more educated, affluent woman and quite possibly was the spark the nation needed to start a hundred years' war for female freedom.*

Vol. 1—No. 1   November 2, 1867

Harper's Bazar

"A Repository of Fashion, Pleasure, and Instruction."

THE Publishers have just commenced the issue of *Harper's Bazar*, a Weekly Illustrated Family Journal, devoted to Fashion and Home Literature. Their aim is twofold: to supply the existing need of a Weekly Fashion Newspaper, and to combine therewith a first-class literary journal, which will be indispensable to every household.

It is the first Weekly Journal of Fashion ever published in the United States. The Publishers have made arrangements, at great cost, with the most celebrated of the Fashion Papers of Europe, so that henceforth the fashions will appear in *Harper's Bazar* simultaneously with their publication in Paris.

Harper's Bazar, besides being the leading Fashion Journal in this country, will also aim to present before its readers the very best specimens of Household Literature. It will contain original and selected Serial Stories, Poetry, Novelettes, Articles on the Topics of the Day (excluding Politics), on Books, Art, Morals, Familiar Science, Education, Amusements, Hygiene, Etiquette, Housekeeping, Gardening, with Home and Foreign Gossip. No subject of household interest will be excluded from its columns.

"Unquestionably the best work of the kind in the World."

Harper's Bazar.

A Repository of Fashion, Pleasure, and Instruction.

Vol. I.—No. 1.]   NEW YORK, SATURDAY, NOVEMBER 2, 1867.   [SINGLE COPIES TEN CENTS.
[$4.00 PER YEAR IN ADVANCE.

Entered according to Act of Congress, in the Year 1867, by Harper & Brothers, in the Clerk's Office of the District Court for the Southern District of New York.

FALL BONNETS.—Fig. 1, Fanchon.—Fig. 2, Catalane.—Fig. 3, Marie Antoinette.—Fig. 4, Trianon.—[See next Page.]

BRIDAL TOILETS.—[See next Page.]

LADIES AT WORK

ARTIFICIAL FLOWER MAKERS

HOOP-SKIRT MAKER

PAPER BOX MAKER

PREPARING CANDIES

2

ENVELOPE MAKER

UMBRELLA MAKERS

TYPE SETTERS

PHOTOGRAPH MOUNTERS

SILVER BURNISHERS

PAPER COLLAR MAKER

3

THE FLIRT.

THE flirt is ubiquitous. There is no nation and no habitable spot of *terra firma* under the sun where she does not spread her snares and weave her spells. It is not necessary for the accomplishment of her vocation that she should be beautiful, or wise, or cultivated, or even well-bred. We find her among the ignorant, the unpolished, and the foolish virgins perhaps oftener than elsewhere. Her type doubtless exists among savage tribes, in the camp of the Comanches, and flourishes no better in the tropic than in the temperate zones. The one quality which seems necessary for her complete success is youth, though the old flirt does not yet share the extinction of the dodo, to be sure. The desire to please, with which nature has endowed us all, is surely an innocent and laudable emotion; but in the heart of the flirt it has become exaggerated into the wish to exact the admiration and attention of every man within her radius of vision. Her chief object in life is to decoy certain of the sterner sex into a declaration of love, and then to retreat into the asylum of friendship. She counts her offers of marriage as the Pawnee counts his scalps, and it makes small odds to her whether she trespasses upon the rights of other women or no. But let her not plume herself upon her acquirements and attractions, since every woman has the making of a flirt in her, if she would condescend to the task, which is alike degrading to sensibility and sense.

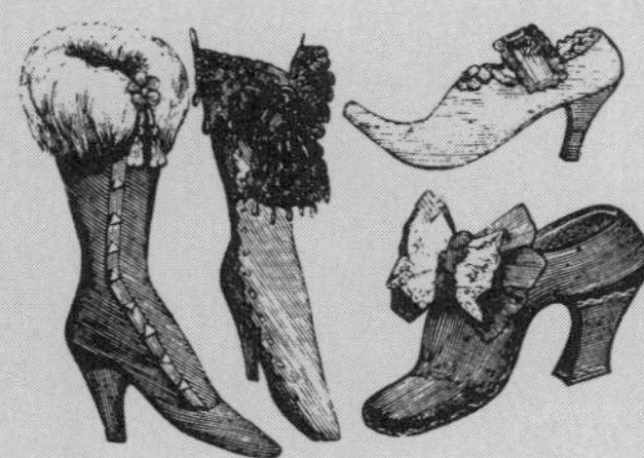

MASCULINE WOMEN.

A FAMOUS divine lately deplored the enlarging opportunities of education offered to women as tending to make them masculine. The finest charm of woman, he thought, would have departed with her ability to "dispense with the protecting and sustaining care of man." This statement seems to mean, if it mean anything, that the woman who can earn her own livelihood is less womanly than her sister who can not.

Those distinctively masculine qualities which enable man to exercise his "protecting and sustaining care" over woman, and which, by inference, are undesirable for her, are courage, energy, ambition, perseverance, industry, probity, and that capacity to adapt means to ends which results from good business training. But what one of these attributes is woman more charming without? Is courage an unfeminine possession? In a crowded mountain hotel, last summer, we knew a young lady to sit up all night, faint with terror because she had seen a house spider run across her bed, and dared not search for the intruder. Another very pretty girl refused to take a single walk, while the forests were in their fullest splendor, because vague rumors of a small garter-snake having been seen a mile or two away peopled the wood with monsters. In all casualties by land or sea more women perish proportionately than men, not so much by reason of their physical weakness as of their cowardice and lack of self-control. But was GRACE DARLING ever called unfeminine, or CATHERINE DOUGLAS, or LUCY HUTCHINSON? Is Elfrida of the blue eyes ever more charming or maidenly modest than when, by her brave self-possession, she saves her lover from an awful death? If our girls are to skate, swim, row, ride, travel, as boys do, they must learn to face danger as boys do, and fortunately the practice teaches them.

Nor are the masculine qualities which command business success to be deprecated in daughters more than in sons. The girls who, every year, without training and without experience, are suddenly called on to earn their own bread; the widows left destitute, or too ignorant of affairs to secure or administer wisely the residue of property fairly theirs, and incapable of earning more; the uninteresting elderly women without kindred to bestow the reluctant hospitality due the "poor relation," without the gift of making friends, or the skill to make a fortune—it is the voice of these which pronounces the cultivation of those masculine qualities whose precipitate, so to speak, is a clear common-sense and aptitude for business, to be the most obvious "right" for which women should plead.

PRESIDENT AND MRS. HAYES.

THE fine full-length portraits of our new President and his charming wife which appear in this week's issue are copied from pictures taken, just before the inauguration, by the skillful photographer, Mr. James Landy, of Cincinnati, and are therefore to be relied on as recent and faithful likenesses of the personages who are destined, for the coming four years, to take rank as the first gentleman and lady of the land.

During the past year all the facts relating to President Hayes's career and family have been so often reiterated that it would be superfluous to repeat them here. We will only say that he is now in his fifty-fifth year, the golden prime of life, a tall, stalwart man, measuring 5 feet 11 inches, and weighing 198 pounds, with a frank blue eye, luxuriant auburn hair and beard, slightly tinged with gray, and a genial, winning manner, which at once inspires confidence. In 1852 he married Miss Lucy Ware Webb, the daughter of Dr. James Webb and Maria Cook, of Chilicothe, and celebrates this year his silver wedding day. Mrs. Hayes is a graceful and accomplished lady, with a pleasing face, regular features, and a peculiarly expressive mouth. She has a *petite* but well-developed figure, 5 feet 4½ inches in height, with dark eyes and dark brown hair, which she arranges in a simple fashion, brushed low over her forehead, without crimps, and fastened in a knot, with a comb, at the back of her head. She dresses richly but plainly, and never wears low corsages. At the inauguration she was attired in an elegant black silk dress, trimmed with velvet and Valenciennes lace, a camel's-hair shawl, black velvet bonnet with a white feather and white flowers, and white kid gloves. Her only jewelry was a handsome gold pin confining a knot of rich lace at the throat. It is probable that she will set an example of good taste and quiet elegance which will do credit to her high position, and which, it is trusted, will be followed by the ladies of the republican court.

FAMILY LIVING ON $500 A YEAR. BY JULIET CORSON. LVI.

MANY practical house-keepers who are interested in economical experiments in a general way do not always believe that they can be successfully undertaken in their own households. They may be sufficiently liberal-minded to conceive the possibility of success under conditions more favorable than they can command; but they are inclined to doubt the feasibility of applying such efforts to ordinary house-keeping, the chief objection being the time required, which they may not be disposed to devote to mere experiment. It may be true that many *Bazar* readers who live the abnormally full life of popular city people will defer testing some of our proposed methods until the ideal suitable hour arrives, which never does come. On the other hand, we have the satisfaction of knowing that numbers do endeavor to carry out the entire scheme here outlined. For just this reason considerable space has been given to some operations which are far from inviting to any housewife less than enthusiastic and thorough. Were these most admirable of their kind numbered only by the tens, it would still be worth our best efforts to clearly show them the way to every successful issue of the economic problem.

As we tried to prove in our earliest articles, the proper use of such usually disdained portions of food as fat and bone assumes importance in this connection. The experiments of Dr. Edward Smith with bones were cited to instance their possible food value; these experiments were undertaken at the command of the English government, and were exhaustive enough to prove that three and a half pounds of mixed bones contain as much heat food as one pound of meat, and six pounds of bones as much flesh food as a pound of meat. As none of the substance of the bones can be eaten except the small quantity of marrow they yield during cooking, two things are needed in treating them, *i.e.*, a vehicle for the extraction of their nutriment, the simplest being water, and the addition of such food elements as will afford the substance needed to meet the requirements of nutrition; these may be chosen from the great variety of vegetables or from the numerous cereals. In order fully to extract all the nutritious substance from bones they must be broken small, and boiled steadily in water for at least nine hours; the result will be a gelatinous broth, the flavor of which depends upon its seasoning, and its capacity for satisfying hunger upon the solid vegetables or cereals added to it; the broth alone, seasoned and drank, would nourish a man relatively as beef broth does, according to the quantity of bones from which it is made.

There should always be water enough to cover the bones, a quart to a pound being the maximum quantity; and at the finish the broth should be boiled down to one-sixth the first quantity of water; if a quart has been allowed for each pound, the proportion of solid food added should be the same required for ordinary broth equal in quantity to this sixth of the first amount. The round bones of the legs, which contain marrow, are much more nutritious than the flat bones of steaks and ribs or the bones of the head. The bones of beef are relatively larger and more nutritious than those of sheep and pigs; the proportion of bone in the entire leg of beef is from one-third to one-half, the best-fed beef having relatively more flesh; the head gives about one-half its weight in bones; the neck, shoulder, and thin end of ribs about one-tenth, and the choice cut from one-sixth to one-tenth; the average weight of bone in the ordinary best cuts of all kinds of meat is about one-tenth the whole.

WOMEN AND MEN. SEX IN DIET.

THERE are certain simple and elementary bits of nonsense which reappear at intervals with the certainty of measles or small-pox, and this sometimes in the very families of physicians. One of these is the theory that whereas men and women differ in important respects, there must therefore be an entire difference in their mode of education. The best way to look at this is by applying it first on the plane of physical structure. This, for instance, would be the line of argument: Boys eat beef and bread; therefore, obviously, girls should not. Yet the moment girls accept this inference and begin living on caramels and ice-cream, the physicians are the first to complain. They point out, justly enough, that while the functions of the sexes are in some important respects different, yet there are many more points in which they are identical; the alimentary and digestive processes, for instance, are the same. We do not digest as men or women, distinctively; we digest as human beings; and so it is with nine-tenths of what physiology includes.

THE BANG.

IT is only a few years since the bang was unknown amongst us, and although it has achieved popularity, we are notified that the day of its glory is passed, that its renown is on the wane, and that we must prepare to return to sweet simplicity and severe, unmitigated primness.

"From thee how shall we part?"

Girls who were almost plain have become pretty under its *régime;* faces past their first bloom have borrowed something youthful from its kindly spell; it has softened the most severe outlines; it covers a multitude of unwelcome wrinkles. Shall we be content to surrender it without a murmur? Will the pretty girl be glad to drop her mask and resume her native homeliness? Will the eye that has been used to the line of beauty be pleased with precision? To be sure, there are some faces upon which a bang would seem like an intrusion, but to most of us it has become dear as the apple of our eye. What hopelessly intellectual foreheads will emerge from seclusion when the flat has gone forth! what disclosure of waning locks which the crimp mercifully concealed! And what shall we do with the shorn tresses before they have time to grow in grace? how shall we coax them to abandon the kink we have been to such trouble to invoke?

PALMISTRY.

SINCE palmistry became a social amusement people have reason to be careful of the inside of their hands, written over with this line and with that, lest they be seized upon and be read to their dismay, the survey of the lines there puffing them up with conceit of themselves, or putting them to open shame in the face of folk. "I would not trust out of sight the best friend I had in the world," said, recently, an enthusiastic prophet of the art, "if I found the line of truth did not join the line of life before leaving the hand!" And if she were justified in her statement, what complications and perplexities might ensue to the adherents of the art! The next thing in the advance of the matter might be that no lover would propose to the damsel who had filled his eye and touched his heart, until he had looked at her wrists and certified to himself the absence of the bracelet of command there, lest he should see before him the fate of Dame Partlet's mate. Perhaps, too, the young lady's father would find it necessary to compare the right hand of her lover with his left when he had stammered his wishes into the paternal ear, and thus discover what traits he had developed in his right hand by scanning the original lines in his left one, what good tendencies had increased, if any, and what evil ones had been suppressed in his growth, and if, in short, he had desirable traits and would make a good husband. The mother-in-law-to-be may also think fit to examine the line of life of the proposed bride of her son, and see if it be crossed by the mark of serious illnesses, or otherwise, in order to judge if it is best for her son to encumber himself with a sickly wife; or she may even look for the stars that signify the number of marriages this young woman is to contract, that she may thus forecast her son's chances of long living. We have heard that it is a custom in our centres of criminal control to take impressions of the ball of the thumb of criminals, each thumb differing from the other in its tale of crime or character. And if this thing goes on, and it becomes an acknowledged fact that we carry about with us a complete police-report description and category of our traits, it will befit those of us conscious of any want of moral rectitude, or only of the absence of immediate perfection, to wear not merely gloves, but mittens, if we do not want our lapses and shortcomings proclaimed to the world about us.

WOMEN IN BUSINESS.

IT is not altogether the fault of women, probably, that the workers among them are looked at by society with a glance of pity. Even the liberal thinkers who concede their right to labor are too apt to praise their success with an air of abatement, as who should say, "They do remarkably well under the circumstances; but alack the circumstances that compel them to toil!"

Perhaps, however, we should rather wonder that this disrespect toward industry is not greater, than that it is so great. How much of it is due to the popular theology which for so many ages was supposed to regard labor as a curse, and so a degradation, is not clear. Some part is our inheritance from the Greek and Roman civilizations. The airy Hellene, who loved leisure for art, philosophy, politics, and the newest news, was content to live simply while his slaves did all his work. Labor was the badge of the servile class. In Bœotia a man who engaged in commerce made himself ineligible to office for ten years. The liberal Plato declared that the trade of a shop-keeper, being a degradation to a citizen, ought to be punished as a crime. Aristotle, though the defender and mouth-piece of the middle classes, thought that in a perfect state no citizen should exercise any mechanical art. Rome, from different motives, practically adopted the Greek habit. Cicero agreed with Xenophon in adopting Aristotle's notion. Augustus condemned to death a Senator found guilty of debasing his rank by taking part in a manufacture.

The feudal system fostered this feeling, and forbade the "gentleman" to do any thing useful. It is but lately that any employment, save that which the army and the church offered, was opened to younger sons in England. Byron thought that his rank compelled him haughtily to return his publisher's check, though an execution was in his house. Even Walter Scott made a half apology for selling "Marmion."

That eminent social philosopher, Mr. George Fitz-Boodle, expected the gratitude of the world for his invention of two new professions for gentlemen, one of them being that of aesthetic auctioneer, and the other superintendent of artistic dining. The fashionable world of London lately felt a shiver creep down its aristocratic back at the news that a duke's son and a princess's brother-in-law had gone into trade.

Our colonial position, our peculiar history, and Necessity, that most radical of reformers, broke down this narrow prejudice in America. Men of all ranks found themselves free to work at whatever business they chose. All the prizes of social and political life were within reach of the tradesman or artisan. But it was inevitable that women should wait for a like liberty, since they have been in all ages practically a servile class, not demanding opportunities withheld.

Now, however, that the complex character of modern society makes it necessary to utilize their capacity, employment after employment has claimed them, until it is easier to count the few industries still refusing their help than the many which exact it. But society is slow-going, and hates innovations. It is only when a revolution is accomplished, and the new order of things is becoming an old order, with promise of stability, that society accepts the fact. If it took generations, dynasties, wars, the subversion of whole civilizations, to make work honorable for men, we ought not to be chagrined that women encounter some opposition, pity, or surprise from the thoughtless when they too claim a right to labor.

Indeed, this reform has advanced in public favor with notable swiftness. And it may not be too much to say that but one obstacle can long delay the recognition of the fact that capacity is of no sex, and that labor, in and of itself, is honorable. This obstacle is the tendency of women themselves to depreciate their own callings. When the saleswoman shall think as well of herself for being a saleswoman as the salesman thinks well of himself for being a salesman; when the female book-keeper takes the same pride in her day-books and ledgers that her brother would take, honoring her business as sincerely, and equally content to make it her life-long occupation, if that be her duty; when the female teacher shall refuse to make teaching a makeshift; when all working-women shall be willing to consider their work final, if need be, and at least always dignified, always worthy of their best service—the world will cheerfully accept them and their industry at their own valuation.

Not that marriage is to be deprecated or postponed to a mean prudence. It is only marriage as an escape from labor, marriage as a selfish, loveless convenience, marriage as a dishonest bargain, that is unlovely. And by honorable toil women may avoid that dishonorable ease.

FEMALE INEBRIATES.

ARTICLES of a highly sensational character have, from time to time, appeared in various newspapers and magazines purporting to give both startling and truthful details of drunkenness amongst women, especially those of the upper classes. Startling these statements certainly have been, but far from truthful save in a few facts already well known. The so-called "ladies' club-houses" and "ladies' gambling parlors," shielded behind ostensible millinery, dressmaking, and like establishments, are simply the height of absurdity, and exist only in the morbid imaginations of the writers who give them, and are intended solely for the delectation of lovers of the sensational.

Female inebriates there certainly are, and to be found amongst all classes, from the poor, weary, scantily clad, gin-drinking washer-woman, to the wealthy, indolent, wine-drinking merchant's wife. Between the two there are numerous gradations both as regards social position and degree of inebriety. The dangers that surround the women of the present day, and which may unconsciously lead them into the habitual use or abuse of stimulants as well as narcotics, are far greater than they were in former times, and are daily upon the increase.

The now common custom of resorting to the use of spirits in times of pleasure, as well as for the relief of pain and despondency, is fraught with dangers but little appreciated by the average individual. That the custom of the free use of stimulants is upon the increase amongst women, especially in our larger cities, is easily demonstrated. A cursory visit to any popular restaurant will result in the visitors seeing ladies both alone, in parties, and with and without escorts, who ten years ago would not have tasted an alcoholic beverage of any kind, even in their own homes, taking beer, wine, or spirits with their meals, almost as a matter of course, and apparently with no idea that they are doing anything unladylike or unusual.

Beer, and especially bottled beer, has of late years become immensely popular with all classes. Ladies stop at restaurants often with the sole purpose of having a bottle of beer to refresh and invigorate them after a long walk, or when tired from shopping; families take it regularly by the box; boarders have it privately at table or in their rooms; and servants, pitcher or pail in hand, no longer make a secret of their trips to the corner groggery or the avenue beer saloon. Grocers keep it, and sell it to families by the bottle or box. The same sentiment that has made the German style of open-air concert so popular in this country seems at the same time to have brought with it a love for conviviality, and to have popularized the custom of beer-drinking.

Beer has been the entering wedge, and following close upon it has come the more or less free use of spirits. And this was natural and to be expected. One thing almost unconsciously leads to another in matters of this kind, and beer has proved itself a stepping-stone to the use of stronger liquors. Women who formerly would have used spirits only under medical advice, and even then reluctantly, now resort to them without objection and upon the slightest grounds, simply because their previous use of beer seems to have broken the ice. To many a poor wreck the first glass of beer has proven a costly experiment, and will be looked back to as the first step in a career the incidents of which make her shudder.

A NEW DEPARTURE.

IN the last number of HARPER'S BAZAR, issued on June 26, our readers found a beautiful colored fashion drawing, given as a supplement to the paper, and showing in grace of outline, richness of tint, and sheen of fabric an elegant costume for the sea-side made of figured India silk. Any lady who chooses may copy this toilette precisely in every detail, the color scheme giving a certain advantage over the ordinary design in black and white. We intend to follow this initial supplement in color with others equally striking and valuable during the summer and autumn.

—Miss LUCIA ZARATE, a dwarf, exhibiting in London, commands a larger salary than any other woman in England.

—JOHN BRIGHT has discovered a curious resemblance between the hand-writings of VICTOR HUGO and CARLYLE.

—While Miss KATE FIELD was in Providence, Rhode Island, a few days ago, she gave a concert to the patients in the Butler Lunatic Asylum, and had a most enthusiastic audience. Several lunatics are said to have fallen in love with her, and a young lady, who is a capital musician, exclaimed, at the end of the concert, "Miss FIELD has made my back hair stand straight out with ambition!" A very crazy old woman declared, after hearing her sing a song in a foreign language, that she was "the craziest of the lot, and ought to be shut up for three months, with medical attendance."

—SARAH BERNHARDT'S charming hat, of bird-of-paradise and ostrich plumes, with miniature wolves' heads, is described by male critics as looking as though "she had rested her head upon a bed of moss, and upon lifting her head had raised her pillow with it."

THE MILLER'S DAUGHTER.*

Ciro Pinsuti.

It is the mil - ler's daugh - - ter, And she is grown so dear, so dear, That I would be.... the jew - - el That trem - bles in her ear; For hid in ring - lets day and night, I'd touch her neck so warm and white, I'd touch,............... I'd

The Art of Facial Expression
by Anne O'Hagan

Photographed by Sarony.
Miss Beatrice Herford.

how little plasticity, how little elasticity, these features of our possess. Our faces, perhaps, show forth our characters. They seem incapable of intelligibly showing forth our moods. They declare us, it may be, ascetics or *bons-vivants,* shufflers with the truth or candid blunderers, worried mothers or conscientiously vivacious spinsters; but to anything more than broad classifications, as little descriptive as a census report, they seldom attain. When we do see a face over which shift lights and shadows, a face expressive of inner feelings, responsive to outer stimuli, it possesses a fascination greater than that of modelled beauty.

There is one place where we look to see all this disproved—the stage. The art of acting we are almost ready to define, off-hand, as the art of emotional expression by means of face and body.

IN the chorus of sighs over graces which our hurrying generation has been obliged to discard—sighs for the lost art of conversation, for which, so it is alleged, we have substituted slang and chatter; sighs for the lost art of letter-writing, which we are said to have replaced by the staccato brevities of telephonic and telegraphic communication; sighs for the abandoned art of tranquillity which went out with the patience-developing stage-coach—in all this chorus of sighs one hears no moan over the lost art of facial expression. Yet it is an accomplishment which we have either long since lost or have not yet acquired in our creeping advance from the primitive stolidity of the savage.

One has only to spend a half-hour in any place where human beings greatly congregate —in Peacock Alley at the Waldorf, in the Grand Central station, at the theatre, at market, at tea, or at mass-meeting, to realize

Photographed by Sarony.
Miss Elsie Janis.

In 1900, Bazar *became a digest-size book. This diversion on the part of the editors lasted till 1907, when it returned to its more regal size—a size it maintains to this very day.*

THE HEIGHT OF THE NEWPORT SEASON
SOME OF THE SMARTEST GOWNS

Three Literary Recipes

By Kate Douglas Wiggin

Which Show that Authors Know Something About Cookery and Humor

Author of "Rebecca of Sunny-brook Farm," "Mother Carey's Chickens," etc.

BELOVED alike of American girls and grown-ups, Kate Douglas Wiggin is to-day a smiling denial of the old saw that a prophet is not without honor save in his own country. It is just there, in her own country, that this woman, who stands as a favorite author to many of us, is most honored. Not for her books alone, however, is she honored in the town of Hollis, Maine, but for herself. It is here that she spends her summers and she has come to be known as the Lady Bountiful of Hollis. Here, in the hours supposed to be given to recreation, she addresses the Hollis Club, advises the Hollis neighbors, delights them with song and story, and is the moving spirit of any enterprise which has for its object the benefit of the town or its people. Hollis has a Dorcas Society, and each member of the Dorcas Society is an expert cook. The exchange of recipes is a favorite pastime among them. Stimulated by this friendly competition, and to prove that the literary gift and a broad and comprehensive knowledge of cooking can be combined in the same woman, Kate Douglas Wiggin recently evolved the following strictly literary recipes. While they may not help Bazar readers to solve the problems of decreasing the cost of living, it is certain that they will lighten the burden with smiles. The kind of nourishment in a joke is relished by all of us.

Substitute Washington Pie

BEAT twenty-five eggs twenty-five minutes in a quick oven, but reserve the whites of twenty-three. Remove gently and set the pan in the sink, adding two-thirds of a gill of old-fashioned home-made yeast. (If you have neither gill nor yeast in the house substitute a plain china cup without handle and a tablespoonful of washing soda.) When passing through the kitchen subsequently, remember the mixture and place it on the ice. (If you have no ice, in the cellar.) Stir in a blue bowl (or a yellow bowl if more convenient) a package of cornstarch and two boxes of gelatine. (If that cannot easily be procured, use flour and Irish moss.) If the cake still seems too thin to roll out, add a quart of lightly sifted flour. (Indian meal will answer if the flour barrel is low.) Bake slowly, trying every five minutes with a clean broom-straw. (In case you are out of broom-straws the little finger of the right hand will do.)

Vegetable Filling for Same

BEAT the whites of your twenty-three eggs until you can turn the platter upside down and count ten. Remove the eggs from the floor and stir in:

One clove of garlic (one ring of onion will produce about the same effect).

One-eighth of an ounce minced string-beans (or pea pods).

One saltspoon of horseradish (or ginger).

Two tablespoons of Infant's Food (or malted milk).

One-half cup grated cheese (apple sauce is a good substitute).

Split the cake as many times as its height seems to suggest and insert the filling between the layers. This recipe keeps well and lasts a long time.

Novelty Cake

THREE Plymouth Rock hen's eggs.
Three turkey's eggs.
Three duck's eggs.
Beat separately, and never under any circumstances allow them to come together. Beat them earnestly, until they can stand alone or you cannot.
Butter size of a gold thimble.
One cup of lard.
One cup of suet.
One cup of buttermilk.
One cup of maple syrup (the kind procured from trees).
One cup of self-raising buckwheat flour.
One cup of oatmeal.
One and one-half cups of talcum powder.
Enough soda to insure that golden-brown color so often secured by young housekeepers, but not enough to settle in dark spots. You have already a substantial novelty here, but if you will add a dust of catnip and a dash of peppermint, vanilla, and witch-hazel, you will have a cake that can be distinguished from any other, even with the eyes closed. Set this mixture (which is either a thin batter or a stiff dough, as it happens) well out of reach of the cat, until it has thoroughly made up its mind what it will be. Meantime, take a white lisle-thread glove or the top of a baby's stocking; wash and boil. When thoroughly dry, butter with it a dozen pop-over cups. Give the mixture an extra stir at the last moment. In cold weather the maple syrup sometimes refuses to mix with the talcum powder, and the suet does not combine easily with the oatmeal. The last thing, add six tablespoonfuls of watermelon seeds, which give a handsome finish. They are not edible, but when eating the cake each person can dispose of his seeds in some genteel and unostentatious way.

Large Family Bread

A LITTLE soda measured in a silver spoon; two-thirds and a half as much again cream of tartar. If the weather is hot simply reverse the quantities and say nothing to the neighbors.

One quart of Graham flour.
One quart of white flour.
One quart of Indian meal, in the order named.
One cup new milch cow's milk.
One cup farrow cow's milk.
One cup ordinary milk; sweet if sweet, sour if it has turned.

Bathe the hands carefully and plunge them into the mixture, kneading it vigorously for an hour, being careful to stand in the draught of an open window all the time.
Grease the pans well with cocoa butter or beeswax.
Pour in the mixture if soft enough; crowd or push it in if it resists force, as it sometimes does with an inexperienced cook.
Never allow the fire to go out when bread is baking, as it often spoils it.
Remove the pans when, according to your best judgment, the bread is done, and never ask advice, as it is always unsettling.
Keep the loaves in a tin cake-box under the spare-room bed, where the children can run and get a slice whenever disposed.

This recipe sometimes cures the bad habit of eating between meals.

A WINTER'S READING

WHAT shall a young girl read?
When she begins to show a strong appetite for novels and short stories she is apt to meet with very little encouragement from the rest of the family. She might better "do something useful, practise, sew—anything rather than hang over a silly novel." But the point is that it should not be a silly novel.

Mothers who understand that this craving for novel-reading is the girl's natural desire to know something about the world opening before her realize that here is the opportunity to give her the best reading, to broaden and train her mind, and to put her in the way of one of the greatest enjoyments life has to offer—the companionship of the best minds of the past and present.

One advice is to turn the eager reader loose in a good library to browse in freedom, but most of us are apt to have haphazard libraries, of which a good part is the choice of our friends who presented the books, and another part, even though it may be distinctly classic, may as well not be read by the too "young person."

As to giving "the best," the discouraging thing is that people will quarrel and disagree about the "best," and also that the "young person" who is thirsting for a novel may not be so ready to devour it served too classically or in hexameters.

A simple advice is to recommend the sort of book you used to close yourself at sixteen with a sigh, wishing that there were some hundred pages more; an absorbing adventure, a fascinating love-story, a descriptive story of the kind that transports you from place and hour, and makes you read long into the blind-man's holiday, forgetting lamps and eyesight. When such a story is written by a hand that handles a pen well, and is guided by a heart which understands other human hearts, you need not fear the company in which you leave your daughter for hours at a time. The hours will be far from wasted.

NOVELS.

THACKERAY: Pendennis, The Newcomes.
DICKENS: David Copperfield, Nicholas Nickleby, The Old Curiosity Shop, The Pickwick Papers, Dombey and Son.
STEVENSON: Kidnapped, David Balfour.
BLACKMORE: Lorna Doone.
SCOTT: Ivanhoe, Kenilworth.
GOLDSMITH: The Vicar of Wakefield.
MRS. GASKELL: Cranford, Mary Barton.
BRONTË, CHARLOTTE: Jane Eyre, Shirley.
BRONTË, EMILY: Wuthering Heights.
JANE AUSTEN: Pride and Prejudice.
DR. BROWN: Rab and His Friends.
HENRY JAMES: Daisy Miller.
KIPLING: The Jungle Books (I. and II.), Wee Willie Winkie and Other Stories, The Brushwood Boy, Captains Courageous, The Day's Work.
CHARLES READE: Christie Johnstone.
WASHINGTON IRVING: The Sketch Book.
EDWARD E. HALE: The Man without a Country.
HARRIET BEECHER STOWE: Uncle Tom's Cabin.
LOUISA ALCOTT: Little Women.
HOWELLS: The Rise of Silas Lapham, The Lady of the Aroostook.
STOCKTON: Rudder Grange, The Casting Away of Mrs. Lecks and Mrs. Aleshine.
OLIVER WENDELL HOLMES: The Autocrat of the Breakfast Table.
HAWTHORNE: The Marble Faun, The House of the Seven Gables.
CHARLES DUDLEY WARNER: A Little Journey in the World, The Golden House, That Fortune (to be read in this order).
CURTIS: Prue and I.
MARY WILKINS: Pembroke, A New England Nun and Other Stories.
COOPER: The Spy.
JAMES LANE ALLEN: The Kentucky Cardinal.

BALZAC: Eugénie Grandet.
DUMAS père: The Three Musketeers.
OCTAVE FEUILLET: The Romance of a Poor Young Man.
HALÉVY: The Abbé Constantin.
VICTOR HUGO: Notre Dame of Paris.
MAARTEN MAARTENS: God's Fool, The Greater Glory.
CERVANTES: Don Quixote.
FREITAG: Debit and Credit.
MARLITT, E.: Gold Else, The Old Mamsell's Secret.
FREDERIKA BREMER: The Neighbors, The Home.
BJÖRNSTJERNE BJÖRNSON: Arne.
DE LA MOTTE FOUQUÉ: Undine.
MÜNCHHAUSEN's Tales.

HISTORICAL NOVELS

KINGSLEY: Hypatia.
WALLACE, LEWIS: Ben-Hur.
GEORGE EHERS: Uarda, Homo Sum, Au Egyptian Princess.
BULWER: The Last Days of Pompeii.

MYTHOLOGY

KINGSLEY: Heroes of Greece.
HAWTHORNE: Wonder-book, Tanglewood Tales.
LANIER: Boys' King Arthur, Boys' Mabinogion, Boys' Froissart.

POETRY

SCOTT: The Lady of the Lake.
LORD LYTTON: Lucille.
TEGNER: Frithjofs Saga.
R. L. STEVENSON: A Child's Garden of Verses, Poems and Ballads.
TENNYSON.
LONGFELLOW.
HEINE: Book of Songs.
GOETHE—SCHILLER: Selected Poems.

FOR THE GIRL WHO ENJOYS ESSAYS AND WISE SAYINGS.

MARCUS AURELIUS: The Thoughts of the Emperor Marcus Aurelius.
PASCAL: Thoughts.
EMERSON: Conduct of Life, Society and Solitude.
MAETERLINCK: The Treasure of the Humble.

Individuality in Dress

The Secret of the Well-dressed Woman

By Paul Poiret

THE art of dressing is an art as complex and elusive as all the others. It, too, has its principles and traditions, known only to persons of taste because they harmonize with their inmost feelings. This art has little in common with money. The woman whose resources are limited has no more cause for being dowdily dressed than the woman who is rich has reason to believe she is beautifully gowned. Except in so far as money can procure the services of a good dressmaker, of an artist who can judge his customer's style and garb her accordingly, the wealthy woman stands no better chances of being correctly dressed than the woman who must turn every penny before spending it.

The contrary is very often true. Whereas the rich woman can satisfy her least caprice in a most haphazard fashion, the woman of average means, simply because she is actually forced to *think* about her wardrobe, is more apt to realize what is suitable to her and what is not. She learns how to choose and what to select. She acquires the art of dressing well.

And it is not an easy art to acquire. It demands a certain amount of intelligence, certain gifts, some of them among the rarest, perhaps—it requires a real appreciation of harmony of lines, of colors—ingenious ideas, absolute tact, and, above all, a love of the beautiful and clear perception of values. It may be resuméd in two words—good taste.

Taste is by no means developed by riches; on the contrary, the increasing demands of luxury are killing the art of dressing. Luxury and good taste are in inverse proportion to one another. The one will kill the other as machinery is crowding out handwork. In fact, it has come so far that many persons confuse the two terms. Because a material is expensive they find it beautiful; because it is cheap they think it must be ugly.

To give you an example!

All women whose wealth may be measured beyond a certain figure, invariably appear with a string of pearls around their necks. Pearls are essentially becoming to certain types only, and cannot possibly be suitable to all women, but they seem to have become a visible sign of social caste. To how many women does a pearl necklace add any beauty? How many women choose their pearl necklaces for reasons of good taste and style, that is to say, in order to set off the beauty of their coloring?

At the theater, in restaurants, you see hundreds of women more adorned than Indian idols. The most sparkling with jewels, the most expensively garbed, are never the most beautiful. Quite the contrary. Those who are most loaded down with precious stones, necklaces, bracelets, and rings rarely attract my attention. Sometimes I try to force myself to admire them. But it is impossible for me to feel anything more for them than for the dazzling setting of a jeweler's window, and the women who appear thus dressed in their fortune only, would not appear one whit less attractive to me if they wore it in their hair as curling papers made out of banknotes!

UNFASHIONABLE TO FOLLOW FASHIONS

THE well-dressed woman is the one who picks out her gown, her adornments, simply because they make her appear more pleasing, not because other people are wearing that style or because it will be a palpable proof of her husband's bank account. Because one woman chooses to emphasize the purity of her Grecian profile by winding a band of gold around her hair, why should twenty the next day and five hundred the day after that do their hair in the same style? But that is the way fashion sways women to-day. The only well-dressed women are those that dare and create original ideas, not those who servilely follow fashion.

In order not to appear entirely out of harmony with her surroundings and the place where she lives, a woman is obliged to follow fashions to a certain extent. But let that be within certain bounds! What does it matter if tight skirts be the fashion if your figure demands a wide one? Is it not more important to dress so as to bring out your good points rather than to reveal the bad? Can any idea of being fashionable make up for the fact of being ridiculous?

I dined the other day in a fashionable restaurant. At the tables around me I noticed at least half a dozen women whose hair was dressed in exactly the same way, with the same number of puffs and switches.

All were dressed in equally expensive gowns, although I was not able to judge of the colors because they were all equally overloaded with beading, embroideries, gold, silver, or steel ornaments, with laces and fringes.

These women, who, I imagine, were neither sisters nor friends, were all shaped in the same mould, that is to say in the same kind of corsets, and they all wore jewels, pendants, and necklaces, which, if not exactly alike, were at least of the same type. Every woman had adapted her body, her movements, and her taste to the commonplace desire of being fashionably dressed. And in looking at them I could not help thinking that in case of a panic their husbands or brothers or friends would be perfectly justified in mistaking one for the other.

Instead of hiding their individuality, why did not each woman try to bring out her personal type of beauty? One woman would have been more attractive without the puffs and switches; another would have been more beautiful in black; jewels were out of place on the third.

A DEFINITION OF THE WELL-DRESSED WOMAN

BUT, curiously enough, women fear being called original or individual, but never hesitate to make fools of themselves in following the latest fashion. A woman will submit to any torture, any ridicule, if she believes she is worshipping the absurd goddess Fashion. Every year a certain very limited number of types of styles are seen, and almost all women may be classified under one of them. Only those who do not fit in under any particular heading are worthy of being called well dressed.

I cannot help feeling a vague contempt for those who ask at the beginning of the season, "What is to be the favorite color?" Choose the color that suits you, madame, and if some one tells you that red is to be worn, dare to wear violet and consider only *what is suitable to you,* because there is only one single rule for the well-dressed woman, and the old Romans expressed it in one word—*decorum*—which means, "that which is suitable." *That which is suitable!*

Choose whatever is suitable to the time, the place, the circumstance, the landscape, the place you are staying, whether it be a large city, a village, or a watering-place!

Choose whatever is most in harmony with your character, for a dress can be the expression of a state of mind if you but try to make it. There are dresses that sing of joy of life, dresses that weep, dresses that threaten. There are gay dresses, mysterious dresses, pleasing dresses, and tearful dresses.

Paul Poiret

Paul Poiret's own career is as interesting as anything he writes. His father, a tailor, apprenticed him to an umbrella-maker. During his leisure Poiret, for the fun of the thing, began designing dresses. The value of these sketches soon became apparent, and his talent was quickly snapped up by the great Rue de la Paix establishments. When his own time came, Poiret left the famous thoroughfare and took a quiet old mansion formerly used by the pages of Louis XVI, in the Chaussee d'Antin. He filled it with period furniture and in this atmosphere were born the styles which have given such vogue to Poiret. The mansion has been the scene of many entertainments at which prominent Americans were guests.—The Editors.

Since Lovely Woman Makes the "Follies" They Are All That Fancy Paints Them

Despite Shot and Shell Paris Inspires Coolness in Midsummer Frocks

Even the weather has been affected by the war. The March lion came in camouflaged as a lamb, and then dropping his disguise roared all day and all night long for weeks. Late in April we were treated to showers of snow driven by a bitter wind, and Parisians went about muffled to the eyes—we can still remember when they were muffled merely to the ears—in furs, while spring frocks bloomed in closed *armoires* or in closets, where even the long arm of Bertha, as Paris insists on calling the German cannon, could not reach them.

Paris is dull. Many people have left the city, and houses and apartments are closed. The Paris of to-day is a city of half-deserted streets —a city where shops are almost empty of buyers and gardens of playing children, but where in spite of war conditions Parisians are determined to "carry on". Which, indeed, is just what the world expected—*vive le Paris!* So we shop wisely and not too much; we search for an *abri* where we may be tolerably comfortable in case of danger; and we go to the theatre when we need amusement. We may still go to the Opéra and to the Théâtre Français, to the Theatre Edouard VII., where they are again playing "La Folle Nuit", so pretty and so shocking; and to several other playhouses. And, grasping our parasols firmly by their carved wood sticks, we even walk in the Bois of a fine morning; but we must explain—for the gentle reader is as yet unaccustomed to these things—that if the cannon thunders while we are walking we do not taxi hurriedly home. It is not good form. Instead, we do not move an eyelash—we walk on.

Milady Dons Velvet So Soldiers
May Have Wool

Celebrated Artists
Wield the Brush
with Spirit to Help
Our Boys to Victory

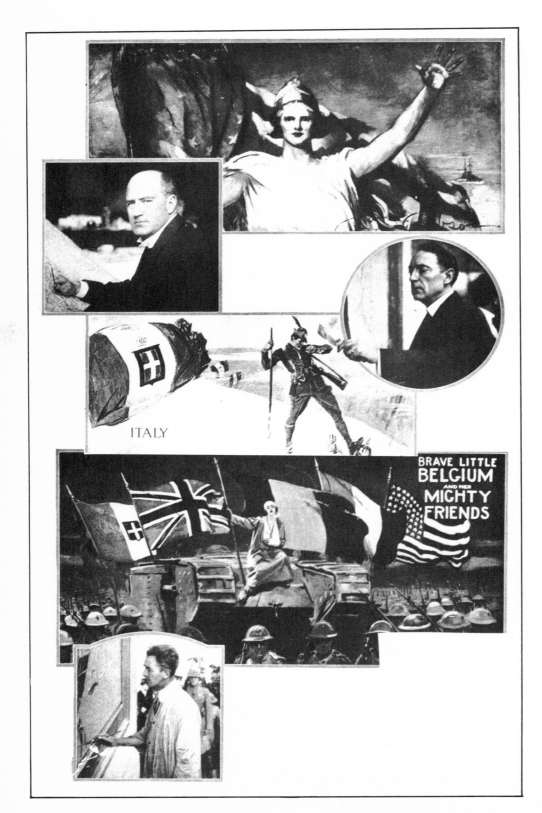

ITALY

BRAVE LITTLE
BELGIUM
AND HER
MIGHTY
FRIENDS

During the three weeks of the Fourth Liberty Loan drive a portion of the New York Library terrace was transformed into an open-air studio. Upon the wall of a war-work building was built a huge frame and every day on a bright and empty canvas a well-known artist painted a picture to help convert Fifth Avenue throngs into bond buyers.

Each artist was confronted with the task of symbolizing as vividly as possible one of the Allied nations. He had but a single day in which to complete his picture. And the appraising eyes of all New York were watching his performance. Yet in spite of the conditions—or perhaps because of them—the paintings in almost every instance turned out to be uncommonly good art.

Top to bottom:

Charles Dana Gibson's "America" gave evidence that Mr. Gibson, if he chose, could have been mightier with the brush than with the pen.

Howard Chandler Christy answered the call with a strong and clean-cut "Italy", interesting in arrangement and also for the idea it illustrates.

James Montgomery Flagg, with his keen sense for the popular appeal, painted this stirring and vigorous conception of Belgium.

*Mid the war's great curse, stands
the nurse . . . she's the rose of No
Man's Land.*

Running a Country House

Is there anything more interesting than an exact account of one's expenditures? Yet, how few of us know them accurately! As we explained last month, Mrs. X knows exactly what she spends—and she spends about two hundred and fifty thousand dollars a year on her wardrobe, her country house, her yacht and her three children. In this article she shows what proportion she devotes to her country house.

One of my strongest characteristics is love of order. That is why keeping these expense books does not bore me. On the contrary, it gives me amusement and satisfaction to know exactly what it costs to run the house, or the garden, or the stables, or the yacht. I always know exactly what I can afford. Most men have a theory that they would like their wives to keep budgets of their expenditures, but they actually don't like it in practice. They will not be annoyed with the details, though they are always able to call in public accountants and ascertain the various costs of their business departments. As for women, most of the women I know keep no books and never know where they stand.

Before I began keeping these books I would often go into town with a hundred-dollar bill in my purse, and next day have no idea what had become of it. I was so annoyed to feel I could spend a hundred dollars, and be able to account for less than half of it, that I began keeping accurate accounts.

I live in the country within easy commuting distance of New York. We have no town house, but keep an apartment which we use when we go to the opera or the theater occasionally.

You will notice that the first item of my house budget is food. You would be surprised to hear some women discuss their household bills. They are just as apt to say their meat bills are $60 a month as $1,000—both utterly ridiculous statements, out of all proportion. There are certain averages in foods—you cannot use more than a certain amount.

Food costs me $1.18 per day for each member of my household, which is about what it should cost. This $1.18 does not include wines or cigarets. All our wines were bought before prohibition. Cigarets average a little over $50 a month.

Our gardens supply most of our fresh vegetables, in season. But where you save on vegetables you spend on labor. We also had $542.65 worth of eggs last year, but keeping chickens cost us $937.43, so there was a deficit of $394.78, if one wished to be accurate.

The next item is house expenses. This includes the coal bill, $3,650.00, which is large, but this takes care also of the heating of the stable where the head chauffeur and his family and the head gardener and his family live. Under this heading come also water, electricity, gas, telephones, telegrams,

HOUSE EXPENSES, 1923

	Water	Electricity	Gas	Coal and Wood	Phone	Telegrams	Express	Laundry	Cleaning House	Books etc.	Stationery	Flowers	Totals by Months
January	$21.74	$103.07	$101.94	$645.99	$43.90	$24.59	$11.93	$172.45	$12.25	$21.61	$3.42	$12.50	$1175.39
February	21.75	103.08	135.66	315.50	39.70	20.39	9.95	135.11	38.20	23.10	8.24	16.50	867.18
March	21.75	103.08	91.59	533.38	35.50	1.27	7.80	172.21	57.50	12.03	5.26	11.90	1053.27
April	40.43	60.77	63.30	.....	38.81	3.58	37.33	149.21	63.00	20.50	9.77	108.70	595.40
May	40.43	60.77	50.92	670.02	47.95	4.53	24.49	148.99	46.50	16.07	17.72	58.90	1187.29
June	40.43	60.77	47.80	115.40	42.20	6.48	52.56	214.04	28.50	22.85	16.64	62.25	709.92
July	73.42	65.74	47.08	.....	41.35	2.02	9.29	192.24	14.75	26.95	5.34	25.00	503.18
August	73.42	65.74	45.40	174.75	38.35	1.75	6.87	156.58	8.25	9.31	5.87	.....	586.29
September	73.42	85.54	41.80	.....	37.45	1.23	14.25	186.50	.....	13.02	9.25	67.00	529.46
October	23.67	85.54	45.76	76.79	41.90	1.24	16.75	147.69	43.50	10.71	4.52	.....	489.07
November	23.68	65.75	50.44	469.78	48.65	....	9.32	170.22	14.00	19.59	3.93	94.90	970.16
December	23.68	85.55	53.32	648.55	42.40	2.79	20.77	189.48	26.75	30.52	12.91	49.45	1186.17
	$477.82	$945.40	$775.01	$3650.06	$498.16	$69.87	$221.31	$2034.72	$353.20	$226.26	$102.87	$507.10	$9861.78

Total House Expenses for 1923 . . . .$9,861.78

express, laundry, books and stationery, flowers, et cetera.

The water bill, $477, seems large, but that is because we have a swimming pool on the place. The laundry bill is really less than the cost would be of having a laundress and assistant in the house.

Repairs to the house average about the same every year. The house is comparatively a new one. It cost about $350,000 to build it, and as much more to furnish, five years ago. There are about fifty acres of woods, lawns, and gardens around the house, but of their upkeep later.

Servants and their clothes cost a little less than $13,000 a year. There are twelve house servants, who are paid monthly as follows: housekeeper, $100; governess, $90; butler, $125; second man, $80; third man, $70; French maid, $65; two house men, $145; two chambermaids, $130; cook, $110; kitchen maid,

$75. In addition to these there is my private secretary, who comes in by the day, and only has her luncheon in the house. The laundry, as I have said, is done outside the house. The servants' clothes are expensive at first, but they do not cost very much to keep in order after the first cost. The butler gets a morning suit with striped trousers and waistcoat, evening clothes, collars and ties. The second man gets a morning suit, a livery, collars and ties, and work aprons. The two house men get aprons and clothes necessary for heavy work. The furnace men get overalls. The cook and kitchen maid get their aprons only. The third man in the pantry gets his aprons. The parlor maid gets her aprons, caps, collars, and cuffs. The chambermaids get aprons and sometimes their dresses. The ladies' maid gets aprons only. The chauffeurs and grooms get their complete liveries.

Doctors' bills seem very small, which means that we have had a fortunate year. Also, the children's doctors' bills are entered in their own expense books, not in mine.

The expenses outside the house, that is, the running of the stable, the garage, and the upkeep of the grounds seem fairly large, but analysis proves that they are not. The upkeep of the grounds last year cost $7,173, which includes the payroll of two men in winter and five to seven in summer, new plants and seeds, stones for the roads, et cetera. We have flower and vegetable gardens, but no hothouses. When I can afford it I shall build a real conservatory and have the luxury of fresh flowers all the year around, but my budget tells me that I can not afford it now. A conservatory is about as expensive as a yacht.

In the stable we have eight horses, four polo ponies which the children use for riding, two hunters, and two carriage horses. Two grooms run the stable. The head groom gets $150, and the second groom gets $130 a month. He acts as emergency chauffeur, and also rides with my two girls. Roughly speak-

ing, it costs about $40 a month to keep a horse.

The upkeep of the garage, including the wages of two chauffeurs, cost $8,308 last year. This takes care of three good cars and three cheaper cars that the children and the servants use. The good cars are a limousine for town use, a small enclosed car which my husband drives at night, and an open car for the country.

I have included the insurance and taxes on the house and grounds in the house budget, because this takes the place of rent. Income taxes are not included.

This budget of mine may seem extravagant at first glance, but I believe that my house is run with as little waste as the house of any conscientious young bride who is trying to make every dollar count. Everything is comparative. It is just as easy to be extravagant on fifty dollars a week as on five thousand a week, and the satisfaction of knowing that one's five thousand is well spent is just as great. I have many friends who spend much more than I do each year, many who spend only a fraction of my income, and I know that the size of the income has nothing to do with the happiness and contentment we derive from it.

HOUSE BUDGET	
Food	$7,813.73
House expenses	9,861.78
Repairs to house	5,288.98
Repairs to furnishings	651.02
Upkeep of grounds	7,173.92
Wages, 12 house servants	12,003.37
Clothes, 12 servants	680.41
Private secretary	1,484.82
Doctors	507.00
Drugs	103.53
Trained nurse	289.00
New things (small) for house	1,231.36
New furnishings	18,551.79
Toilet articles	386.33
Sewing articles	20.34
Taxes on house and grounds	14,000.00
Insurance on house and grounds	12,160.68
Garage	8,308.20
Stable	4,895.94
Chickens	937.43
Total house budget	$106,349.63
Total miscellaneous expenses	$30,461.44
Total	$136,811.07

MISCELLANEOUS EXPENSES	
*Clothes for the family	$16,985.06
Traveling	2,029.81
Hotels and restaurants	2,272.87
Presents	1,080.01
Christmas presents	2,130.23
Charity	2,140.95
Tips	249.01
Taxicabs	243.44
Auction	2,093.50
Amusements	1,086.56
Lawyers' fees	150.00
Total miscellaneous expenses	$30,461.44

*Does not include Mr. X's clothes.

Erté

Erté, an illustrator-writer-fashion reporter, designed many of the Bazaar *covers of the twenties that delighted the* Bazaar *reader. From the sundry descriptions of the clothes he sketched, one sometimes had the thought that if Erté couldn't find what he wanted to sketch, he got what he wanted to sketch, designed.*

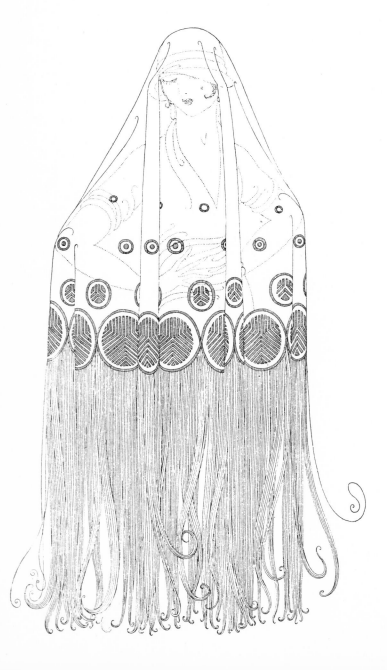

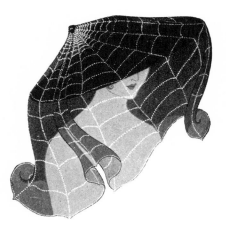

To be flung over a wide summer hat is a black veil, embroidered in silver to look like a spider web. It is fastened to the hat by a pin made to represent an anxious-looking spider, of onyx and silver, a confident spider in the center of its silver web waiting for the inevitable victim.

Not the summer sun nor the tiniest gnat that goes about on its impudent gauzy wings can penetrate this écru veil embroidered with turquoise-colored silk, and finished with a deep turquoise silk fringe. Designed for the beach or the sun-drenched veranda.

The Improvised Cage

A bathing-suit that makes the lady in it look like some exotic species of mauve and gold fish has a foundation of mauve silk tights, embroidered with orange silk, held up around the neck by a twisted cord of orange silk, ending in a long tassel. The little pointed skirt is of layers of mauve and orange silk strands that flutter in the water like the delicate fins of some great "China silk" gold fish.

The Wife's Share

Of the Husband's Income—What Proportion?

After I had been married three months I awoke to the fact that all my own money was gone, my purse was empty, and that not one word on the money subject had been spoken either by my husband or myself. Of course, I expected him to broach the subject, thinking he surely would not want me to ask him for money. This thought was humiliating, but so was an empty purse. I had no idea what to do and was beginning to think I had either married a very stingy or a very thoughtless man, when, observing the unusually solemn expression of my face, he anxiously inquired what was the matter. Without stopping to consider I blurted out the truth. He laughed, then said, remorsefully, "It never occurred to me. Of course you will need a little money," and handed me $10.

My husband is a fire-insurance agent, and during the year we lived with his family (which was the first of our six years' married life) I had no knowledge of the amount of his income nor of how much or little it was right for me to spend. I did some hard thinking on the subject, however, and when we decided to go to housekeeping I made two conditions. He was to tell me exactly how much he earned and give me an allowance to be used as I deemed best. He finally confessed that his income was only $900 a year or $75 a month, and asked how much I should need for household expenses. I promptly asked for $60. It may seem that I was greedily demanding the lion's share, but I had my reasons. I had learned by now that if there was any saving to be done I was the one who must do it. It was simply not in my husband's power to save.

We rented a small house in a good neighborhood for $25 a month, reduced to $20 by agreeing to give the use of the stable and lot to our landlord, who lives next door. I spend $4 a week for table expenses and $1 for laundry. Some months being longer than four weeks my monthly expenses average as follows:

House rent	$20
Water rent	1
Telephone	2
Food and laundry	21
Gas (25 cents per 1,000 feet)	2
Total	$46

This leaves me $14 a month or $168 a year for other expenses. Out of this I pay $6 a month or $72 a year on a thousand-dollar share of building-loan stock maturing in eight years from date of buying. My church dues, clothes, and incidental expenses (which include two magazines) are paid out of the remaining $96, and as my clothes seldom average over $40 or $50 a year I usually have a balance of from $15 to $25 at the end of the year. So far we have kept well and had no doctor's bills. My husband does not smoke and finds his $180 sufficient for his clothes and individual expenses. As his business increases we hope he will soon be able to take out a life-insurance policy. M. C.
FORT SMITH, ARKANSAS.

Twenty-eight Years' Experience

Shall I boast? Shall I say we have been married nearly twenty-eight years, and know a thing or two? Perhaps I am old-fashioned, but to me the words "Economic value in women" are distasteful. Can I say to her, "Take this — the rest is mine"? Shall I say she can have as her share so much only of the social atmosphere that belongs to both? Shall I say just so much of the blessed sunlight and God's green earth to see or walk upon is yours—the rest, as far as I can control, is mine? God forbid! That is what I think about an allowance.

Now, as to bills. Let no young wife begin by believing that a man can long be loving and kindly paying bills. He will at first, perhaps, when the process is as new to him as the pleasure of buying is to her, but it won't last. Under the process the evolution of the cheque signer into the grouch is slow but sure. Ask for cash when you want it and pay cash. If you don't get it, don't buy. Talk understandingly and sympathetically about the finances for the home. Don't get into debt. Don't live separate lives morally or financially, and you will avoid the rocks. J. C. H.
PLAINFIELD, NEW JERSEY.

ON $850 A YEAR

As a girl I worked at housework and in a factory, so I learned economy before I was married. My husband earns from $70 to $75 a month. He is a brakeman on the railroad. He gives me $60 to $65 a month for the bills. This is the way they usually run:

Rent	$11
Food	28
Clothing	10
Gas	5
Insurance	5
Total	$59

He keeps $10 for himself— his clothes, and groceries, etc., when he is at the other end of the road. We each have a little for emergency and amusements. We have four little children. We have a garden in summer, and fruit of our own. E. E. K.
BELLEVUE, OHIO.

Reine, Rose, Ethel and Marion Davies

"The Swan Dance"
by Anna Pavlowa

Marilynn Miller of the Follies

Quand Même . . . The Divine Sarah

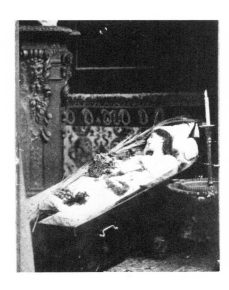

Above: Bernhardt, The Eccentric, Posing in the Celebrated Coffin Where She Often Slept. About 1875

Opposite Page: Sarah Bernhardt, Sculptress, in Her Studio, 1869

Early in this decade—on October twenty-second, 1944, to be exact—there will occur what would have been the hundredth birthday of the Frenchwoman whose name stands as triumphantly today as it did in her long and effulgent prime for the one thing that mattered to her: the Theatre. Her detractors—and they have been many, during her lifetime and since—argue that she was never the Theatre, but what they are prone to consider its enemy number one: the Actress. She was not Sincere, they say, she did not Suffer. . . . Ah, well. If Sarah Bernhardt were alive on that hundredth birthday, it is likely that she would shrug her shoulders and remark indulgently that the same discussion was raging around her before the Franco-Prussian War; and after all, her answer must be what it was then. She would go gaily off to her theatre, as was her inviolable custom, one hour before even the stage hands put in their appearance. First alone, then with her company, she would make certain that not the slightest detail of the evening's performance was left to chance. Then, just before the curtain rose that would find her on the stage, she would reach for a couple of contrivances resembling clothespins, with the palms of her hands pull her centenarian folds and wrinkles to the back of her neck, mercilessly pin them there, signal to the waiting stage hands, and . . . APPLAUSE! That would be Sarah Bernhardt's answer: a miracle, no more, no less, produced with no fuss other than the divine Sarah thought pertinent to the theatre. It was an answer that never failed her.

When the great actress was a young girl, she chose for her motto the valiant and untranslatable phrase *"Quand Même";* it was inscribed on her note paper, on the celebrated coffin in which, during her most bizarre period, she used to sleep "to get used to death," and finally over the portals of her own theatre, the Sarah Bernhardt, in Paris. *Quand Même* — "just the same" or "nevertheless" — but no, not really: let us say that, to the actress, it meant that come hell and high water, the show and Sarah Bernhardt were going on. In her earliest days in the theatre, she was a prey to indecision, frail health, and a fantastically morbid nature; she had to fight her way through a jungle of scandals and theatre politics that more than once forced her to quit the Parisian stage; it was whispered that she had flayed alive a pet dog, thrown cats on the fire, and hidden in a closet the skeleton of a lover who had refused to recognize that Sarah was fed up. So the strange young woman spoke of retiring to a convent, or to a life as a sculptor, or possibly . . . *Quand Même!* And ambition's flame leaped high, never to be quenched: she was forevermore Sarah Bernhardt, *la grande Sarah,* idol of Paris and the world.

The "Incomparable Sorel"
Embodies the Glamour, Gaiety, and
Beauty That Is Paris

Early color presentation
the beach costume—18

HARPER'S BAZAR

AUGUST 1912

FIFTEEN CENTS

HARPER & BROTHERS
Publishers · · · New York

Miss Ina Claire
A Subtle Impression of
Certain Elegance

So This Is Greenwich Village
Where All Those
Queer Artists Live

Here is that hot bed of art and iniquity that has fostered and sent forth into our fair land the bobbed head, the cigaret, The Washington Square Players, The Theater Guild, The Greenwich Village Follies, The Provincetown Players, a bit of pure revolt, some free verse, and lots of music, laughter and dancing in the streets.

Bazaar readers tried gamely to spot all the famous Villagers like John Dos Passos, George Bellows, Eugene O'Neill, Carl Van Vechten, Edna St. Vincent Millay. To help them identify the place and the face, *Bazaar* had Reginald Marsh paint a portrait of Greenwich Village. Here were some of the hints. The car racing through Washington Square to a picnic contains the Young Intellectuals Gilbert Seldes, Edmund Wilson, Jr., Steve Benét, John Dos Passos, Ben Hecht, Scott Fitzgerald. Descending the stairway (subway) in the middle of Sheridan Square is Marcel Duchamp. On the bus under the Arch sits Clara Tice, and behind her, Ray Long and O. O. McIntyre. Diving into the fountain is Mrs. Scott Fitzgerald. In the window, Mr. and Mrs. John Barrymore. Sinclair Lewis stands on the platform of the Sixth Avenue "L" train. On the lower right stage (playing O'Neill's *Diff'rent*). In the audience, Edna St. Vincent Millay, Djuna Barnes and Rollo Peters.

Katherine Cornell, who will create
in America the leading role in
W. Somerset Maugham's play,
"The Letter." Miss Cornell is
considered the outstanding figure
among our younger actresses. Her
career has been deservedly meteoric.

Paris Has Now Adopted the
Small Grosgrain Hat

The Low Crowned Hat Is Smartest

Vamps

In 1919 "Vamp a Little, Lady" was a hit song, It was the heyday of the never-to-be-forgotten movie vamps. Unabashedly flamboyant in sequins, lamé, feathers and transparent veils, the sultry charmers writhed and clawed and enraptured their victims, only to lose them, inevitably, to the ingénues with fluttering eyelashes and sugar-water curls.

Left to right:

Greta Nissen, the Scandinavian threat to America's sweethearts.

Gloria Swanson dressed for the kill in three thousand ermine tails.

Bee-stung lips and honey-spun hair were stock in trade with Mae Murray. As a gilded lily she strolled in the park in a form-fitting dress, with a cane and fawn-color boots to match her borzoi, the symbol of shady high life in the silent movies of the Twenties.

Top left to right:

Barbara La Marr spelled temptation and a sexy afternoon at the local Bijou.

Ann May Wong, the Oriental temptress, slinking under metallic rain.

Bebe Daniels added an authentic exotic note by cuddling an obliging leopard cub.

Bottom left to right:

Theda Bara, a 1915 rage in *A Fool There Was*, taken from Kipling's "The Vampire."

Silent screen siren Lenore Ulric in black lace leotards for *Frozen Justice*.

Greta Garbo, uninhibited, as Mata Hari, the infamous courtesan-spy of World War I.

Shall It Be Trousers
for Women?

The possibility is only a step ahead—perhaps a long one

Paul Poiret says that women of the next generation will all wear trousers as a matter of course; yet, some gentlemen hope that the men of this same generation will soon renounce pants in favor of knee-breeches and long silk stockings. The trouser has been established for a hundred years or so for the masculine wardrobe. How long will it take to win the feminine one? Men seem, as a whole, to be pleased with a woman's dress and totally discontented with their own, while women are, on the contrary, beginning to revolt against the skirt and hanker after a fabric cylinder for each leg. When a man wishes to lounge, he takes off his trousers and puts on a dressing-gown, ample and flowing. A woman, on the contrary, slips into trousers with a contented sigh. As for sex, there is no denying that skirts in movement are revealing, whereas trousers are concealing. Of course, in China, Turkey, and the Far East, men wear the robes and women the trousers. In ancient Greece, both sexes wore robes. In Rome, trousers for men came in only with the conquering barbarians, thus furnishing a splendid argument for the adoption of the "rational dress" to the would-be conquering modern feminist. In the frigid North, both sexes dress alike. And here, perhaps, we have the final explanation of the desire of the modern woman for a trousered costume. Her daily life is being masculinized; why should her costume not follow suit?

Four ways, all equally quaint, for arranging the hair that has just passed the bobbed stage. They are all reminiscent of the Second Empire modes.

 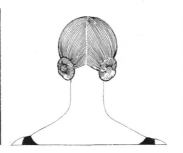  

The Coiffure de Garçon

The coiffure *de garçon* shown in the middle of this page is one of the most startling that has appeared this season. One lady who wore it was very dark, her hair was very straight, and cut short like a boy's. The hair was brushed straight and uncompromisingly back, with both ears showing as they were originally planned, and the whole coiffure looked like a little lacquered cap on the lady's small head. The effect was exquisite. Needless to say, she was one of the rare souls who could wear so exotic a mode. With this black satin hair she wore the great carved ivory earrings shown here.

The Smartest, Most Practical Negligée for Pullman or Steamer

The strictly tailored suit is the only thing to wear during those hours of lounging in one's transcontinental drawing-room; of silk or velvet in various colors.

(Left) For the dusty Pullman journey the serviceable lounging robe of a man is the smartest thing a woman can wear; here of brocade in green, blue, and rose. When a feminine negligée will be rumpled a masculine lounging suit will come out of the trunk crisp and fresh. Coat and trousers of tan and blue figured silk.

The Uncompromising Masculine "Costume Complete" Cannot Be Surpassed

As a Feminine Lounging Robe

Here is the masculine negligée at its most chic—a "costume complete" in three pieces consisting of trousers and jacket (with kimono sleeves) of a beautiful Egyptian-figured silk, prevailingly blue and red, and a matching robe lined and trimmed with an unfigured grosgrain *tête de nègre* silk.

The vogue of the masculine lounging robe has increased incalculably since the first showing of these robes for women a year ago in *Harper's Bazaar*. Women find them both comfortable and smart. This lounging suit in green corduroy is cut exactly like a man's dinner jacket suit.

These purely masculine garments are smartest when bought at a man's shop where no compromise with the feminine angle is attempted. Here are pajamas of a soft Oriental silk, predominantly yellow, the jacket cut like a man's, and over them is worn a matching robe, brilliantly lined.

Miss Amelia Earhart is wearing, in the above photograph, a warm tweed coat, which came from Abercrombie and Fitch. Her close-fitting felt hat was supplied by Dobbs and her scarf is voluminous enough to fill in her open coat.

Plane Clothes

by Amelia Earhart

What does the woman aviator wear? This question is asked me as often as any other connected with aviation.

Ten years ago I could have described a flying costume. It would have consisted of helmet, goggles, leather jacket, breeches, and some sort of high boots. There were no traditions but those of wartime flying to follow, and both men and women adopted or modified it to suit commercial needs. Also, flying fields were usually dirty, planes were crude, and there were no refinements in facilities, such as passenger waiting-rooms, and so forth. Altogether, the clothing had to be rather rough.

Since the war, flying has undergone the same sort of changes that automobiling did previously. Do you remember the dashing linen dusters and gauntlets and veils of 1908? They constituted an "automobiling costume," and of course one couldn't tour without the proper accessories.

At the present time, with the development of luxurious passenger planes, which very much resemble the finest buses, there isn't the necessity for special dress. One wears ordinary street clothes. Why not? There are comfortable upholstered seats, one can move about at will, read, or write, or sleep. On one line a buffet luncheon is served at no extra charge. Unlike railroad or automobile travel, one has a clean face at the journey's end, as there are no cinders or dust in the air.

Even the pilots wear street clothes, usually, unless they are in the uniform of the transportation company. In the enclosed planes they do not wear goggles. From observation it appears that one of the most popular outfits for summer flying is knickers and a sweater. These pilots look more as if they belonged on the fairway than on the runway.

When I am flying my little plane, I usually wear a sports costume with a rather full skirt and a close-fitting hat. Sometimes I slip a leather windbreaker on under my coat, for the temperature drops as one ascends. Most cabin planes are heated, by the way, so even this precaution isn't necessary in them. Usually, on a solo flight, I wear low-heeled shoes, because with low heels it is easier to keep my feet braced on the rudder bar. Then, too, high-heeled shoes suffer from the exercise. As you know, driving a car with them rubs the back of the shoe, and the same condition applies in a plane.

Commander Byrd one day showed me some beautiful fluffy fur suits he was planning to take to the Antarctic. He told me they were warmer than the flying suits now used, and I think such a rig would greatly appeal to those women who will eventually try flying as a sport. On the *Friendship* flight I couldn't follow the rule of wearing sports clothes. The trip was a pioneering one, and comforts were not thought of. Clothes suitable for "roughing it" had to be taken. For instance, there was no step from the pontoons to the door, and I couldn't have jumped into the plane in a skirt. Further, though we could walk about in the after cabin, we had dumped everything to sit on, to save weight. Squatting on a rolled flying suit, or kneeling on one knee, or sliding between the large gas tanks wouldn't have left much of a ladylike ensemble.

There are other adjuncts to flying you might be interested in hearing about. On my transcontinental flight, recently, I had to battle against a severe sunburn. The wind and the sun really blistered me. Through Texas, Arizona, and New Mexico, the heat was intense and very drying, even at a fairly high altitude. I kept a tube of cold cream in the cockpit, and when I was not otherwise engaged I tried to keep some on my face as a protection. I flew the same plane that Lady Heath, the famous English woman flier, used on her trip from London to Cape Town and back. I remember her telling me one of the absurdities of her journey was pulling out a powder puff and powdering her nose over the South African wastes. She always carries a mirror and powder puff with her. I hope some time that flying fields will have cold cream and powder service for women fliers. Getting gasoline and oil and mechanical help only, I am sure will not be adequate in time.

Seriously, women can make a great contribution to aviation by demanding comfort. Without patting ourselves on the back, I think we are responsible for the development of the gasoline service stations which adorn automobile roads today.

Clockwise:

That air travel has ceased to be a thing of hardship, a complicated endurance test, is evidenced in the cabin of the air yacht Pegasus, built for Mr. John Hay Whitney of New York by Sikorsky.

Lady Heath tries for altitude in an open cockpit and dresses for the part, sensibly and effectively, in helmet, boots, coats, and gauntlet gloves of leather and beaver fur.

Could anything be more comfortable than this cabin of a Fokker plane, fully equipped and with room enough to move around in?

If you are dégagé enough to become bored with the landscape, just lie down in your bunk, or read; this in a Ford.

Making Air Travel Simple, Practical, Comfortable and Luxurious for 1929

America's New Society at Play

At Newport, at Palm Beach, on the Riviera and all the chic spas the "darlings" frequented when the season was on.

Top left to right:

Mrs. McLean, after her swim, is on her way to Whitehall for luncheon.

Mrs. J. Francis A. Clark and her small son, John Poultney Clark, found the pony classes the most interesting of them all.

Miss Muriel Vanderbilt attended the Newport horse show with Mrs. Deering Howe.

Among those present at each session was Miss Natalja Willard, a daughter of Colonel and Mrs. Joseph H. Willard.

Mrs. Charles Amory answering the call of the sunlit waves at Palm Beach.

Bottom left to right:

Although Mr. and Mrs. T. Suffern Tailer have their own golf links out on the Ocean Drive, they found time to attend the annual horse show.

Prepared for the last meet of the season are M. F. H. Lederlin and his wife and the Count and Countess Pastré.

Jean Patou pauses for a chat with Madame Cérès and evidently approves of her fawn ulster.

MUNKAC[

Ramon and Renita, snatched for
the moment from the Warner
Brothers, whirl gloriously in the
clouds, at the Rainbow Room.

Why Not Brunettes?

By Anita Loos

Wherein Both Lorelei and Dorothy Discover Unmistakably that

EVERYTHING'S FOR THE BEST

MANUEL FRERES

Well, the Little Stranger has turned out to be a boy. And Henry has settled quite a large settlement on me. For, I always seemed to know by instinck that nothing makes any husband become so sentamental in a financial way, as the day he can call a girl "Little Mother." And on top of all that, I have got into the Social Register. So I really suppose that now I could forget everything, and enjoy myself, if I wanted to. But I never seem to be so happy enjoying myself, because I always want to be getting somewheres or other. So I suppose I shall keep on getting myself more and more promanent in Society, because Dorothy says that any girl who wants to keep on getting somewheres, without enjoying herself, was really cut out to be a Social Leader.

But practically the most wonderful thing that has occured to me is the feeling it gives a girl to be a Mother. I mean, even if a girl does have to go through quite a lot, your character takes quite a change for the better. I mean, I never used to know what it would feel like to

want to give up and *make sacrafices*. But, for instants, the day the Little Stranger was born, Dorothy and I were having luncheon at the Ritz. And a very delightful gentleman friend we knew introduced us to a very famous society leader. So this society leader was giving a tea that afternoon and she invited Dorothy and I to attend, because she wanted to show us to a titled lady friend of hers from England, who wanted to see practically everything before she went back. So Dorothy and I excepted the invitation, and went, and if I had not been expecting the Little Stranger at practically any moment, nothing could have kept me from staying through the whole tea party. But after a few moments, I began to feel as if I really wanted

to go home, which is quite an unusual feeling for a girl that enjoys society, to have in the midst of an exclusive tea. But when they put the Little Stranger in my arms that evening, I really felt repayed for giving up a party. And I think the state of Motherhood is the most wonderful state a girl can get into after marriage.

Well, when the society leader who gave the tea and her titled English friend read in the newspapers that a Little Stranger had arrived to me that very evening they could hardly believe it. So they called up the nurse on the telephone to find out. Well, I always have quite a habit of 'listening in' on a cute gold and ivry telephone of the French period that I have by my bedside. So when I heard the society leader's voice, I chimed in, and invited her and her English lady friend to come over and look at it. Well nothing could keep them from excepting.

So I sat up in bed with my pink maraboo bed quilt and my pink ostrige feather negligay and we held quite a delightful party. And before the afternoon was over, my bodoire became quite a rendeyvous for callers. And quite a few girls from the Follies came in with their escorts. Because nothing touches their hearts as much as a girl they know personally going through 'The Valley of the Shadow' and coming out with a baby. And the more the news spread, the more they kept coming in, and I had to keep telephoning and telephoning to Rubens for more sandwitches. But the nurse would only give us a small glimpse of the Little Stranger, because noise and cigarette smoke are not so good for babys the day after they arrive.

Well, the titled English lady said that it was her most enjoyable afternoon in the United States, but she knew that when she got back to London and told everybody, nobody would believe her. And she paid me the compliment, that being such a well poised hostess under all of the circumstances, made me the kind of a Mother that gave birth to giants. So I had to thank her, but I really hope that the Little Stranger will not turn out to be tall to soon, because I always think that when a baby starts in to become tall, he stops being a baby.

Well right on top of that I had my largest quarrel with Dorothy. And it really seemed as if our friendship had almost reached the point of becoming strained. And our conversations had really become nothing but bickering.

Because right in the midst of Dorothy's engagement to Charlie Gwynn, who is a millionaire's scion, she fell madly in love with Gerald, her dancing partner at the Club Zig Zag. And practically everybody knew it, with the exception of Charlie Gwynn. Because when Charlie has quite a few drinks he gets into quite a congeneal state of seeing everything through rose colored window glasses. So he never knew what was going on, because he was constantly having quite a few drinks. So he thought that Dorothy was only putting in her time dancing with Gerald until the ceremony took place.

Well, every time that Dorothy and I came in contract, it really seemed to end in a misunderstanding. I mean, I think it takes quite a lot of self controle to stand a girl who is madly in love with a ball room dancer. Especially when the only reason that Gerald was in love with Dorothy was because she was the only partner he could get for $50 a week while he put the remainder of the $500 a week they got into his own pocket. But every week when Gerald presented Dorothy with the $50, he would spend quite a few moments telling her that she was not even worth that.

Well, any time that an admirer places a girl like Dorothy in an unfavorable light, Dorothy gets the idea that it is the result of his own superiority. And then she places him on a pedestal. And once a gentleman is placed on a pedestal, Dorothy starts in to look up to him. And that was the condition that Dorothy had gotten into about Gerald.

But as far as poor Charlie Gwynn was concerned, he spent all of his time telling Dorothy that she was wonderful, while he was really nothing at all. So naturally Dorothy thought so to.

Well, one night Gerald was even more harsh to Dorothy than usual. And he really was right for once, because Dorothy would never practise or concentrate her mind on her steps. So sometimes they would get out on the floor at the Club Zig Zag and Dorothy would forget what went next. So then she had to do something quick, on the spur of the moment, and Gerald could not keep in step. So he would have to stand on one side, with quite a graceful sweep of the arm toward Dorothy, and pretend that he was proud of her while she did it. But the audience used to applaud Dorothy more than usual, and it was quite difficult for Gerald to look well poised, while the audience was applauding Dorothy. And when he got her back of the curtain, he did not even try to hide his contempt. And he finally told Dorothy that she would have to go up to Ned Wayburns dancing school and learn some steps that had really been thought up by somebody, and then stick to them, so that he could accompany, or else hand in her notice.

Well, that made Dorothy feel very very humbel. And when Doro-thy becomes humbel, the gentleman who did it to her, always seems more wonderful than usual to her by comparison. And Dorothy got into quite a worried condition for fear Gerald would give all of her opertunities to some other girl he might select.

But I told Dorothy to hand in her notice to any gentleman who gave a girl $50 a week out of $500. So then Dorothy and I had our largest misunderstanding, because I could not understand what she was getting out of her friendship with Gerald. So Dorothy said that it could not be explaned to a girl whose chief emotion was mental arithmatick. So I told Dorothy it would be a good thing if she would use her own brains for once. And Dorothy said that brains did not enter in. So I asked her what *did* enter in, for instants. And Dorothy said that even the perfume of the hair tonic that Gerald put on his hair, gave her a feeling inside that she had never yet been able to get enough of. But I told Dorothy that any such a feeling as that, was not Love, but it was a feeling that ought not to even be mentioned out loud, called Infatuation. Well, Dorothy said, that she would not trade 10 seconds of it, for a whole career of being well supported by someone who was born to be a husband. So I told Dorothy that if she was looking for dishonorable intentions, she was certainly looking in the right quarters. And we practically parted in anger.

Well, Dorothy even went to dancing school and put her mind on it, to win Gerald's heart, and of course it was poor Charlie Gwynn who paid for the dancing lessons.

Well finally one morning quite a peculiar thing happened to Dorothy, that was a mistery practically up to the time we found out the reason why. I mean Dorothy received a box of flowers, and when she opened it, the card was Gerald's card with his own handwriting saying 'Oh you wonderful girl.' Well Dorothy could hardly believe her eyes, because it was practically the first time that Gerald had ever given her such a kind word, especially in writing accompanied by flowers.

Well, no sooner did she get over her surprise, than the telephone rang. So Dorothy answered it, and it was Gerald's voice, saying "Hello, Beautiful." And then Dorothy could hardly believe her ears, because Gerald's comments on her personal appearance had generally been the reverse. And on top of that, Gerald even invited Dorothy to go to the Ritz to tea. Well Dorothy went into a daze. But she met Gerald in the lobby of the Ritz, and he led her into tea, with quite a new found galantry. And over the tea cups he broke her the news that he had made up his mind to marry her. Well Dorothy was really to overcome to even make a reply. But Gerald took it for granted, and after tea, on the way out, he stopped everybody they knew and told them to congratulate Dorothy. And when they got on the street, instead of letting her find herself a taxi, as usual, Gerald helped her into one himself and even let her know that he would escort her home.

Well Dorothy was just beginning to realize that Gerald had actually invited her to become a wife, so she decided to come and tell me, to prove that his intentions had been honorable all along.

Well, as Gerald was handing Dorothy out of the taxicab at my front entrants, he told Dorothy, by the way, that he had gone into the Club Zig Zag that morning and found a telegram from Mr. Ziegfield which made them the offer to go to work in the new Ziegfield Follies at $1,000 a week. But he forgot to mention it before, on account of their new found happiness. Well, it started in to look quite peculiar to Dorothy that anything could make Gerald forget $1,000. I mean she could hardly believe it. So she asked Gerald to let her see the telegram, but he was sorry that he left it in his other clothes.

Well, while Dorothy was coming up in the elevator, she had an opertunity to think everything over, away from the glammer of Gerald's personality. And Dorothy began to realize that there must be something back of everything or else why would Gerald suddenly become so gallant?

And by the time Dorothy came into my bodoire to brake me the news, instead of being overcome by her happiness, Dorothy's feeling seemed to be more subdued. I mean, it really seems as if an honest proposal of legal matrimony does not give a girl like Dorothy as much of a thrill as the oder of some gentlemen's imported English hair tonic when she is not even sure his attentions are honorable.

Well, I was overcome by my surprize, but I told Dorothy that in the case of gentlemen like Gerald, legal matirmony is just as much of a mistake as something worse. But Dorothy said, that she might just as well marry Gerald and get it all out of her system, because, after all, she always had Charlie Gwynn to fall back on when things came to greif.

Well Dorothy decided to keep all of her plans to get married very very quiet on account of her engagement to Charlie Gwynn. But it seems that Gerald never cared to keep anything quiet when publicity was at steak. So he went to the publicity agent of the Club Zig Zag and explaned to him what an astounding piece of news it was for him to become engaged. So the publicity agent went to work, and managed to get it on the front page of a few picture newspapers, with large size pictures of Gerald showing Dorothy how to dance.

Well, when Charlie Gwynn got up that afternoon and saw the morning papers, he did not believe his eyes, but he thought it was the publicity idea of some agent. So he called Dorothy up, to correct the impression. Well Dorothy's maid answered the telephone and when she told Dorothy who it was, Dorothy became unnerved. I mean she really did not want to go into the subject, so she let her maid break it. And when Charlie Gwynn heard that the news was true he let go of the telephone receiver and could not even say good-bye. So Dorothy felt quite an uncomfortable sensation all day.

Well, when anything unusual happens to Charlie Gwynn he takes more drinks than usual. So Dorothy's new engagement was no exception, except that he even took

more. And when Charlie drinks quite a lot, he is the kind of an intoxicant who always becomes very very humbel. And the more he drinks, the more he seems to think that he calls for an apolagy.

Well after Charlie had quite a few highballs, he started in to apolagize to his valet for being unworthy to even touch the hem of the girl he loved's garment. And after he had a few more drinks, he decided to go over to his club where his audience would be even larger. So he went, and then he started to go around the lobby and ask them, 'Who he was to think that the greatest little woman in the world would have him?' Well nobody seemed to care to take up the arguement so Charlie decided to go one step further and kill himself.

Well, then Charlie's friends began to take an interest. So they held a consultation and decided that Charlie had better not drink any more. So then they formed a committee to sober Charlie up, and one or another of them never left his side all day.

Well, it was quite a novel thing for Charlie Gwynn to drink a cup of coffee. I mean at first he would not even agree, until they put it in a tall glass and put a piece of ice in it. But after quite a few glasses, he started in to listen to reason, and he finally agreed to take it right out of a cup. And the result was that he started in to become sober. And it was the first time in years and years.

Well, at first, the sensation seemed to be even more depressing than usual. But after he had a sandwich and another cup of coffee, his real nature started in to come forth. And his real nature had not come forth for years, on account of always being in such a congeneal state of thinking that everything was wonderful except himself.

But when Charlie Gwynn's real nature came forth, he started in to become critical. I mean, instead of apologizing for himself, he gradually started into get the idea that it was Dorothy who stood in need of the apolagy. And he started in by calling Dorothy ungrateful. And after a few more cups of coffee he almost reached the verge of becoming ungalant. So by eleven oclock, he had had practically no food, but sixteen cups of black coffee, and he decided to go over to the Club Zig Zag and tell Dorothy to her face what a conclusion he had reached about a girl like her.

Well, Dorothy was in her dressing room in quite a state of nerves. Because in the first place, Dorothy did not feel so comfortable about Gerald's new found galantry. I mean Dorothy knew that something must be strange somewhere, because it was not Gerald's real nature. And after all, it was Gerald's real nature that won Dorothy's heart.

And Dorothy had quite a premonition that Charlie Gwynn might try to hold an interview with her at any moment, and break into tears, which always seems to embarass a girl like Dorothy. So she had told the keeper, who kept the back door, that if an intoxicated gentleman arrived, not to let him in. So when Charlie Gwynn arrived sober, the keeper really could not be to blame for not recognizing the guest who Dorothy told him to keep out.

Well Dorothy was sitting there getting ready to appear, when there was a loud knock on the door. So Dorothy jumped with quite a start and asked who is it?

So Charlie replied who it was, quite sharply.

Well such a tone of voice from Charlie Gwynn was practically new to Dorothy. But she thought quite quickly and said that she was not in the proper clothes to receive a gentleman caller.

But Charlie Gwynn said, *"Never mind that. You open the door."* And the tone that he used was quite masterful. Well, it was such a shock to Dorothy that before she could realize it, she did.

Well Charlie stood there in silence, but he looked at her and looked at her with quite a dark expression. Well Dorothy always feels embarassed when a silence is going on, but she finally found her tongue and told Charlie that she was glad he had come over, because she wanted to explane to him that, even if she did get married to somebody else, they would go right on being the best of friends.

But, greatly to Dorothy's surprize, Charlie spoke up in a harsh tone and said

"The hell we will!"

Well, Dorothy could not believe her ears. I mean she knew that his new found harshness was not because he had been drinking, because he always was. And to believe that he had become sober, was even more unbelievable. So all Dorothy could do, was to find her voice and ask Charlie what was the matter.

So then Charlie said "I have figured you out at last, you *mongrel*."

Well Dorothy had been called quite a few harsh names in her life by gentlemen, but no one had ever used the word "mongrel," and it really made quite a deep impression. Because it was practically the first time that Dorothy ever heard Charlie pass a remark that seemed to call for attention.

But Charlie Gwynn had not even commenced. And the words that he called Dorothy were new to her vocabulary because, after all, Charlie had a colledge education that came to his ade. I mean, where Dorothy's other admirers could only use words that were quite common, Charlie knew classical terms that reminded the girl of terrible thoughts, on account of not knowing what they meant. And when he finally termed Dorothy an *Undisciplined Troll* the sensation was tremendous. And all Dorothy could do was swallow.

Well then Charlie stopped long enough to catch his breath, and he started in on Gerald. And the first word he called Gerald was a French word called "macaroo" which is the word for the kind of a gentleman who does his living off of girls. And then he went on to translate it into an English word, that I would not even write down.

Well, as Dorothy listened to Charlie Gwynn, she lost more and more of her self possession. And quite a lot of respect for Charlie began to take its place. And finally Dorothy broke in, and grabbed Charlie by the hand and invited him to listen to her side. I mean, in Dorothy's heart, she knew that she did not have any side, but she was trying to do some quick thinking and think up one.

But Charlie Gwynn said that he was in a hurry, because he had begun to realize that he had neglected his own kind of people long enough. So he was going to attend an exclusive party, where he would find Muriel Devanant, who had breeding and knew the defanition of the word called Honor. And he was going to make her a proposition to become his bride that very night.

Well Dorothy became frantick. And she held Charlie by the hand and tried to use force. But at that, Charlie Gwynn turned on Dorothy and gave her a vigarous push into a corner that knocked her down. And then he said a permanent good bye and went out and slammed the door.

Well Dorothy sat there in the corner like a stone. And Dorothy began to wonder. And then she began to think. And then she began to realize that under all of his social polish and delightful manners, Charlie Gwynn was really more competent to make her feel humbel than anybody she had ever met.

Well that night Henry and I dropped in at the Club Zig Zag. I mean I always like to drop in at night clubs because I always like to be sure that the nurse is giving the Little Stranger his bottle at 3 A.M. and all of the night clubs have to close at 3 A.M. So if I come home at 3 A.M. every night, everything always seems to work out by skedule.

So Henry and I were sitting there in the Club Zig Zag, when the Orchestra Leader came out and made the announcement that Miss Dorothy Shaw would not be able to appear because she was vialently taken ill in her dressing room. Well, of course Henry and I went right back to Dorothy's dressing room to find out for ourselves and when we got there, Dorothy was violently sick to her stomack. And between times, she was in quite a bad case of histericks.

Well it seems that what happened was, that after Charlie Gwynn left Dorothy, she felt that she did not feel as if she could face her audience. So she went over to Gerald's dressing room to tell him that she had a vialent headache. Well

Gerald was not in his dressing room, but while Dorothy was awaiting, she noted a telegram on his dressing room shelf, that was opened. And then she noted that it seemed to be addressed to her. So then she read it. And it was the famous telegram from Mr. Ziegfield. But instead of Mr. Ziegfield offering *Gerald* and she $1000 dollars a week, the telegram was addressed to Dorothy personally, and it offered Dorothy $1000 a week, alone. But it said that she would have to get rid of her dancing partner, on account of his noncompetency. So then Dorothy began to realize that Gerald's intentions were not really so honorable, but he wanted to have his rights to the $1000 a week made legal.

Well Dorothy stood there reading it over and over again, when Gerald came in. So Gerald was not sure that Dorothy had read far enough to incriminate him, so he made quite a quick grab to snatch it. So then it became give and take, back and fourth with vialence on both sides. So finally Dorothy reached for something to throw, and picked up a bottle of Gerald's hair tonic. Well, in the crash that followed, the hair tonic got strewn all over Dorothy. And the oder of all that perfumed hair tonic, added to Dorothy's state of nerves, was what made Dorothy so vialently sick to the stomack. And that was when she decided that she did not care to smell it any more.

Well as soon as I calmed Dorothy down she started in to become quite a problem. I mean she had broken her engagement to Gerald in the midst of the struggle, and I have never seen anybody so vialently in love as Dorothy had suddenly become toward Charlie Gwynn since she lost him. And she decided to start out in a taxi cab and go to the Ritz, and Sherries, and the Park Lane and practically every spot on Park Avenue where exclusive parties are the rule, to find Charlie, and get hold of him before he committed the errer of getting engaged to Muriel Devanant.

Well, I told Dorothy that she could not go into exclusive parties, and make a scene where she had not

been invited. But Dorothy said that she would not make a scene, but she just wanted to tell Charlie in a few plain words that she had heard rumors that Muriel Devanant had the reputation of going with a girl friend, to the exclusion of the male sex. So Muriel was never cut out to be a housewife.

Well I told Dorothy in a case like that, Muriel Devanant would probably refuse Charlie's proposal. But it seems that the Devanant family was in need of the Gwynn family fortune, and Muriel was no exception, even to the point of personal inconvenience.

Well, I tried to stop Dorothy, by telling her that she ought not to deal in personalities at a party where she had not been invited. But Dorothy kept right on getting into her clothes to go out, so I had to start in to think. So I thought up a plan. And I told Dorothy that Henry and I would accompany her, and then she and I could wait outside in the taxi cab, while we sent Henry inside enquiring for Charlie Gwynn. Because anybody that looks like Henry does, can walk right in and out of exclusive parties and practically never be noticed. But if girls like Dorothy or I went in, we might be deteckted. And as soon as Henry found Charlie, he could bring him outside and the whole scene could take place in the privacy of our own taxi cab.

So Dorothy finally gave in. And we started at the Ritz and we stopped at every place that we came to. And finally at Pierres, Henry heard the fatal news that Charlie Gwynn had attended, but he had left half an hour ago to escort Miss Devanant home.

Well, I really became quite unnerved about the state of Dorothy. I mean, I was even afraid to let Dorothy go home to her own apartment in her condition. And Dorothy did not seem to mind where she went, so we took her home to our apartment. And we led her to the salon, with quite a vacant stare, and when we got inside the door, who was sitting there but Charlie Gwynn?

Well, then it all came out. And it turned out that Charlie had heard

rumors about Muriel Devanant himself, but when girls are athletic in the first place, how can anybody tell why they dress that way. So in the heat of his anger he went to Pierres to get revenge on Dorothy at any price.

Well, in the lobby of Pierres he met Muriel Devanants Mother, who was going home, and he told her that he must see Muriel to ask her something. So Mrs. Devanant was quite thrilled. And she told Charlie, that when he brought the dear child home, she would be awaiting to hear the good news.

Well, Charlie went into the party looking here and there for Muriel. But when he found her, she was dressed in a new black evening model of the modern day, that was practically a dinner coat, holding quite a quarrel with her girl chum because she caught her at a florist sending a bouquay of vialets to a French actress who was notorious for her reputation of having practically no gentlemen acquaintances of any virility. And Charlie had walked up behind and listened to the quarrel. So he changed his mind. And he made the excuse to Muriel, that what he wanted to ask her, was the question of some polo pony or other, and he saw her home from the party and left her at the foot of her stairs.

And besides, by that time, Charlie had decided that it was practically no use to fight with the kind of feeling he held about Dorothy. Because, after all, he is the kind that only has one woman. So he wanted to find out what Dorothy wanted to do next. So then I made a motion to Henry to tip toe out of the salon, to avoid their embarassment.

Well the Gwynn family always automatically disinherited Charlie whenever he did the wrong thing, but this time they could not do it, because Dorothy's lawyer had collected so much legal evadents on them that he practically held them in the palm of his hand, provided they wanted to remain outside of jail. So they could do nothing against the romance in a financial way, but socially they preferred not to be present.

So I told Dorothy that under the circumstances, the wedding really ought to be in some justice of the peace's back room, where the bridegrooms family's absents would be overlooked by gossip. But Dorothy said that she was going to have just as large a ceremony as Muriel Devanant or any other of Charlie's admirers would have, if they had been selected. And what was even worse, Dorothy had telegraphed to California for her father to arrive for the ceremony. Well, I told Dorothy that a large ceremony in a church would be sure to be a social failure, especially with a father, giving the bride away, whose only public appearance had been jumping off of roofs of buildings into a tank full of water at street fairs. But Dorothy said that there was a rumor going on in New York about her that she wanted to spike, and she could do it by having a father make a personal appearance in a large gathering.

Well, I began to feel very very worried because, after all, I was to be the Matron of Honor, and if it turned out to be a social failure, it would reflect on me. So I gave Dorothy a last warning, but her only reply was to order steel engraved invitations at Cartiers. So I helped Dorothy address the envelopes with quite a few forebodings to everybody in the Social Register, and Dorothy's personal set besides.

Well finally all of the refusals and exceptences started to come in. And the younger society set excepted, but the older set refused with only one exception, and that was old lady Vandervent, who does not know all of the evil that is going on in the world, on account of only reading The Christian Science Moniter. So she did not know that Charlie Gwynn was marrying a girl like Dorothy.

Well, when Dorothy and I went down to the Grand Central Station to meet Dorothy's father, he got off of the train with four large valises, that it took two red caps a piece to even lift off of the ground, on account of the heavy pacific gravity of the liquor which was practically all they contained. And he had made it all himself, in a solid copper still, presented to him by Dorothy on a birthday he had. And the reason he brought it to New York was not so much that he cared whose liquor he drank, as it was personal pride in his own acheevement. But that kind of an acheevement is not the kind of an acheevement that ads anything to a large church ceremony.

But the way it all turned out, sending for Mr. Shaw was really quite a happy thought. Because he has had quite a lot of experience, handing girls down off of trapezes with galantry and bowing to the throng at street fairs. So when he gave Dorothy away, he did it with the most graceful gesture that I have ever seen inside of a church.

And, after the ceremony, came the wedding reception at my salon. And I really must pay quite a few compliments to the way a few of us behaved. I mean, all of the girls who were outside of the Social Register, were so impressed by the impression Dorothy's wedding had made on them, that they were practically overcome by the sanktity of the occasion. And, as far as Dorothy was concerned, she would not even touch a drop of it, because she might do something to bring down the new found rath of her Lord and Master. And, as far as Charlie was concerned, he had never touched it since the time that he became sober. Because, being hypocritical was what won Dorothy's heart, and Charlie never wanted to get tolerant again. And when it came to the Bride's father, he was really drinking as if he had been born and bread in the Society set that was making all of the noise. But, while they were becoming more and more vulger, Mr. Shaw was only becoming more and more galant. So he was an ornament at any reception.

Well, I tried to lead the younger set a good example, by refusing champagne in quite a loud tone of voice, especially in the earshot of Mrs. Vandervent. But the way that they were drinking, finally became so obvious that I had to go and sit in a corner by Mrs. Vandervent to hold my dignity. So then we went into a conversation. And it all came out, that she and I had practically the same ideals about everything.

Well, the Society guests finally reached a point where Mrs. Vandervent said that she could not remain without giving her sanction, so she decided to go home. And she said that she wanted nobody else but that delightful Mr. Shaw to be her escort.

Well Dorothy told her Father to do it but when they went out the door, Dorothy whispered to her father and said, "If you make a pass at old Lady Vandervent, Pop, you take the first train right out of New York Society in the morning."

But the next day Mrs. Vandervent's footman told my chauffer, and he told my maid, that Dorothy's father did 'make a pass' at Mrs. Vandervent, but she enjoyed it.

So Dorothy's wedding really turned out for the best after all, because the next morning Mrs. Vandervent called me up on the telephone, to apologize for the way all of her social born friends had behaved in the privacy of my apartment. And Mrs. Vandervent said that it was girls like Dorothy and I who could remain sober under such an occasion and be impressed, that had got to carry on the fabrick of Society. So she and I have become practically inseprable, and that is how I came to get into the Social Register.

Well, the last I saw of Dorothy was when Henry and I went down to see she and Charlie off on a boat that went to Havana. And Charlie, in his sober state, kept ordering Dorothy around, until she was practically in the 7th Heaven.

And if Charlie keeps on ordering Dorothy to do the right thing at the proper moment, I really should not be surprised if Dorothy would be the next one to get into the Social Register. I mean, the way they are having to put Society people out of it, somebody or other has got to take their place. And I shall be quite delighted when Dorothy does, because Dorothy and I have been in practically everything else together but that. And if Dorothy does get in it, at the finish, I shall really have to begin to believe, after all, that the World is quite a good place to live in, even in the case of a girl like Dorothy.

Dreams

by Sigrid Undset

LOUISE DAHL-WOLFE

I dream nearly every night. I dare say my dreams are now like everyone else's dreams. Odds and ends of thoughts I hadn't time to think out during the day, faces casually seen, a paragraph in a paper that I paid no attention to while awake—these are the things that usually turn up again now in my dreams. And as a rule the dream is forgotten when I wake up . . . now.

It was different when I was a child. From the age of ten or twelve and onward through the years of transition.

No doubt the sleeping brain always acts according to the same laws—plays with impressions that are left over like chips and shavings from the day's work. If my dreams in those days were so different it must have been due to the great number of impressions I was already picking up. But child as I was, I could do nothing with them—nor had I time to think about such things.

I have made up stories as long as I can remember—long and marvelous stories full of strange happenings—for the entertainment of my brothers and sisters. And still more wonderful stories for myself alone.

Of course in those days I had no idea of what poetry was—that it was the true inwardness of human beings and of all that concerns them.

Rarely did anything happen to me in these dreams. I simply *was*. Suddenly I found myself in some beautiful tract of country, or floated through many regions, dreamlands, unutterably beautiful and charming. But the whole of this dream world had the features of the world I knew. The Christiania valley, places in Eastern Norway where I had stayed, the country round a little town in Denmark where I often spent the summer—my dream world was like a strongly scented essence of their peculiar beauty.

I don't remember that it was ever winter in any of these dream pictures. And rarely summer or autumn, rarely sunshine—almost always my dreams were of bare early springtime with pale green meadows, moist and flowery, and a soft light of rainy weather. The heavy gloom of sleep surrounds these visions—only the little picture itself stands out sharp and clear. I have seen Japanese woodcuts which appear to represent a dream landscape of this sort.

At intervals of years one of these dreams may suddenly rise up in my memory, making me close my eyes to retain the fleeting vision. While walking in the street, while sitting at my work, it is there all at once—and it brings a painful longing, like homesickness, for the beautiful world that does not exist—for my own fresh, keen senses of long ago.

A misty swamp—a wet meadow where I have plucked yellow

dream peonies, which looked like gigantic globe flowers—a flooded tract where I floated in a strangely low boat among sedges and tree-tops, whose foliage I could trace with my eyes deep down in the gray water, under a gray sky which shaded into a shining white, like a mackerel's belly, toward the horizon—a yellow sandy road on which I walked between peat bogs and lean brown meadows toward a high bank overgrown with scrub, where I knew there was a robbers' den in the steep sandy bluff—and I shall never, never get so far.

But there were very few dreams in which anything happened. They are the ones I still remember, and the ones I liked best to dwell on in those days.

Only one of these dreams was of an erotic nature. I believe I dreamed it in the winter when I was between twelve and thirteen.

No doubt it was to be referred to something that happened to me in the previous summer. But when this happened it made no impression on me.

I was walking along a road with two grown-up ladies—who they were I did not see in my dream. On the other hand, I saw the road quite clearly. It ran by the side of the fjord outside the little town in Denmark. It was dusk; I had the impression that the beacon on the point was alight, but what was on either side of me I did not see, merely divined its presence in the half-light of the dream. The field on one side was thick with little white labiate flowers in the dry, short grass; on the other side the water lapped very softly on the beach. And a pale silvery light lay on the skyline, between the water and the clouds.

I was waiting for someone—for something—in my dream I did not know for what. But I was happy, in a deep and tranquil way—as though the air I breathed were happiness itself.

Then we met some people. The two ladies walked on with some of these—passed out of the dream. One of those we met had stopped behind me. And I too

stood still. In my dream I did not know who he was—no one in particular, or that I had ever met before—merely one for whom I had been waiting.

From behind he laid his hands on my shoulders and bent me backward, till my face was looking up into his. But I remember that I did not see his face; I believe he vanished at that moment. . . .

What I do remember is the overpowering sense of my own existence. Presumably I had never before been conscious that I was a being, detached and isolated from the world around me and from other people. The feeling was so sudden and so powerful that I woke with a start.

I was a child when I had this dream. And I remained a child—for a long time after it. All the same—how much of the boundless possibilities of love, of what is new each time, as it comes afresh to each one—how much of all this was essentially revealed in this dream?

But I was a child in those days. There was another dream which at the time made a far more powerful impression on me.

It was a dream I had at the age of sixteen.

Again I was in the same little town. I dreamed I was sitting on the stone wall surrounding the little park which is the pride of the place. And this time I knew very well for whom I was waiting.

Behind me the foliage of the park hung dark as the edge of a forest. Before me lay the undulating country, checkered green and yellow with meadow and cornfield. The thorn bushes below were alive as usual with the shrill metallic voices of sparrows, and above the fields the larks were trilling as usual. It was summer and bright sunshine in this dream.

Then there came a dark man walking through the big rye field—the one I was waiting for. But he was even taller, even slighter, he stooped and had a black, broad-brimmed hat on. No, it wasn't he. . . .

All at once he stopped on the

narrow sandy path between the rye field and the thorn bushes. He raised his head and looked at me. The larks stopped singing, and the twitter of the sparrows broke off suddenly in a sort of gasp, and the birds shrank into the bushes in dead silence. I saw his face——

Why didn't I wake in terror——?

It was like the face of a man with a concertina whom we children used to call "the leper"—our horror. A face from the dead whiteness of whose skin every feature seemed to have perished; only round the eyes were there living red sores, and the mouth was like a narrow, bloody rift. . . .

But the eyes of the vision were not dead like those of the street musician—from their bleeding rims they stared at me, alive and shining, into me, through me—more alive than life. And his mouth broadened in a soundless laughter.

Then he raised one hand and thrust it into the hedge: as children strip the currants from a bunch, he stripped the stunned and frightened sparrows from the branches of the thorn bush and clenched his hand. I felt the tender bones being crushed, and I saw the blood run out on his thin white hand, heard it drip on the sand of the path.

And he laughed up at me soundlessly.

—Then I suddenly found myself in an attic, where I used to play as a child, and the golden sunshine poured in among the old trunks and boxes and lumber. But outside, underneath the window stood the man, sweeping up the sparrows in his hands and crunching them. And his mouth called me without a sound, and his eyes with the bleeding sores around them ordered me to come, right through the brick wall.

I was over by the window. I saw the yellow high road winding up and down, where I had walked in happiest hours—the light suddenly went out over the bright landscape, and I saw nothing but *him.*

He was standing among the sweet briers. He had raised his white, wasted face and was looking up at me, smiling with his narrow, bloody lips and his sore eyes; he laughed and called me silently, raising one bloody hand.

And I knew I must obey—that hand, which would crush me to pieces, as it had crushed the terrified sparrows.

So I flung myself out of the window. And then I awoke. . . .

I thought of nothing but my dream for the next few days. And there have been many times since when it has been often in my mind. I shall never forget the face I saw in that dream.

I used to wonder, in those days, what that dream might mean. For I was certain it meant something.

That face—I have called it the face of Death, and the face of Life, and the face of Love.

But of course it was only something I dreamed. Scientists say that a dream lasts at the most three minutes. But they say, too, that there is no such thing as time. . . .

—*Translated from the Norwegian by A. G. Chater*

Life Sentence

by Kay Boyle

The boy lay on his side, back turned against the light as well as against the sound of the woman's voice reading aloud, and stared through the bars of the long narrow crib at the wallpaper's red and white design. The wall was so close that with a fingernail he could draw what he liked on it, alter the women in the toile de Jouy until strips of paper hung like saliva from their mouths as he distorted them, or scrape their eyes until only circles of white plaster showed blank as horror while they still sat, unable to rise and gather their skirts up and go, fixed there, their little parasols open under the big round softly dipping branches of the crimson trees.

It was warm and he had kicked the covers off and his legs, tapering, slender, fretful, bare almost to the knee because the pajamas had been bought new two years back, were drawn up double. In a little while the long crib would be too small the way the pajamas were already too small, and after-

LOUISE DAHL-WOLFE

ward it might be the room and then the flat and then the street outside that would have to be thrust aside or else exchanged for something bigger. Because of the hot black look in his heavy eyes and the color in the sulky mouth things would have to keep on altering for him, one thing be quickly, arrogantly discarded for the next, objects kicked hard and impatiently enough eventually giving way to something better or worse or merely to something different. Now he turned over on his back and beat his bare feet in the bed.

"I'm thirsty. I want to get up," he said, and the woman's voice which had been reading high,

young and pretty in the room now stopped. The boy gave a flap with his body like a fish tossed out on land, not in desperation for life but in fury with the summer heat and the soreness in his throat and the simple childish words she read. "I want a drink," he said again.

One lamp was lit in the room, one with a chromium base that stood on the corner of the marble mantelpiece. The shade was imitation parchment and the light it funneled fell on the divan made up as a bed where she had been lying reading the book about the donkey. The sheet and pillowslip were green and now she sat up from them in a thin green dress, half dressing gown, half a housewife's overall in artificial silk, clean, trim and tailor-made. She thrust her bare legs out from the covers and they hung down toward the floor, the skin pure white, the ankles and insteps veined blue, and with her toes, the nails on them varnished ruby and opaque, she felt a moment for the high-heeled gaping slippers which had fallen sideways as if just home from a dance and dropped in weariness there by the bed.

"When you're all right we'll go to the zoo," she said and the boy saw her head drop to stop the yawn or to seek the slippers too. "Next Sunday if your throat's all right." Her hair was short and light and artificially curled and oiled; but the color at least was its own, a misty yellow like the hair of little girls who later on will darken, with no copper or even gold in it, almost as if it had succeeded in having no describable color at all. Even growing up, even marrying and having a child she hadn't darkened, or perhaps the white hair growing imperceptibly into the blond had kept it light. When she leaned over he could see the scalp where the part was, white and clean and the smooth curls twisted up from it. "But you'll have to begin sleeping the night through if you want to get well. If you don't sleep you won't get well nearly so quickly," she said.

She crossed the rug and the waxed parquet to the door into the hall and from his crib the boy watched her in the short green almost transparent dress and the high heels going out for the bottle of lemonade in the kitchen. When she came back carrying the little bottle and the glass, he beat his feet in the bed again.

"I want to go out now," he said.

"Yes," she said, pouring the lemonade out. "At one or two o'clock in the morning. It's a very good idea." He pushed himself up, half sitting against the pillow, his face hot, his eyes black and, like objects glazed with varnish, singularly magnified and bright. "You drink this," she said, "and then try to go to sleep a little."

"If I want to go out I don't see why I can't go out," he said. He drank some of the warmish lemonade and the needles of it pricked behind his nose. Every time he took a swallow he looked up under his brows at her, hot, feverish, resentful. She looked very clean, the skin of her neck fresh and pale, and the arms naked almost to the shoulder thin and weak-looking and perfectly white. "If my father was here he'd make you let me do what I wanted," he said.

She took the empty glass out of his hand.

"Do you want to drink some more?" she said.

"No," he said, looking at his feet. "It's not cold enough and I don't like the taste. It's not good. It went bad because you left the top off."

"Now you try to go to sleep," she said. She stood by the crib holding the bottle and she might not have been talking to a child at all but talking to someone old enough to know, perhaps older than herself, but at least someone born cannier. "You know what happens tomorrow morning. You know the shops open."

"You said it's one o'clock," he said. He knocked one foot against the bars of the bed. "So if it's one o'clock then it isn't tomorrow morning; it's this morning. It's today the shops open."

"All right," she said. She put the glass and the bottle of lemonade on the mantelpiece and put the stopper back in it. "All right, this morning. In a little while now, in just a few hours Camille will come and make the coffee and I'll have to get up and dress——"

"If it's today then get dressed now," the boy said. She came to the crib and leaned over it and moved the pillow slowly, inch by inch against his resistance, from behind him. "I don't want it smoothed out," he said, holding hard and furiously to the bars, his head turned from the sight of her as she beat the pillow out and laid her hand beneath his head to slip it under him again.

In the daytime, lying on his other side, he could see across the carpet and the furniture to the window and through it the chimneys of other houses standing against the colorless city sky, and one unpainted wooden dome—a theatre's or a church's—a little below the thick forest of jointed stovepipes and tin crowns that turned fluctuating in search of the wind's or any air's direction. He could see all day this portion of the city's roofs, the faded sky, and these repairs, as individual as millinery, that had been made to chimneys so that clogged smoke could escape them; or he could see Camille in the room, sweeping, or see the doctor when he came, but the thin white breakable arms and the high heels and the black put on the lashes were as transient, as fragmentary, as alluring as a movie-actress's passage across the screen. All afternoon the air quivered with heat above the chimneys' heads, passive until the evening cooking began and the smoke stammered out across the sunset, and Camille walked in bedroom slippers in the hall or kitchen, slowly doing the room, slowly washing the dishes, slowly on but she could not quite find the words to say it. "Then I'd be with you more, I wouldn't have to get up and go out to work and I'd be here when you got home from school at night, and then on Thursdays . . ."

Don't tell me, he said, holding the sound in. Don't tell me.

"And then in the summer," her voice went musically on, clearly, effortlessly speaking like a bird's notes shaped in the dark. "Then next summer we'd be able to go away somewhere, you and I, perhaps to the seashore, instead of me having to stay here working in the city . . ."

Don't say it, he thought fiercely to himself. Don't say his name. I know it.

"When you grow up and when you meet a nice girl you like and you want to marry her," her voice went on, "then I'd do everything I could to make it easy for you. If you love a person you want them to be happy and I'd want you to find a girl your own age and I'd want you to marry her. I wouldn't be jealous of her or make trouble.

I'd understand everybody belongs to people their own age, and I know you'll fall in love with a girl sometime and then you'll want to marry——"

He lay hard on his back, his hands clenched.

"No, I'll never want to," he said. "I'll never want to get married."

"Oh, yes, you'll want to get married some day," she went on quietly, "and I won't say a word. I'll do everything I can to make it easy for you because I'll understand. Even if I mind I won't show it so you won't know and you won't be unhappy. People aren't supposed to live alone. No one ought to be expected to live alone," she said, the ego's whimper as they whirled almost resorted to, almost heard.

He lay still, tense and straight and hot in the bed, his hands holding tight to the pillow under his spine and hair. And what about my father, he thought savagely. What about him? What are you going to do about my father if somebody—if anybody—if someone else . . .

He had never got the story consecutively from anyone, only in pieces over the period of years he had been alive, and told in different voices. One year she had sent him away for the summer; she had sent him to Trouville where a cousin of hers had taken an apartment for July and August, not near the beach or anywhere near the hotels but in a back street of the town. That was two years ago, when he was nearly six, but he had not forgotten. He remembered the look even of the liquid in their glasses at the café table, perhaps the first time he noticed that this wine poured out clear green and then, when the water was spilled into it, turned to milk. He remembered the cousin although he had not seen her since that July, and only the hat of the friend sitting at the café table with her, and the words not for an instant confused with the value of the bucket and shovel they had bought him but just as absolute, just as enduring.

She said "his father" as though talking of someone who had passed by in the street, and she even looked toward something else until for a little while he still believed she was not speaking about him at all. The rain was falling beyond the café awning, a slanting broken downpour of seaside rain sliding drop by drop from the umbrellas and the awning fringe, and in the same voice that she might have said he couldn't go down to the beach that day she said to the friend who didn't know: "His father's in prison. I never believed a thing like that could happen in our family; but then it's his side not hers. . . ."

He was thinking about the new bucket and shovel and about his mother coming up from Paris on Sunday when the stores were closed—because the thing hadn't happened yet, it was just about to happen. The words had been said but it was as if they had not yet been heard: the cousin and the friend, the two women sat there drinking and talking together while he looked out beyond the cornice of the awning at the rain and swung his bare legs in his sandals underneath the table's edge.

"My father was killed in the war. He was killed in the war," he said, as pleased and certain as if it was the conscious, not the subconscious taking the defense up now. "My father was a general in the war," he said louder so that they must stop and hear. "I never saw him because he was killed before I was born in the war. That's why I never saw him."

The cousin turned away from her friend and looked across at him and smiled. Her cheeks were full and high and hard and he could see the grains of carelessly put on powder lying on the skin, and in the lenses of her glasses he watched the people under open umbrellas passing, no signal or gleam of sight behind the glass but the perfect, the absorbing motion picture of the wet shining street.

"Yes, of course he was, of course," she said. Her face was mottled with color now from the drink or heat and she put one short hand forward in its white cotton glove and lifted the hair back off his forehead where it clung to the skin. He was sitting up straight on the café's red tin chair, not having started to be afraid yet or to know, still watching in her glasses the movement of the people and the cars, and then the friend leaned toward him. Under the brim of white braided straw there was nothing, a small curiously bright cipher in which stood the edges of her two gold teeth. In two years the words had not altered but traveled intact through inconceivable time and space toward another and profounder hearing.

"What war?" she had said, leaning over the table. "What war, my little Maurice?"

He looked at the cousin's face again, and because it was not that year but the year following that he began to count back to 1918 and see the impossibility of it by ten years at least, he looked in surprise and mystification again at the woman friend.

"You tell her, you say what war it was," he said to the cousin. She sat silent, smiling at him, putting his curls back clumsily with her fingers. He could see the button of her glove forced into the buttonhole beneath the crushed pink oval of her palm's squeezed flesh as the hand moved just above his brows. "You tell her what war," he said, and then he stopped saying it abruptly and stopped looking at their faces, not out of bewilderment any longer but now because he knew. So it was my father she meant, so it was me.

When the cousin spoke she did not give him any answer but said: "I think her mistake was not to tell him. That's where she's made a lot of trouble for herself. Letting him have his father's picture beside his bed and this thing about being a general . . ."

The next time anything was said about it, it had another sound, clearer, simpler, more accurate than the truth. It was Sunday when his mother came and he asked her; she was going to stay until Monday morning but because he asked her they went away before. For a long time after she came he did not remember; they went to the beach and sat down in the sand, the three of them, eating raw tomatoes and drinking grapefruit juice out of the bottles, and then he went in wading. But when he remembered he came running back, the pail and shovel left near the water in the damp sand, coming back to ask her to keep on telling the story to him or else make up another. Lie to me, he said with his lips against her bare smooth knee, lie to me, my love.

"Why didn't you say they didn't kill him in the war but put him in prison?" he said out loud.

She was sitting in her bathing suit rubbing her arms with the oil and when he said this her hand stopped moving, the brown slender fingers motionless but clasping still the forearm's even flesh.

"Who?" she said, really in fright, as if the ghost had walked toward them and stretched out his hand.

"My father," the boy said. He rubbed one finger, with the sandlike pepper on it, across her knee and watched the grains fall away. And suddenly she began moving, the legs drawing up to stand, the hand putting the cork back in the sunburn lotion, the head jerking to look at the cousin. When she stood up she stooped at once to pick up the towel and bag and then she let them drop again and started tying the ribbons of her bathing shoes. But her hands moved so quickly that she could not make the laces hold around her ankles and she picked up the towel and flowered-cretonne bag out of the sunlight again and tried to speak.

The cousin was sitting spread upon the sand, wearing a big straw hat and embroidering under the shade of it, working with silks, dark green and yellow, knot after silky fraying knot into the crumpled grayish linen on which the

pattern was stamped in ink. She made no sign that she had heard them speaking and her hands did not falter. Only when his mother said in a quick low trembling voice, "You bitch, you dirty bitch," the cousin's face choked with color and she began quietly, embroidering still, to cry.

He stood with his bare toes moving in and out of the sand watching the tears fall black and separate on the linen in her hands, and then his mother seized him by the shoulder and turned him savagely away and up the beach. She did not say anything until they got to the wooden walk and had gone along it until they stood opposite the street he and the cousin took twice or more often every day. There, facing the two rows of big-headed golden nails studding the way in the avenue for pedestrians to cross, she said: "They had no right to put him in prison. That's why I didn't say it."

Then he remembered the bucket and shovel left standing in the damp sand, but he could not go back. They packed their things before the cousin got to the apartment, and then they left for Paris, traveling at night, and on the train she told him a little more. She said: "I didn't tell you because it was a mistake. I always thought something would happen and the mistake would be corrected and I paid lawyers, I paid lawyers for three years and then it seemed nothing else could be done. Then I began telling you he was dead."

"When will he be dead?" he said, and he felt his heart rushing forward in bliss with the swift rushing of the train.

"What do you mean? What are you trying to say?" she said. She was looking out the window, her head turned from him so she would not have to look at him and know.

"When are they going to kill him? When will they guillotine him?" he said, and a fresh and inexplicable joy gushed from his heart; for the first time seeing prison as a pause, troubled and

vague as purgatory and like it suspended between life and death, for the first time believing in the possible silencing of one man's voice in her ears, the perfect blotting out of one man's face.

Almost at once the girl began coming to the apartment that summer in Paris. At first she came back with his mother from work at night, and then she began coming earlier, perhaps an hour or less before his mother rang the bell. She would hang up her coat in the hall before coming into the sitting room where the beds were, and on her way to the mantelpiece she'd say, "Hello, kid" when he looked up from his lessons or the Meccano set. She wore low heels and fringed tongues slapped on the front of her shoes as she walked. She'd put her shell cigarette case down on the mantel by the lamp and take her plain hat off and throw her head back so that the short narrow nose looked smaller even, and stand there with her legs spread running the pocket comb through her dark short-cropped hair. Or she might not wear a hat but come in and fling herself down on the divan where his mother had slept and stretch and yawn and lean up on one elbow to read the evening paper she had brought, carrying it rolled tight as a stick in her hand. She wore a square silver watch strapped on her wrist and she'd look at it from time to time until some time after seven the doorbell rang and Camille walked out of the kitchen to open it; or else he jumped up and went to open it first; or else the girl sat up abruptly and swung her feet off the bed and said, "I'm going! Wait," and crossed the room and pushed past them in the hall, stoop-shouldered, tall and thin, and reached the door before them.

In the late afternoon or early evening the girl was this one thing: silent except for the sound of her yawning or humming, carelessly, casually insulting as she came in and flung herself, with her shoes on, down on his mother's bed. But at night she altered;

with the darkness, like a miracle, the alteration came. She became so young, so reckless that Maurice sitting at the table with them and seeing the wine come and go and the things to eat getting better when she stayed watched with excitement first one bright wild face and then the other. After the month of July was over he began liking the way they shrieked their words with laughter at each other and the dances they did together to the radio music once the dishes had been taken out. If he woke late at night, he knew she was there still even before he quite heard the sound of their voices from the kitchen where they sat on the two stools smoking, or doing their nails, or merely talking after the light was out in the sitting room and he was put to bed. All night it seemed he could hear their voices: the high delicate one and the lower, quieter, surer one, as if it was the first that always asked the questions and the second that answered, mingling like the drowsy voices of people mingling in sleep.

She was a Russian princess, or that is she had been a princess before the changes had come about in Russia, his mother told him. Once she had joined a roving White Russian company of cavalry and for two years she had passed for a man among them, and once she had walked up to the glass the body of Lenin lay under and cursed him in front of the guards, before all the people, and ended by spitting right on the glass.

"And then?" said Maurice, still too young to ask how she had got back to Russia or why she had been allowed to stay but listening to this story his mother might have invented for someone younger or else more guileless.

"And then she came to France, she had to leave the country after that, and she became an automobile racer," his mother said. She was getting ready to go to work in the morning, standing in her black velvet dress in front of the bathroom mirror and putting the mascara on. "Sometimes she wears her cap like an automobile racer now, on the side of her head sort of. You notice when she comes in if she doesn't make you think of an automobile racer."

Or another time, getting ready in the bathroom in the morning and looking at her own face in the sunlight that came in through the window from the court she said quickly: "Look, Maurice, I'm getting a little gray in my hair now and I haven't done anything with my life. I'm just the same age as Baya and she looks so young and she's been to nearly every country and ridden camels across deserts and I never do anything but sell perfume and powder and sometimes go out dancing somewhere. That's all I'll ever be able to do and Baya—she's my age, she isn't any younger than I am—she's going to be an aviator."

"Are you and Baya twins?" Maurice said, sliding on the bathtub's edge.

And his mother said: "Yes, we're twins. We're twins, we're almost like sisters. Only she's braver than I am. She's more like a man."

It was on another Sunday that his mother and Baya had oysters and wine before lunch on a café terrace in the Avenue de la Grande Armée; it must have been March because his *trottinette* was new still and he went pedaling fast up and down the sidewalk while they sat at a table in the sun, Baya with no cap on, and her short hair brushed back, wearing a dark green jacket with a green leather flower in her buttonhole. The man, the implacable rival who had lived in photographs and in remembrance and legend with them since the beginning, was dead this spring; wiped out without the aid of war, without the guillotine by the two women's laughter as they rocked over the empty blue oyster shells in the first sun together. He had stopped fearing his possession, stopped needing him almost, since he knew he lay quiet now, the spring earth flung down upon his face, finally expired in his mother's memory. When they had finished, the two women took arms and walked slowly, their heads down, talking, not looking up or seeing the people coming back from church, but moving through them like dreamers walking.

Once back in the apartment they could not eat because of all the things they had to say. They sat at the table with their cigarettes while he ate steadily and rapidly, great sides of crust pushed into the gravy and carried dripping to his mouth, while his mother rose at the required moments and as if moving in a dream changed his plate and brought the cheese to him; dreamily, speechlessly moving around the table with her eyes on the girl who sat talking with the cigarette burning down short in her fingers, talking and talking in meaningless intensity and gravity of things that had happened in other places with other people, her head lowered so that only the thick black brows and the forehead and the dark uncombed pompadour showed. When his mother passed by her with the fruit, Baya caught up his mother's hand and pressed the long slender fingers against her mouth as if in pain.

"Maurice, darling, have an apple, have a pear," his mother said quickly and she put the plate of fruit down on the table near him.

About four o'clock that day Baya came into the sitting room with the clothes on. She had got them out of the trunk in the closet in the hall. She was dressed as a French army officer, the visored cap, black with gold braid on it, tipped on the side of her head, even the boots seeming to fit exactly, and the crop stuck under her armpit, and the face small tough and reckless. It was something so palpable this time that all the rest he had been told or overheard or merely imagined about his father seemed as scant and as equivocal as fabrication. He followed her in wonder out onto the balcony in the sun where she leaned on the railing, and his mother followed, laughing.

"I'm going to let all the neighbors see me and make a scandal for you," Baya said. She lit a cigarette and dropped the dead match down onto the pavement five flights below where the Sunday afternoon families were wandering by, even the children dressed elegantly in black, the little boys as sailors in heavy mourning, the palefaced girls in serge and patent-leather slippers walking two by two.

"What kind of a scandal? What do you mean by a scandal?" Maurice said, looking in wonder at her.

"They'll think your mother has a gentleman calling on her," Baya said.

"No, she wouldn't," he said. He stood with his hands behind him near the window, looking in stupefaction at the jacket, the breeches, the polished leather. "I wouldn't let her. I wouldn't let a man come here."

It seemed as if it were the first day of spring, even the earth that had been left in the flowerpots and forgotten all winter in the corners of the balcony asking for life now that the reviving of the world's life had begun; and his mother, weak with laughter at the sight of Baya, leaned against the sun-heated stone of the apartment house's wall and gasped out the high-pitched and partially broken sound he sometimes believed was singing beginning.

"My dear, the weather is truly remarkable today, truly remarkable," Baya said in a manly deep and artificial voice, in imitation of what might be an army officer's elegant French or what she thought the neighbors expected of her, and his mother put her handkerchief to her lips and cried with laughter. She did not stop even when Maurice, standing motionless in the sunlight, said:

"When did my father wear that uniform?"

Baya shook the cigarette ashes down toward the street and smiled at two girls passing on the other side, and Maurice's mother touched the ends of her lashes with her finger.

"My mascara's running. . . . He had it for his military service," she said. There was no strangeness or emotion in her voice and she went right on saying to Baya: "You know, his mother took it out of camphor when we were first married and she said, 'It's such superior cloth that I wake up at night and think of it lying wasted here in a trunk.'" She gave another burst of laughter. "She said, 'Let's hope they get on with their next war before the moths have a chance to get at it!'" Baya looked back over the epaulette on her shoulder for an instant and then went on smiling at the girls below. "And then when she was dying, poor thing, it all came out in the rest of them, the things she'd taught them young," his mother said and she blew her nose again and laughed. "She was

dying in the clinic in Rouen and when they found there wasn't any more hope for her, he sent me to the station to find out how much it was going to cost to have her sent from Rouen to Paris to be buried, and when he found out—of course, his sisters were in it too—it was more than the fare and so he said she'd have to come to Paris alive instead of coming dead by freight."

Maurice stood watching the blue figure leaning on the rail, unable still to walk across the balcony's stone and impersonally touch the cloth or lay his hand against the belt.

"Where did my father wear it? How long did he wear it? Why didn't you ever show it to me before?" he said.

Baya turned back to them from the street below and crossed her legs facing them and leaned backward on her elbows on the iron rail. She stood there looking at his mother's face, one smooth toe of the officer's boot tapping on the stone, her lip drawn up and softly whistling, before she began speaking.

"His uniform, his wife, his kid, the life he can't live handed me like a present," she said scarcely aloud, the casual, rakish smile neat as a boy's, the visored emblem of a nation's valor tipped carelessly over one ear.

This is an excerpt from Kay Boyle's novel Monday Night

The Lion in Love . . . To Mlle. Sévigné

A Fable by La Fontaine
Translated by Marianne Moore

Mademoiselle—goddess in-
    stead—
In whom the Graces find a school
Although you are more beautiful,
Even if with averted head,
Might you not be entertained
By a tale that is unadorned—
Observing without more than a
    quiver
A lion whom love knew how to
    conquer.
Love is a curious mastery,
In name alone a felicity.
Better know of than know the
    thing.
If too personal and thus trespass-
    ing,
I'm saying what may seem to you
    an offense,
A fable could not offend your ear.
This one, assured of your lenience,
Attests its devotion embodied here,
And kneels in sworn obedience.

Before their speech was ob-
    structed,
Lions or such as were attracted
To young girls, sought an alliance.
Why not? since as paragons of
    puissance,
They were at that time knightly
    fellows
Of mettle and intelligence
Adorned by manes like halos.

JERRY BAUER

The point of the preamble fol-
    lows.
A lion—one in a multitude—
Met in a meadow as he fared,
A shepherdess for whom he cared.

He sought to win her if he could,
Though the father would have
    preferred
A less ferocious son-in-law.
To consent undoubtedly was
    hard;
Fear meant that the alternate was
    barred.
Moreover, refuse and he foresaw
That some fine day the two might
    explain
Clandestine marriage as the chain
That fettered the lass, bewitched
    beyond cure,
By fashions conducive to hauteur,
And a fancy that shaggy shoulder-
    fur
Made her wilful lover handsomer.

The father with despair choked
    down,
Said though at heart constrained
    to frown,
"The child is a dainty one; better
    wait;
You might let your claw-points
    scratch her
When your heavy forepaws touch
    her.
You could if not too importunate,
Have your claws clipped. And
    there in front,
See that your teeth are filed blunt,
Because a kiss might be enjoyed
By you the more, I should think,
If my daughter were not forced to
    shrink
Because improvidently annoyed."
The enthralled animal mellowed.
His mind's eye having been shut-
    tered.
Without teeth or claws it followed
That the fortress was shattered.
Dogs were loosed; defenses were
    gone:
The consequence was slight resist-
    ance.

Love, ah Love, when your slip-
    knot's drawn,
We can but say, "Farewell, good
    sense."

Ghostly Father, I Confess

by Mary McCarthy

My gostly fader, I me confess,
First to God and then to you,

That at a window—wot ye
how?—
I stale a kiss of grete sweteness,
Which don was out of aviseness;
But it is doon not undoon now.
My gostly fader, I me confess,
First to God and then to you.

But I restore it shall doutless
Again, if so be that I mow;
And that to God I make a vow
And ells I axe foryefness.
Gostly fader, I me confess,
First to God and then to you.

The eyes gleamed benevolently behind the glasses. If she turned her head on the cushion, she could see them, and she kept doing this from time to time, hoping to surprise them in an expression of disapproval, of astonishment or regret—anything but that kindly neutrality. But they did not change, and finally she gave it up, dropped her head back on the cushion, and tried to relax. It was really against the rules (she sup-

CECIL BEATON

posed) to be flopping around there like a fish. He had never scolded her for it; now and then he would say gently, "Don't worry about what I think. Just let your own thoughts come."

"I dreamed I was seventeen," she said, "and I was matriculating at a place called Eggshell College." She could not resist a teasing smile and another glance up at him. "I must have dreamed that just to please you. It's custom-made. The womb fantasy."

"Go on with the dream," he said.

"Well," she continued. "There was a sort of an outing cabin. We had one at college. It was supposed to be great fun to spend the week-end in it. I never did. I

thought it was silly—you know, a vestigial trace of the goofy old days when they had chafing dishes and spreads and college sings and went to the Cider Mill for a binge. My aunt had the idea that college was still like that," she went on. "She tried to give me an electric doughnutmaker to take away with me when I was a freshman. It was the only present she ever offered me."

She knew without looking that she had coaxed a smile out of him. It was all right, then; she could go on. He understood her attitude toward the outing cabin. Often it was not so easy. She would spend half a session trying to show him, say, that a man they both knew was a ridiculous character, that a movie they had both seen was cheap. And it would be hopeless, absolutely hopeless, for he was that man, he was that movie; he was the outing cabin, the Popular Front, the League of American Writers, the *Nation* the *Liberal,* the *New Republic,* George S. Kaufman, Helen Hayes, colonial wallpaper, money in the bank, and two cocktails (or was it one?) before dinner. When she had worn herself out, he would remind her patiently, "It doesn't matter what I think, you know." But it did matter, of course. Sometimes it seemed to her that her analysis could never be finished until he could purge himself of the maple furniture in his waiting room, the etching of the Cathedral at Chartres that hung above his desk, the subscription to *Newsweek* that never ran out. Someone had once suggested to her that all this was a matter of policy, that a psychoanalyst in the decoration of his professional quarters aimed deliberately at that colorless objectivity, that rigorous job-lot asceticism that can be seen in its purest form in the residential hotel room.

The notion was pleasant but not really plausible. It was impossible to think of Dr. James as a male Cinderella who lived dangerously every night after office hours, and all day Sundays.

"What are you smiling about?" he asked.

"I'm thinking rude thoughts about you."

Damn my stream of consciousness, her mind said. Why must it keep harping on this embarrassing topic?

"Let's have them," he exclaimed, with that ghastly, hand-regulated cheerfulness that seemed to spurt out of him the more eagerly the more unpleasant were the facts to be faced. To listen to him, you might think that someone had just set a wonderful dinner before him.

"Oh, Dr. James," she sighed. "Let's skip it this time. You know what I think about you. It doesn't give me any pleasure to say it to your face."

"But your picture of me is very important," he said, in his pedagogical manner. "Not for what it says about me, but for what it says about you."

This angered her slightly. So he took no stock in her opinion, labeled it "aggression against the analyst," and dismissed it from his mind. Very well, then . . .

"I was thinking," she said, "how utterly fantastic it is to imagine you on a tear."

"Don't you suppose I have any fun?" There was a certain wistfulness in the question that must have got in by mistake.

"No doubt you do," she said, "but I bet you have to work awfully hard at it."

"What do you suppose I do for relaxation?"

Relaxation, she thought; there is the key word. There the poor pedant betrays himself.

"Well," she said, "you see about six plays a year. Your wife makes a list of the things that are really worth while, and you check them off one by one. You get the tickets well in advance, and you generally take another couple with you. You never go on the spur of the moment; you never take standing room. Sometimes somebody in your party knows the girl who is playing the ingénue, and then you go backstage afterward. You meet some of the actors and think it's a lot of fun. Once in a while, you go to a benefit concert with your mother or your wife's mother. Myra Hess for the British Relief. You like the movies, and you never miss one that the *New Yorker* recommends. Now and then, if your party is feeling particularly reckless, you go to a swing-music joint. You're not much of a dancer, but you ask the other guy's wife to dance once; after that you sit out because the floor is too crowded. In the summer you commute to your mother-in-law's place at Larchmont or Riverside. There is a nice crowd of young doctors there, and you kid each other about who is going to go in the water first. Probably there is a certain amount of splashing, but nobody loses his temper, and afterward you play medicine ball on the beach. Your wife likes tennis, but you don't go in for it, on account of your eyes. Your wife has a three-quarter-length silver-fox coat and several very dear girl friends. You take excellent care of your health. You have small feet and are proud of it, and this is your only foible."

"What makes you so sure of all this?"

"It's not magic. I've got a good eye for social types, and I've had a lot of practice. When I was in college, I was a perennial house guest. I never went home for vacations, you know."

She was anxious, now, to change the subject. She had enjoyed doing that malicious portrait, but suddenly toward the end her self-confidence had wavered. Supposing she were wrong? He would not tell her. She would never know. It was like doing an algebra problem and finding that the answers were missing from the back of the book. She felt the ground give way beneath her.

"Nothing I could do would surprise you?" he said.

She began to cry.

"Oh!" she exclaimed. "Why do you lead me on so? It's not fair! You make me say all these awful things to you, and then you won't even tell me whether I'm right or not."

The tears streamed from her eyes. She opened her pocketbook and found, as usual, no handkerchief. He took a box of Kleenex from a drawer and handed it to her silently.

"Thank you," she said, still sobbing. "Do you keep that specially for me or do all your patients weep?"

He did not answer. He never answered questions of this sort.

"What made you cry?" he said at length, in that falsely casual tone he used whenever he asked her an important question.

"You made me feel like a fool," she said. "I extended myself and you sat and watched. It was like one of those exposure dreams. You go into a restaurant and you think how beautiful and chic you are. You even pose a little, toss your head, draw off your gloves very, very slowly, like an actress. And then all of a sudden you look down and you see that you have nothing on but a pair of pink pants. And the worst of it is that nobody shows the slightest surprise; there is no commotion; the headwaiter doesn't come and ask you to leave. Everyone goes on eating and talking, so that you think that maybe your eyes have deceived you, and you look stealthily down again, hoping to find your clothes back on. But no; you are still in the same condition.

"Then you try to tell yourself that perhaps nobody has noticed anything, that if you behave very, very quietly and do not call attention to yourself, your lapse will pass unobserved. But all the time you know that this is not true. They are all watching you, but out of cruelty they will give no sign. If one of your companions were to say, 'Why, Meg, you're undressed,' the situation would be saved. You could exclaim, 'Why, gee, I am,' and people would lend you things and laugh and fuss over you, and the whole thing would turn into one of those jolly Embarrassing Moments that readers send in to the *Daily Mirror.* 'Imagine my mortification, but there I was without a stitch of clothes!'"

Dr. James laughed.

"Yes," he said. "But what is there about you that you don't want me to see?" He spoke softly now, in the tone of a conspirator in a Grade B movie. "What is it, Meg, that you are ashamed of?"

She pressed her hands wearily to her forehead. If he would give up this whispering, she could forgive everything. It made them both ridiculous. She longed to reply in a sepulchral voice, "Dr. James, when I was a little girl, I buried my four-year-old cousin alive." (Sensation in the courtroom!) "But don't tell anybody." However, these miserable jokes of hers wasted a great deal of time. She knew exactly what would follow. He would scribble furiously in his notebook for a few seconds, and then the questions would come. Did you ever play with a four-year-old cousin? Did you ever want to bury anybody alive? Where did you get this idea of interment? And so on, through "The Last Days of Pompeii," "The Cask of Amontillado," and the giant, whatever his name was, who slept restlessly under Aetna.

Matthew Arnold, Empedocles. And Karl Marx: "weighs like an Alp" on the something-or-other.

"Nothing, Dr. James, nothing. There's nothing I ever did that I haven't told you." (But what about the time she had stolen the ring from the five and ten and her aunt had made her take it back and confess to the manager? Could it be that? Oh, surely not, her common sense replied. All children steal, and she had already told him of a half a dozen other childish thefts: the cookies from the pantry, the small change from her aunt's bureau, the dime for the collection plate she had spent on candy. Oh, surely not! And yet . . . What if it were important and she failed to tell him? What if her reluctance to delay over a trifle really masked an unconscious fear? In this game, you never knew whether you were putting obstacles in the way or clearing the path. It was a question of relevance, but how could you determine what was relevant to the Unknown?)

Fortunately, he was speaking and she did not have to decide.

"Understand me," he said. "I don't think it's anything you did. It's a feeling that you have about yourself, a feeling that there is something about you that you have to conceal."

He means sex, she thought with relief. It was not the ring, after all. She could feel her mind wrinkle into a smile. We are heading for the castration complex, she told herself, the horror of the little girl when she discovers that an important part of her is missing.

"I don't believe in it," she said aloud.

"Don't believe in what?"

"All this castration nonsense."

"How do you know I was going to mention that?"

"Weren't you?" She pressed him.

"Well, as a matter of fact, I was." (Ah, she thought, without pleasure, I can read him like a book.) "But," he continued, "I am not trying to foist this idea on you. It was you who brought it up."

"Oh, Dr. James," she murmured reproachfully. "You turn everything to your own advantage. If I can read your mind, you say that I put the idea there."

"No," he said. "Think! What are the pink pants in your dream there for? What are they hiding?"

She looked up quickly at him, struck by his question, proud of him for having asked it. Perhaps he was not so stupid as she feared.

"It's true," she admitted, "when men have exposure dreams, they're always completely naked. Most women, too. The pink pants are a little idiosyncrasy of my own. Maybe you have something there." She felt suddenly excited and gay. Everything was going to be all right. They were on the scent. The fugitive, criminal self lay hiding in a thicket, but the hounds of the intellect were hot in pursuit. Ah, she thought, thank God for the mind, the chart, the compass. Of course, the universe had to be meaningful. There can be no question without an answer; if you throw a ball up, it must come down. Her life was not mere gibberish; rather, it was like one of those sealed mystery stories where the reader is on his honor not to go beyond a certain page until he has guessed the identity of the murderer. She had come to that imperative blank page again and again and stopped and retraversed her ground, looking for the obvious, unobtrusive clue, the thing that everyone overlooked and that was nevertheless as plain as the nose on your face. "The Clue of the Pink Pants," she said to herself. "The publishers take pride in announcing a new kind of detective story by a young author." But, seriously, if that were really it . . .

Then she could go on. She paused to examine this phrase, the vague, dramatic resonance of it, the hollowness of the two o's echoing in a triumph of onomatopoeia the emptiness of the mind that framed it. It was a phrase that came to her lips a dozen times a day. Bumping along on a Madison Avenue bus, she would find herself hammering her fist on her knees and crying out to herself in a sort of whispered shriek, "I can't go on, I CANNOT GO ON." And at home, in the apartment on Sutton Place ("not one of the really smart ones, my dear, just one of Vincent Astor's remodeled tenements"), she would suddenly set her fork down on her plate and say to her husband, "I can't go on. Listen to me, Frederick, I can't go on." She would watch the surprise invade his anxious face, the pain, the irritation, the do-we-have-to-go-through-all-this-again, the doubt (tact or brutality, which was the better method?), the desire to get through the meal in peace, the final decision to humor her until the maid brought the coffee in. "Finish your supper, my dear," he would say, calmly, easily, so as not to put pressure on her. In the end, she would pick up her fork again and, with an exaggerated listlessness, begin to eat.

This was what she could not forgive herself: the capitulation. If she had any strength of character, she would commit suicide. But they would never find her body in the river. Ah, no, not she! She knew which side her bread was buttered on. Better a live coward than a dead hero, as her colored maid always said. "Cemetery's full of heroes," she could hear the soft, wicked Negro voice . . . "Lacedaemonians, shed a tear . . . *Maestius lacrimis Simonideis.*" The distich of grief was not for her. She remembered how in boarding school, bemused by sad poetry out of an anthology, she had sat half one night with her feet hanging out her window, knowing that she would never have the heart to jump, yet telling herself from moment to moment that of course in five minutes, ten minutes, fifteen, she would. When, at last, she had crept back into her bed, cold and dispirited, the romantic melancholy had blown away, leaving her with a mild depression, for she had in truth seen her own grave, the narrow, schoolgirl's bed with its regulation blanket which she would always, however late, return to. It was characteristic, she thought

now, that she had not even caught a cold.

"But why should you have committed suicide?" Dr. James had said. "You reproach yourself unnecessarily." "You have got everything upside down," her husband told her. And from their points of view, they were quite right. Why shouldn't she finish her dinner, love her husband, have a baby, stay alive? Where was the crime? There was the class crime, to be sure, yet it was not for having money that she hated herself, but (be honest, she murmured) for having some but not enough. If she could have been very rich . . . It was the ugly cartoon of middle-class life that she detested, Mr. and Mrs., Jiggs and Maggie, the Norths in the *New Yorker.* And the more stylish you tried to make it, smearing it over with culture and good taste, Swedish modern and Paul Klee, the more repellent it became: the cuspidors and the silk lampshades in the funny papers did not stab the heart half so cruelly as her own glass shelves with the white pots of ivy, her Venetian blinds, her open copy of a novel by Kafka, all the objects that were waiting for her at home, each in its own patina of social anxiety. Ah God, it was too sad and awful, the endless hide-and-go-seek game one played with the middle class.

If one could only be sure that one did not belong to it, that one was finer, nobler, more aristocratic. The truth was she hated it shakily from above, not solidly from below, and her proletarian sympathies constituted a sort of snub that she administered to the middle class, just as a really smart woman will outdress her friends by relentlessly underdressing them. Scratch a socialist and you find a snob. The semantic test confirmed this. In the Marxist language, your opponent was always a "parvenu," an "upstart," an "adventurer," a politician was always "cheap," and an opportunist "vulgar." But the proletariat did not talk in such terms; this was the tone of the F.F.V. What the socialist movement did for a

man was to allow himself the airs of a marquis without having either his title or his sanity questioned.

No, it was not really the humanitarian side of socialism that touched her; though she was moved by human misery when it was brought to her attention, if she went to buy a suit at Bonwit Teller, she was never troubled by irrelevant memories of the slums she had passed through on her way. Her aunt had been one of those pious women who could not look at a garbage pail without being reminded of the fact that there were people in the world who had nothing to eat. "It's a sin to throw that away," she was always saying, and her hyperaestheticism on this point allowed her to practice an extreme parsimony with a good conscience. But she herself, thank God, was not like that. In this respect, she took after her father, who in his rather uninspired way had been fond of good cigars, good Bourbon, *eau lilas végétale,* crabmeat, alligator pears, and hotel suites. It was curious, she thought, that all the Puritan penny-pinching should have been on the Catholic side of her family, while her father, that stern Yankee, with his thin skin, his methodical habits, his civic-mindedness, his devout sense of what was proper, should have spent his life buying encyclopedia sets, worthless real estate, patents on fantastic inventions, and have died, to everyone's astonishment, overdrawn at the bank. What a strange childhood she had had! ("No wonder," Dr. James sometimes murmured, in a slightly awestruck voice, "no wonder," meaning no wonder she had turned out so badly. And it was true, she supposed, Freud would have labored in vain if she had not ended up, sobbing, on a psychoanalyst's blue couch. She was a real Freudian classic, and as such faintly monstrous, improbable, like one of those French plays that demonstrate as if on a blackboard the axioms of the romantic movement. It was not merely a distaste for the obvious that had led both her and the doctor to avoid, insofar as it was possible, lengthy discussions of her childhood. The subject frightened them both, for it suggested to them that the universe is mechanical, utterly predictable, frozen, and this in its own way is quite as terrible as the notion that the universe is chaotic. It is essential for our happiness, she thought, to have both the pattern and the loose ends, to roughen the glassy hexameter with the counter-rhythm of speech.)

Up to the time her mother had died, she had been such an elegant little girl. She remembered her ermine neckpiece and the ermine muff that went with it, her two baby rings with the diamonds in them, the necklace of seed pearls. All a little on the ostentatious side, she admitted, but it had been an era of bad taste. Then, after the flu was over, and Mamma did not come home from the hospital, Aunt Clara had moved in, the rings were put in the vault ("to keep for you until you're older"), the ermine set wore out, the velocipede broke, the white sand darkened in the sandpile, there were prunes and rice pudding on the table, and the pretty little girl who looked (everybody said) so much like her mother was changed into a stringy, bowlegged child with glasses and braces on her teeth, long underwear, high shoes, blue serge jumpers that smelled, and a brown beaver hat two sizes too big for her.

Ah, she said to herself now, I reject this middle-class tragedy, this degenerated Victorian novel where I am Jane Eyre or somebody in Dickens or Kipling or brave little Elsie Dinsmore fainting over the piano. I reject the whole pathos of the changeling, the orphan, the stepchild. I reject this trip down the tunnel of memory which resembles nothing so much as a trip down the Red Mill at Coney Island, with my aunt and her attributive razor strop substituting for Lizzie Borden and her ax. I reject all those tableaux of estrangement: my father in his smoking jacket at the card table with his nightly game of solitaire forever laid out before him, my aunt with her novel by Cardinal Gibbons that she is reading for the fifteenth time, and myself with the cotton handkerchief that I must hem and rehem because the stitches are never small enough; I deny the afternoon I deliver my prize-winning essay at the town auditorium and there is no family there to applaud me because my father is away on a hunting trip, and my aunt, having just beaten me for my error in winning the prize ("You are too stuck-up already"), is at home in her bedroom having hysterics; and also the scene at the summer resort where the lady looks up from the bridge table and utters her immortal tag line, "Surely, Mr. Sargent, this isn't your daughter!" It is all too apropos for acceptance.

Yet what were you going to do? You could not treat your life history as though it were an inferior novel and dismiss it with a snubbing phrase. It had, after all, been like that. Her peculiar tragedy (if she had one) was that her temperament was unable to assimilate her experience; the raw melodrama of those early years was a kind of daily affront to her skeptical, prosaic intelligence. She remembered the White Russian gentleman she had met once at a party. They were asking him about his escape from the Soviets, and he had reached the point in his story where he saw his brother shot by the Bolsheviks. Here, at the most harrowing moment of his narrative, he faltered, broke off, and finally smiled, an apologetic, self-deprecatory smile which declared, "I know that this is one of the clichés of the Russians in exile. They have all seen their brothers or sisters shot before their eyes. Excuse me, please, for having had such a commonplace and at the same time such an unlikely experience." That terrible smile had filled her with love and pity; she had "recognized" him at once, and afterward on the street she had kissed him, because she, too, knew what it was to have a sense of artistic decorum that like a hoity-toity wife was continually showing one's poor biography the door.

If only she could have been disinherited in some subtle, psychological way. . . . If her alienation from her father could have been expressed in any terms but those crude, shameful ones of food, money, clothes. If that tactless lady's question had not been written quite so large in all the faces she remembered. She had seen it a thousand times, wherever she went with her father, in the eyes of the Pullman porter, the traveling salesman, the waiter in the ladies' annex at the Athletic Club downtown. How she had looked forward to those excursions with him, and how disastrously they had always ended! It was impossible for her to be a credit to him, to be anything but an anomaly, the shabby daughter of a prosperous lawyer, the underbred Irish offspring of a genteel New England parent. Her appearance, her conversation, her appetite— everything was wrong. The sight of a menu would be like a poem to her (buckwheat cakes and country sausage with Real Vermont Maple Syrup); inevitably, she would order too much to eat. But when the food came, her shrunken stomach could not accommodate it: a few bites would instantly bring on that stuffed feeling, and she would set down her fork in despair, seeing the feast on her plate as an image of the Unattainable. Her father never reproved her for this, but each time it happened, his lean face with its prominent lantern jaw would set in sharper lines, and she would know that he was grieved, both on her account and his own. He would have liked to "make it up to her" for the loneliness, the harsh, antiquated discipline that his sister-in-law had brought into the house, but it was impossible. Aunt Clara could be bodily left at home but her spirit presided over her niece like a grim familiar demon.

In a way, it had been better at

home, for there the social and religious differences had been given a kind of spatial definition and it was easier to move about. Upstairs there were red votive lamps, altars, and holy pictures (the Sacred Heart, Veronica's Veil with the eyes that followed you about the room, Saint Cecilia in sepia striking a heavenly chord on an anachronistic piano), a rich, emotional decor that made the downstairs with its china shepherdesses, Tiffany glass, bronze smoking sets, and family photographs look matter-of-fact and faded, just as the stories in the *Century* in the magazine rack in the living room seemed unendurably tame after the religious fiction she found in her aunt's favorite periodicals, where people were always being bitten by tarantulas or cobras, struck by lightning, plagued with leprosy or cholera, cursed in the most ingenious and striking ways by an implacable and resourceful God. It was as if the Catholic Church began on the landing, where her father's suite branched off from the stairway that continued on up to her own room, her aunt's room, her mother's empty room with the French perfume slowly evaporating in the silver atomizers on the dressing table. Her father never entered her bedroom (except once, with the doctor, when she was sick), yet she knew that he was fond of her, thought her clever because she got high marks and talked back to the sisters. It was some peculiar delicacy that kept him from intruding, the same delicacy that made him say, "Aunt Clara knows what's good for you."—"You must do what the Mother Superior says."

If he had been truly indifferent to her, she thought, her position would have been more tolerable. She could have set herself to win his love, or fought him as she did her aunt. But she could not win what she had already, and she could not fight him either. For a long time, she believed that perhaps he did not notice, and she began to behave badly in order to attract his attention. She ran away from home and spent the night in

a museum, behind a cast of the Laocoön, where an attendant found her the next day and immediately called a policeman. The idea on the surface of her mind was that she wanted to be put in an orphan asylum, but in the end she confessed her name and allowed herself to be led home, because the thing she really desired was to hear her father say, "Why are you suffering so? Is it so terrible for you here that you honestly cannot stand it?"

When the policeman brought her in, her father's face flushed, and she knew that she had disgraced him. He did not scold her, but neither did he ask any questions. "Get her something to eat," he said to the maid, while the young policeman shuffled his feet, glancing from father to daughter with that expression she was so familiar with, not knowing whether to leave because the case seemed somehow unsolved. She watched his eyes take in the living room. She knew precisely what he was saying to himself. "Good home, nice kid, prominent family, what the hell is the matter here? Maybe I was wrong about the kid. Maybe *she's* the nigger in the woodpile."

And she did not blame the policeman for thinking this. In fact, she expected him to think it. All the way home on the streetcar, seeing him begin to like her, seeing the sympathy spring up (her old man probably beats her), she had known that it was merely a question of time, that as soon as he met her father, a stupid, suspicious look would come over his cop's face, and he would feel a little angry and ridiculous, hurt in his professional pride, as if somebody had picked his pocket. Nevertheless, when he had offered to buy her an ice-cream cone at the drugstore at the end of the car line, she had accepted and gobbled it up quickly, just as later on she would gobble up friendship, love, compliments, with the full prescience of what would come afterward, the reproachful look, the averted head, the "You are not what you seemed."

Yet what was she to have done?

How explain to the policeman a thing she hardly understood herself, that her father's being a good man was precisely what was the matter, that she was the victim of his conscience, as Isaac nearly was of Abraham's? But here there was no God to step in and say, "That's enough, Mr. Sargent. You have convinced me that you are a man of honor, that you practice religious tolerance and pay your debt to the dead. You may now give in to your natural feelings and get that woman out of your house." Her father had never liked Aunt Clara. "Your mother," he said once, succinctly, "was cut from a different bolt of cloth." This, she recognized, was for him the sustaining myth, the classic delusion of the frontier, where a pretty woman is a pretty woman, poverty is no crime, and all the nonsense of family and religion and connections has been left behind in the East, and you do not look down on anybody for his race, except of course a Chinaman or a Jap. You do not permit yourself to remember New England and the Irish workers thronging off the boats, the anti-Catholic riots in Boston; you forget your mother, who would draw aside her skirts when a nun passed, and your father with his stack of Know-Nothing pamphlets. If you are to cut down the forests, lay the trolley tracks, send up the skyscrapers, you need partners in business and domesticity, and there is no time to be choosy. You cannot pause to consider that your wife's grandfather is the historical enemy, the jostling, elbowing immigrant whose cheap labor power pushed your own father out into Illinois and sent you as a young man hurrying farther west, where there was still a little space left.

Her mother's youth and beauty had tempered the amalgam. Nobody could have foreseen that she would die and bequeath her husband Aunt Clara, whose complaints, whose tears, whose blue-white mottled complexion would put his egalitarian principles to the severest kind of test. Aunt Clara was, in truth, more than he had bargained for, and a more realistic man would have felt himself perfectly justified in calling the deal off, repossessing his daughter, bringing her up according to his own ideas. Yet the very injustice of the legacy, its unwarranted, unforeseeable character, had moved her father to accept it. The fact that Aunt Clara was personally distasteful to him put her beyond the pale of his criticism, rendered her untouchable, sacred, just as the very real aversion he felt toward Catholic doctrine drove him to punish his daughter if her mark in Catechism was low. She understood this now very well, for she had inherited from him the twisted sense of honor that was always overpaying its debts, extorting from herself and from others the coin of unnecessary suffering to buy indulgence for a secret guilt, an unacknowledged shame.

Not until she was fifteen, however, did she guess the real nature of her father's sin, and the bitterness of his protracted penance. She saw, then, that to have been locked in closets, beaten, forbidden to read, have a doll, go to the movies or the pantomime was as nothing compared to the agony of permitting these things to happen to your child in the interests of a religious tolerance that you did not really feel.

He had taken her to a dance at the house of one of her cousins. It was her first evening party. She wore a pink moire dress with a big, dark red velvet bow. She was new to the crowd of Irish boys home for Thanksgiving from a prep school, and they kept cutting in and cutting in and bringing her glasses of weak punch from the buffet. Suddenly, her father had shoved his way past her admirers and snatched the glass from her hands. "Get your coat on," he exclaimed in a strange voice, and began to push her toward the door. She was nearly crying when they reached the street, but he took her by the shoulders and shook her. "Damn it," he said, "you ought to have more sense than to let those little

micks get you drunk. Can't you see they're trying to make a fool of you?" "Why, Father," she said, "that's not true. They liked me. They thought I was the prettiest girl . . ." "Stop your nonsense," he shouted, "Don't you know that they're all laughing at you?"

She had walked sullenly along beside him telling herself that it was hopeless, that she would never have a chance to get married if her father was going to act like this. At the same time she had sensed that he was right; there had been something degrading about her success. The boys were awfully common, with their red faces and black hair; the whole party was common. Yet it was strange that her father should have noticed this, for he never made social distinctions. She pondered the word "micks," which came so unexpectedly from him, who had taught her that you must never say nigger or sheeny or dago. All at once she understood; it was as if he had told her the story of his life, and she was both sorry for him and frightened. In that terrible look on his face, in his hoarse voice, she read the living history of the Irish, the Jews, the Negroes. She felt closer to him than ever before; yet there was no doubt in her mind that her allegiance belonged elsewhere. Let her father vote for Hoover! She was for Al Smith. It would have been pleasanter, of course, if Al Smith had been a gentleman, if the Negroes were not colored, and the Jews were not Jewish. Nevertheless . . . Her heart quickened with romantic defiance. She shook off her father's arm and stepped proudly into the car.

But by this time she was free. Aunt Clara had been turned into a housekeeper, to whom no one paid any attention, she herself was in her second year at a good boarding school, she had a clothes allowance and charge accounts, took her friends to lunch at the country club, went to the movies and the theatre, and read whatever she pleased. She had lost her faith. That was what had done it. In her first year of high school,

she came home from the convent one day and announced that she was an atheist. Her aunt had had a fit of hysterics and sent for the parish priest. Her father had said nothing, but when she refused to go to Mass the following Sunday, he picked her up and carried her out to the car, while she kicked at his legs and screamed. "You can send me there," she kept repeating, "but you can't make me go in." At the Catholic church she declined to get out of the car. The chauffeur drove her around for an hour and then brought her home. "I didn't go," she said.

That night her father called her into the library. "You're old enough now," he said, "to know what you want. I can't make you go to church. I've tried to have you brought up a good Catholic because I thought your mother would want it so. I've let your aunt have her way, though I've told her she was being too strict with you, that there was bound to be an explosion. I can't do any more." He paused. "Are you willing to finish out the year at the convent?" She knew that she must take a strong line. "No," she said firmly. "All right." He smiled for the first time. "You'll have to be tutored then till I can find a good school for you. I don't want you to fall behind." "I won't," she declared intensely, promising herself that she would repay his confidence in her by having a brilliant career. A great writer, an actress, an ambassador's gifted wife. Perhaps he would like it best if she were to study for the bar. But no, that was out of the question; women lawyers wore flat-heeled shoes. A great lady of some sort who spoke six languages fluently, Diane de Poitiers, Ninon, or Margaret of Navarre.

With a conscious sense of drama, she walked over to the bookshelves and took down "The Queen's Necklace." Dumas had been forbidden her because he was on the Index. "Can I have this now?" she asked. Her father glanced up at the long line of novels in the worn, burgundy-colored bindings. "I ate those up when I was a boy." She smiled and turned to go. "You can read it in here," he said. "No need to rub it in. Your aunt is going to be pretty upset. You must go easy on her." Her face fell. "You must learn to be a good sport, Meg," he said gently. "It's a poor winner that gloats."

Would she have had the courage, she wondered, to have taken up that extreme position if she had not known, unconsciously, that deep down in his soul her father was cheering her on? She was not sure. "You must stop belittling yourself," said Dr. James. "It doesn't make any difference what you would have done under some different circumstances. The fact is that you did the best you could with the circumstances you had. Anybody on the outside would say you acted very bravely." Ah yes, she thought, but again you miss the point. It had not been a real test. That was what she feared and desired; the real test, the ordeal, the burning tenement house with the baby asleep on the fifth floor (would you rush in and save it if there were absolutely no one looking, no God in heaven to welcome your charred but purified spirit, no newspaper account the next day, YOUNG WOMAN DIES SAVING SLUM CHILD; if there were nothing in the world but you and the baby and the fire, would you not say to yourself that it was undoubtedly too late, that the baby must already have suffocated, that the fire was not serious, that the baby was not there at all but in the house across the street?). And of course, as Dr. James said, life is not like that. In life there is always the mitigating circumstance: "Conditions were not right yesterday for the experiment that was to have been performed."—"Findings of observers are open to serious question because of the cloudiness of the atmosphere." Yet actually all this is misleading; the details, the environmental factors, the conflicting accounts of witnesses serve merely to obscure the fact that the question has been put, is being put, will be put, but worded so ambig-

uously, tucked into such an innocent context, that the subject cannot learn whether or not he had taken the test, let alone what his mark is. It therefore becomes important—for the subject who is interested in his status (there are many who simply don't care and doubtless they are the ones who graduate *summa cum laude*)—to examine the data of his life with the utmost severity and cunning, turning the facts every which way, sideward, upside down, as one turned those old newspaper puzzles to find the face in the cloud.

In her own case, appearances were certainly against her. (Don't look now but isn't she the girl who stirred up all that trouble a few years ago? Treated her husband so badly he drove his car off that cliff. Of course, he was drunk and luckily he wasn't hurt, but still . . . And then that other guy—what was his name?—she worked on him till he left his wife and then wouldn't have anything to do with him. And there was another story . . . he was sick and she didn't go to see him . . . The time she made poor so-and-so quit his job on that Foundation because it wasn't radical enough to suit her . . . Got them to introduce her to some publishers and then dropped them like a hotcake . . . Her best friend . . . Now she's married to that architect, you know the one, that does those houses with ramps . . . I guess she's got what she wants, but they fight like cats and dogs . . .) A shady case unquestionably, a sordid history of betrayal. Yet, in some way, she was not like that. She would look at her face in the mirror and recognize in her features something direct, candid, sincere, some inward innocence engraved there that made strangers trust her on sight, tell her their troubles, ask her to watch their babies, help her carry her parcels. Policemen and taxi drivers smiled at her, truck drivers laughed at her hats. There it was, the unreasonable vote of confidence, which was not quite unearned. She would be, she felt, half entitled to it so long as she re-

fused to become reconciled with herself, so long as the right hand remained on guard, the angry watchdog of the left. Yet in Dr. James's eyes all this was sheer folly.

"Accept yourself as you are," he said. "Stop trying to dig in to your motives. You have set yourself a moral standard that nobody could live up to. Your early religious training . . ." Ah dear, she thought, how they all deplore my early religious training. "For God's sake," her husband said, "give up worrying about your imaginary sins and try to behave decently. You use your wonderful scruples as an excuse for acting like a slut. Instead of telling yourself that you oughtn't to have married me, you might concentrate on being a good wife." "But I do try," she said sadly. "I really do." "Oh, hell," he said, "you overdo it or you underdo it. One day you're a miracle of a woman and the next morning you're a hellcat. Why do we have to live like that? Why can't you be like anybody else?"

That was what he had sent her to the doctor for—a perfectly simple little operation. First comes the anesthetic, the sweet, optimistic laughing gas of science (you are not bad, you are merely unhappy, the bathtub murderer is "sick," the Dead End kid is a problem child, poor Hitler is a paranoiac, and that dirty fornication in a hotel room, why, that, dear Miss Sargent, is a "relationship"). After consciousness has been put to sleep, it is a very easy matter (just look the other way, please; it isn't going to hurt, but the sight of the instruments seems to disturb excitable people like yourself), it is a very easy matter to cut out the festering conscience, which was of no use to you at all, and was only making you suffer.

Then the patient takes a short rest and emerges as a cured neurotic; the personality has vanished, but otherwise he is perfectly normal; he never drinks too much or beats his wife or sleeps with the wrong person. He has returned to the Garden of Eden, the apple is back on the tree, the snake is a sportive phallus. If there is something a little bewildered, a little pathetic about this *revenant,* it is only that the ancestral paradise is, like all the homes of our childhood, smaller than he remembered.

Already, in her own case, the effects of treatment were noticeable. "You have lost those unnatural high spirits," her friends told her. "You are not so tense as you used to be. You don't get so excited about causes." It was true, she was more subdued; she did not assert herself in company; she let her husband talk on his own subjects, in his own vein; she told white lies, where before she had only told black ones. She learned to suppress the unpleasant unnecessary truths: why let an author know that you do not like his book, why spoil a party by getting into an argument, why not tell your friend that her ugly house is pretty? And why mention to your husband that you have spent too much money on an evening dress, gone to the races and lost, had too much to drink, let a man kiss you in the pantry? Pay your debt with the housekeeping money, take your mother's bracelet to the pawnshop, stifle the hangover with benzedrine, say the ice tray stuck and you were a long time getting it out. Do, in other words, what every normal wife does, agree and go your own way (it would only upset him if he knew; it is not important anyway; he would think I was silly to mention it). And if you want the last chop on the plate, the last drink in the bottle, take it, do not force it on him merely because you want it so much—that would simply be making a nuisance of yourself. Stop trying to be fair; only a child insists that everything should be divided equally. Grab whatever you need; he will do the same to you.

What Frederick had not foreseen was that the good would vanish with the bad, that man may easily over-reach himself in making provisions for his comfort. His situation was like that of a woman who gets a hat altered to suit her features. It is only a small adjustment, the crown is lowered or heightened, the rakish feather is removed; there is no longer any fault to be found, but the customer looks in the mirror and weeps for her folly, because the hat is no longer stylish. Moreover, it is not returnable; it must lie in the closet for a certain number of seasons, till it is old enough to be given to a charity. And she herself was not returnable either. She could no longer go back into circulation, as she had done so often before. The little apartment in the Village, the cocktail parties, the search for a job, the loneliness, the harum-scarum Bohemian habits, all this was now unthinkable for her. She had lost the life-giving illusion, the sense of the clean slate, the I-will-start-all-over-and-this-time-it-is-going-to-be-different.

Up to the day that Frederick had sent her to the doctor, she had believed herself indestructible. Now she regarded herself as a brittle piece of porcelain. Between the two of them, they had taught her the fine art of self-pity. "Take it easy,"—"Don't try to do too much,"—"You are only human, you know,"—"Have a drink or an aspirin, lie down, you are overstrained." In other words, you are a poor, unfortunate girl who was badly treated in her childhood, and the world owes you something. And there is the corollary: you must not venture outside this comfortable hospital room we have arranged for you, see how homey it is, the striped curtains, the gay bedspread, the easy chair with the reading lamp, why, you would hardly know it was a hospital—BUT (the threat lay in the conjunction), don't try to get up, you are not strong enough; if you managed to evade the floor nurses, you would be sure to collapse in the street.

Certainly, Frederick could not have intended this. He had sent her to Dr. James because he was unimaginative, because he believed in science in the same way that as an architect he believed in model tenement houses, and slum-clearance projects, and the Garden City of the Future, which would have straight streets, and lots of fresh air, and parks of culture and rest. When she had wept and cursed and kicked at him, he had not known how to "cope with" her (the phrase was his), and out of timidity, out of a certain sluggishness, an unwillingness to be disturbed, to take too much spiritual trouble, he had done what the modern, liberal man inevitably does—called in an expert.

How characteristic of him, she thought, smiling, this great builder of cities, who cannot fix a leaky faucet! Poor Frederick, she murmured to herself, he did not see it in the cards at all that his spirited termagant of a wife would be converted into a whimpering invalid who no longer raged at him so often, who no longer wept every morning and seldom threatened to kill him, but who complained, stood on her prerogatives, and was chronically, vocally tired. And yet . . . Perhaps he had seen it, and accepted it as a lesser evil to living with her on terms of equality or allowing her to leave him. He was always talking about what he called her "bad record," a divorce, three broken engagements, a whole series of love affairs abandoned *in medias res.* Perhaps what counted for him more than anything else, more than love (did he love her, did he know what love was all about?), more than a stable household with a pretty wife across the dinner table, was that this should not happen to him, that no one should be able to say, "Well, she's done it again." Furthermore, the fact of her illness, a fact she could not talk away, since she went to the doctor daily, this fact was invaluable to him as a weapon in their disputes. He was always in a position to say to her, "You are excited, you don't know what you are saying," "You are not a fit judge of this because you are neurotic," "We won't discuss this further, you are not sane on the subject," and "I don't want you to see your old friends because they play into your morbid tendencies." And under the pressure of this, her own sense of truth was weakening. This and her wonderful scruples were all she had in the world, and both were slipping away from her. Overcome by the pathos of her situation, she began to cry.

Dr. James, who was still talking about castration, stopped in the middle of a sentence.

"What is it?" he said. "What upset you?" He had his notebook ready.

"I wasn't listening," she said, knowing this was not quite accurate. She *had* heard him, but the mind's time is quicker than the tongue's. Through the interstices of one of his measured paragraphs her whole life could flood in. "Everything you tell me may be true, but it's irrelevant. Supposing at a certain time in my life, a time I can't remember, I found out that girls were different from boys. No doubt this was a very poignant moment, but I can't go back to it. My horrors are in the present."

"But you have never learned to accept that difference."

"Ah," she said, "now you are on Frederick's side. You think I ought to welcome my womanly role in life, keep up his position, defer to him, tell him how wonderful he is, pick up the crumbs from his table and eat them in the kitchen."

"No," he said, "no. You have a lot to contend with. The marriage is not ideal. It's unfortunate, for one thing, that you should have chosen to marry exactly the kind of man who would make you feel most enslaved and helpless."

"Feel!" she replied indignantly.

"Well," he said in his most reasonable and optimistic manner, "you could always get away from him. I think you want to stay with him. I think you are fond of him and that the two of you have the possibility of a solid relationship. Mutual interests . . . you could have children . . . you can't keep on the way you were going, flying from one hectic love affair to another."

"No," she said ruefully, "you can't."

If one only could . . . But it required strength. It took it out of one so. The romantic life had been too hard for her. In morals as in politics anarchy is not for the weak. The small state, racked by internal dissension, invites the foreign conqueror. Proscription, martial law, the billeting of the rude troops, the tax collector, the unjust judge, anything at all, is sweeter than responsibility. The dictator is also the scapegoat; in assuming absolute authority, he assumes absolute guilt; and the oppressed masses, groaning under the yoke, know themselves to be innocent as lambs, while they pray hypocritically for deliverance. Frederick imagined that she had married him for security (this was one of the troubles between them), but what he did not understand was that security from the telephone company or the grocer was as nothing compared to the other security he gave her, the security from being perpetually in the wrong, and that she would have eaten bread and water, if necessary, in order to be kept in jail.

To know God and yet do evil, this was the very essence of the romantic life, a kind of electrolytical process in which the cathode and the anode act and react upon each other to ionize the soul. And, as they said, it could not go on. If you cannot stop doing evil, you must try to forget about God. If your eyes are bigger than your stomach, by all means put one of them out. Learn to measure your capacities, never undertake more than you can do, then no one will know that you are a failure, you will not even know it yourself. If you cannot love, stop attempting it, for in each attempt you will only reveal your poverty, and every bed you have ever slept in will commemorate a battle lost. The betrayer is always the debtor; at best, he can only work out in remorse his deficit of love, until remorse itself becomes love's humble, shamefaced proxy. The two she had cared for most (or was it

that they had cared most for her?) had, she believed, understood all this during those last hours when the packed trunks stood about the room and the last pound of butter got soft in the defrosting icebox (it seemed a pity to waste it, but what were you going to do?). They had consoled her and petted her and promised that she would be happy, that she would soon forget them—just as if they had been leaving her, instead of the other way around. The most curious thing about it was that their wounds, whose seriousness perhaps she had exaggerated, had been readily healed by time, while her own, being self-inflicted, continued to pain her. There are other girls in the world, but there is only the single self.

She remembered Frederick's impatience when she had tried to explain this to him. "You couldn't have cared much for him or you wouldn't have wanted to leave him," he had said in a grumpy voice. "Really, Frederick," she had answered, "can't you possibly understand . . . ?" "By their fruits ye shall know them," he replied, sententiously. This was one of his favorite quotations, a quotation which, of course, damned her utterly. Yet, she said to herself now, be fair. This is precisely what you want, to be condemned but condemned unjustly, on circumstantial evidence, so that you can feel that there is still some hope for you, that the very illegality of the proceedings against you will advance your cause in some higher court. The prisoner has been under duress; she has been treated with great harshness; let me show you, your honor, the marks of the cat-o'-nine tails. It was for his incomprehension, his blunt severity, his egoism, that she had married Frederick in the first place. She had known from the very beginning that he would never really love her, and this was what had counted for her, far more than the security or the social position.

Or rather perhaps she had felt that she was free to accept these things because the gift of love was lacking. When that man on the train had offered them to her she had had to refuse because love had been offered with them. And yet, she thought, she was being unfair again, for she would never under any conditions have married the man on the train, while there had been something about Frederick (the so-called mutual interests, a certain genuine solidity of character of which the mulishness was only one aspect) that had made her marry him and even believe for a short while that surely it would turn out well, that this time she would be happy and good, that a strong, successful architect was exactly what the recipe called for. An architect, she said to herself scornfully, the perfect compromise candidate, something halfway between a businessman and an artist.

"What you don't see, Dr. James, is that I was better then than I am now. You and Frederick do wrong to be so deeply shocked by my past. Why, if I forget to send out his laundry, he can't resist reminding me of my former sexual crimes. 'You always were a slut,' he says."

"Come now," said Dr. James. "Don't take it so hard. He doesn't mean everything he says, any more than you do."

"Ah," she exclaimed, sitting up, "but he thinks he does. I still know when I lie, I can recognize a frame-up when I make one. But Frederick is his own stooge, his own innocent front. He has a vested interest in himself. He is the perfect Protestant pragmatist. 'If I say this, it is true.' 'If I do this, it is justified.' There is no possibility of dispute because Frederick has grace, Frederick belongs to the Elect. It's the religion of the Pharisee, the religion of the businessman. It's no accident that Catholicism is the religion of the proletariat and of what is left of the feudal aristocracy. Our principles are democratic; we believe that original sin is given to all and grace is offered with it. The poor man is democratic out of necessity, the nobleman is democratic out of freedom. Have you

ever noticed," she went on, forgetting her quarrel with Frederick, warming up to her subject, "that the unconscious hypocrite is a pure middle-class type? Your aristocrat may be a villain, and your beggar may be a criminal; neither is self-deluded, puffed up with philanthropism and vanity, like a Rockefeller or an Andrew Carnegie. And the French, who are the most middle-class people in the world, have produced satirical literature that is absolutely obsessed with this vice."

Dr. James frowned slightly. It was plain that the subject did not interest him. If only her analysis could be kept on the plane of intellectual discussion! But with Dr. James this was out of the question. Whenever she did manage it, she was sorry almost at once for, divested of professional infallibility, Dr. James was a pitiable sight. He was no match for her in an argument. It was murder, as they said in the prize ring. And the brief pleasure she got from showing herself to advantage (now he sees me at my best) curdled quickly into self-contempt, as she perceived how abject indeed was her condition, if she could allow this blundering sophomore to get his hands on her beautiful psychology.

Would she have done better, she wondered, to have gone to one of the refugee analysts, or to one of the older men like Brill? Many of them were intelligent, and they had another merit, they were peculiar. You could see at a glance why psychoanalysis had attracted them. They suffered from migraine, divorced their wives, committed suicide, bullied their patients, quarreled with their colleagues; they were vain or absent-minded or bitter or dishonest—there was hardly a one of whom it could not be said, "Physician, heal thyself." And popular opinion was wrong when it held that an analyst's personal failings disqualified him as a healer. Psychoanalysis was one of those specialized walks of life, like the ballet or crime or the circus, in which a deformity is an asset; a tendency

to put on weight is no handicap to a professional fat lady; moral idiocy is invaluable to a gangster, and the tragedy of a midget's life occurs when he begins to grow. What Dr. James and his young American colleagues lacked was, precisely, the mark of Cain, that passport to the wilderness of neurosis that the medical schools do not supply.

Yet for all their insight and cultivation, the others, the marked men, were dangerous. They might give you their own neurosis; they might neglect you or die or go insane or run away with their stenographers, and then where would you be? With Dr. James you were safe. He might never cure you, but he would not kill you. He would try to make up in conscientiousness and sympathy what he lacked in the other departments. Whatever you did or said, he would be unfailingly kind, and now and then in his blue eyes you would see a small, bright flame of pain, which told you that he was suffering with you, that you were not alone. And if, in many ways, he seemed Frederick's ideal apostolic delegate (for Frederick would have been afraid to have you go to one of those showy, gifted analysts), if he seemed a symbol of compromise, of the mediocrity you were rapidly achieving, you must forgive him, pretend not to notice, since he was all you had left. Your father was dead, your first husband, your first lover, and your next-to-the-last, even your Aunt Clara. Your other lovers were married, your friends were scattered or disgusted with you or on bad terms with Frederick.

One reason, it occurred to her suddenly, that she continued to go to Dr. James long after she had admitted that he could do nothing for her was simply, if the truth were acknowledged, that she had no one else to talk to. Her conversation had become official conversation—the war, the Administration, the Managerial Revolution, Van Wyck Brooks, Lewis Mumford, the latest novel by a friend. Even on these public subjects, Frederick did not like it if she was too "sharp," and she could never guess ahead of time whether he would laugh uproariously at one of her jokes or rebuke her for a want of taste. Frederick, she thought, must have known that with all the will in the world she could not transform herself overnight into a "public" character like himself, that a certain amount of isolation was desirable but too much might bring on revolt. Dr. James was the Outlet, paid for by the month, the hygienic pipe line that kept the boiler from exploding.

"Let's go back a little," he said now. "It made you angry when I told you that you felt enslaved. Understand me, I don't mean that this is a delusion. It's true that you've put yourself in a position that isn't easy to retreat from. You have gone and burnt all the bridges that could take you back to your old life. But you have done this on purpose." She nodded.

"I asked for it all right," she said bitterly. "I haven't any call to blame Frederick. It's my own cowardice that got me into this, and it's my own cowardice that'll keep me there. Every time I say to myself that I can't go on, it's a lie. Or maybe it's a kind of prayer. 'Let me not go on.' "

"Wait!" He sustained a dramatic pause. In this moment he was very much the magician. Behind him you could see Mesmer and then Cagliostro, the whole train of illusionists, divine, disreputable charlatans, who breathe on the lead coin, and, lo, it is purest gold. In spite of herself, she felt a little excited. Her hands trembled, her breathing quickened. She was ready for the mystery. "I am going to suggest to you a different view of your marriage." He paused again. Now she hung ardently on his words. She would have liked a cigarette, but she was afraid to reach for her pocketbook, lest the movement disturb him. She held her body perfectly still, like a woman who is expecting that any minute now

the man by her side will kiss her.

"Yes?" she said in a soft, weak voice.

"You accuse yourself every day of having done something cowardly in marrying your present husband. I want to suggest to you that the exact opposite may be true, that this marriage took more real daring on your part than anything you have done since you left your father's house."

"You're crazy," she said, mildly.

"No!" he declared. "Think! In your childhood you had a terrible experience. Your mother died and you found yourself the prisoner of a cruel and heartless relative."

"She wasn't really cruel," she protested. "She was just misguided."

"I am talking about the way it appeared to you. Your aunt was the wicked stepmother that you read about in the fairy tales. Now where could you turn for help? To your father, obviously. But your father refused to help you. He even refused to notice that anything was wrong."

"He was away a great deal."

"That was what you told yourself. You began by trying to excuse him, but all the time you had the feeling that there was something queer going on, something you couldn't understand. Maybe your father and your aunt had a horrible covenant between them, maybe your own subjection was somehow part of the deal."

He is trying to imitate the way I talk, she thought, but it sounds silly when he does it.

"At the same time, you suspected that you would have been treated differently if you were a boy. You've described the arrangement of your house to me, and you lived in a kind of harem. Your father never went into your bedroom. You began to think that there was something ugly about being a girl and that you were being punished for it."

"Yes. There was something odd there. It seems to me now that my father felt that he had committed a sexual crime in marrying outside the clan. Race pollution.

That was why he was so strict with me about boys. He wouldn't let me walk down the street—in broad daylight—with a boy I'd known all my life. The temptations of the flesh must have seemed very lively to him."

"We can't go into your father's psychology here. Something like that probably happened. In any case, you were made to feel unclean about your sex. And your religion got into the picture. You compared the upstairs with the downstairs."

Ah, yes, she thought, you are right. How schematically it had all been lived out, the war between the flesh and the spirit, between women and men, between the verminous proletariat and the disinfected bourgeoisie.

"You thought that you belonged with your Aunt Clara, that you were a dark, disgusting person, and that your father, though you could not acknowledge this, was the real jailer."

"I see," she said. "And I felt that I deserved my imprisonment, that my father in segregating me from the community was performing a social service, throwing a *cordon sanitaire* around a slum section that was full of typhus."

It was all true. Yet there had been some ambiguity in the situation, arising from the fact that she was, after all, her father's daughter. Yet this element, far from easing her lot, had made it the more intolerable. The ugly duckling might be able to get along in life, adjust, resign itself, if there were not the charming, tantalizing possibility that at any moment it might turn into a swan. And, of course, that was what had happened. The second transformation had been quite as magical as the first. The little girl who looked like her mother had suddenly reappeared, seven years older, but otherwise unchanged. Or so, at any rate, it had seemed. She was pretty, she dressed expensively, she was gay, she made friends, and the only remarkable thing about her was that she had the air of coming from nowhere, of having no past. Her classmates in boarding school could not understand why they had never met her before. When they asked her about this, she would blush and say that her father had kept her in a convent. Questions of this sort annoyed her, for she was anxious to think of herself as a completely new person. If anyone would have believed her, she would have pretended that she had spent her former life in some different, distant city, where she had gone to dancing class every Tuesday and been just like everyone else. Unfortunately, her father was too well known; her lie would have been discovered. In a way, she supposed, it was to escape from these questions, from the whole unfair business of having to have a verifiable history, that she had gone East to college. There, if you had money and used the right fork, no one could suspect an Aunt Clara in your vague but impeccable background. Later, when she had grown more sophisticated, Aunt Clara had been converted into an asset. It was amusing to have an aunt who said "ain't" and ate her peas with a spoon, amusing because it seemed so improbable that you could have an aunt like that.

Moreover, the change had not been merely superficial. Her whole character had altered, or, rather, she had believed that it had. She, who had spent seven years in crying fits, spent the next seven without shedding a tear. Where her artistic tastes had been romantic, they quickly became realistic. Everything she had formerly admired became detestable to her. The sight of a nasturtium or a pink cosmos could make her tremble with anger, though these were the very flowers that, at her aunt's suggestion, she had chosen to grow as a child. Most extraordinary of all, she had suddenly developed wit and, even now, she never failed to be surprised when people laughed at her jokes, because for years it had been a household axiom that poor Meg had no sense of humor.

How remarkable it had all been! How very strong she had felt! She used to think back over her childhood and marvel, telling herself that it was really extraordinary that "all that" had not left a single trace. Yet as soon as she had married for the first time, she had begun to change back again. The first time she cried, she had said to herself, "This is very strange. I never cry." The first time she got angry with her husband and heard a torrent of abuse pour from her own lips, she had listened to herself in astonishment, feeling that there was something familiar about the hysterical declamatory tone, something she could not quite place. It happened again and again, and always there was this sense of recognition, this feeling that she was only repeating combinations of words she had memorized long ago. She had been married some time before she knew that she sounded exactly like Aunt Clara. Yet she could not stop, she was powerless to intervene when this alien personality would start on one of its tirades, or when it would weep or lie in bed in the morning, too wretched to get up. And when it began to have love affairs, to go up to strange hotel rooms, and try to avoid the floor clerk, she could only stand by, horrified, like a spectator at a play who, as the plot approaches its tragic crisis, longs to jump on the stage and clear up the misunderstanding, but who composes himself by saying that what is happening is not real, those people are only actors.

"This isn't like you, Meg," her first husband would tell her, in that gentle voice of his, and she would collapse in his arms, sobbing, "I know, I know, I know." She was inconsolable, but he would almost console her, since he shared her own incredulity and terror. It was as if she had lent her house to a family of squatters and returned to find the crockery broken, the paneling full of bullet holes, the walls defaced with obscenities, her beautiful, young girl's bedroom splashed with the filth of a dog. And it was as if he had taken her hand and said, "Don't look at it. Come away now. Everything will be just the same; we will send for the cleaning woman, the house painter, and the restorer. Don't cry, it has no connection with you." She was glad to believe in him, naturally. Nevertheless, before long, she began to think him a fool.

At the outset, it had seemed to her that he was right, that she was being impersonated by some false Florimell; however, as time went on, she herself became confused. She was losing the thread of the story, which was getting fearfully involved, like one of those Elizabethan dramas in which the characters change their disguises so often (Enter the Friar disguised as a Friar) that the final unmasking leaves everyone more perplexed than before. She came at last to the place where she wondered whether the false self was not the true one. What if she were an imposter? The point could only be settled by producing the false self in all its malignancy, and asserting its claim to belief. To say, "You were wrong about me, look how dreadfully I can treat you, and do it not impulsively but calmly, in the full possession of my faculties." Her first husband, however, had not been convinced. (And how could he be, she thought now; it was far easier for him to believe in her innate, untarnishable virtue than to believe that for three years he had been the dupe of what her present husband called a natural-born bitch.) He had grieved over her and let her go, remarking only that her fiancé would never understand her as he did, that she must be out of her senses.

At once she was restored to herself. She knew that she did not cry or make disgusting scenes or have cheap tastes or commit adultery (unless she were very much in love). Yet whenever a new love affair grew serious the usurper would crowd in again. Each time she would persuade herself that with this particular man her defenses would be impregnable, and each time the weak point, the crumbling masonry, would be discovered too late, when the enemy was in occupation. And she would reflect sadly that of course she ought to have realized that this one was too selfish, that one too lazy, the other too pliant to permit her being herself, though actually it was these very qualities that she had relied upon for protection. And unfortunately she had used very little realism in her selections. She was not in a position to ask herself any of the conventional questions (are our tastes congenial, will he be able to support me, will I still want to sleep with him after the first few weeks?) because precisely what she dared not look into was the Medusa face of the future. "I will have to take a chance," she would always say, and her friends, marveling at her recklessness, did not see that she was exactly as gallant as a soldier who moves forward flourishing the standard, because he knows that if he does not do so, his officers will shoot him in the back.

"Now," said Dr. James, "you were helpless, you had no one to turn to, not even the Juvenile Court. And yet . . ." He paused again, even more impressively. This is the moment, she said to herself. This time surely he will get that rabbit out of the hat. "You won your freedom. And the thing to remember, Margaret," he pronounced her full name with all its syllables, "is that you did it yourself!" His voice was full of triumph.

"Perhaps," she said sadly. "But I can't do it again."

"I think you can," he answered. She felt belief stir, faintly, fondly, within her. It would be nice if he were right. However, the whole tone of his address was so deplorably YMCA. "I think you can," he repeated. "The very fact of your marriage indicates that you can."

She looked up at him. At last he had surprised her.

"Let me suggest to you, Margaret, that this ordeal of your childhood has been the controlling factor of your life. You forgot it, blotted it out of your consciousness, just as you blotted your aunt out of your family history, yet you have never ceased to think about it for a single moment. You did not understand how you had escaped, you could never really believe that you had. Everything that happened afterward seemed unreal to you, like a story, but you disguised this from yourself by turning everything upside down by pretending that your childhood was the fantasy, the thing that never took place. Nevertheless, as you grew older, as you found yourself able to get along, to graduate with honors, have friends and a husband and a job, as you began to feel more secure in your role, the past reasserted itself. This could not have taken place earlier because you were still too frightened. When it did come out, however, it expressed itself in various ways, not all of them bad. It expressed itself in neurotic symptoms, but also in your political beliefs, in a taste for colorful language that has been useful to you as a writer. It expressed itself in what you call emotional greediness, which has done you good as well as harm.

"As soon as the past showed itself, you tried to run away. At the same time you set yourself various tests to find out what you were like. None of the results appeared to be conclusive, though, because the tests did not seem to you real. What you were being drawn toward all the time was a reenactment of the old situation, but your first marriage and your other relationships fulfilled practically none of the conditions that had prevailed in your father's house. And the essential thing was lacking: you felt free; you were an equal; you could always get away. You say that you were happier in these relationships. In the end, though, they proved unsatisfactory. You dropped them abruptly. However, as you got older and—you must not forget this—stronger, you began to choose men who more nearly resembled your father. A middle-aged man, married men, even once, a New Englander who came from your father's home state."

"That was nothing," she said. "A flash in the pan. One afternoon."

"Yes. All these affairs are mere signposts of a direction. Finally, however, your father dies, and you are free to make a real marriage. You at once marry Frederick and imitate, as much as it's possible for a grown woman, your own predicament as a child. You lock yourself up again, you break with your former friends, you quit your job; in other words, you cut yourself off completely. You even put your money in his bank account. You are alone: if you cry out, no one will listen; if you explain, no one will believe you. Frederick's own weaknesses contribute to this picture; they affirm its reality. His own insecurity makes him tyrannical and over-possessive; his fear of emotional expenditure makes him apparently indifferent. On the one hand, he is unjust to you, like your aunt; on the other, like your father, he pretends not to notice your sufferings and to deny his own culpability in them. Religion appears again, but now (this is very significant) it is the Protestant religion. A doctor enters the scene. If I remember rightly, you say that the only time your father came into your bedroom, he was bringing a doctor with him."

She nodded, unable to speak.

"You reproach yourself with cowardice for having contracted this marriage. But look at the facts. Isn't this the most dangerous action you have ever performed as an adult? You have run a terrible risk, the risk of severe neurosis, in putting yourself to this test. For that's the thing you are asking: will I be able to get out? And once again you have the answer in yourself."

"No, I haven't," she said. "I'm turned to water. I'm finished, I'm overrun by barbarian tribes. Two or three years ago, perhaps . . . Not now."

"Two or three years ago, Margaret," he said gently, "you wouldn't have had the courage to put yourself in this situation, let alone to save yourself."

"It's not true. I was wonderful then."

He smiled.

"In those days, you were avoiding the things you feared. Now you are eating breakfast with them."

"Not eating breakfast," she said. "Frederick prefers to breakfast alone. I disturb his train of thought."

"The weakness you feel is a result of living with these fears. You must find your way out, and you'll discover that you are just as strong as Frederick."

"But what can I do? He won't allow me to leave him. I have nobody left to borrow money from. I could run away and sleep on a park bench, I suppose."

But she did not want that. Ah, no! The days of romantic destitution were gone for her. It was no longer possible for her to conceive of herself as a ribbon clerk at Macy's. Now there was not so much time left in the world that you could spend two years or three in the unrewarding occupation of keeping yourself alive. Her apprenticeship was finished. If she took a job, it would have to be a good one, one that would keep the talents limber. No more secretarial work, no more office routine, that wonderful, narcotic routine that anesthetizes the spirit, lulls the mind to sleep with the cruel paranoiac delusion of the importance, the value to humanity, of the humble-task-well-done.

"You tried running away as a little girl, and it didn't work," he said. "No. You misunderstand me. I'm not advising you to leave Frederick. You must win your freedom from him, your right to your opinions, your tastes, your friends, your money. And, of course, your right to leave him. Once you have it, I believe, you will cease to want to exercise it. You can become truly reconciled with Frederick, and you may even be happy with him."

"It sounds impractical," she said. "How am I going to get these rights?"

"You did before," he answered. "You did it with your mind. That and your beauty are the two weapons you have."

He closed his black notebook.

"All right!" he announced in a totally different voice, high and unnaturally sprightly, as if he were giving a bird imitation. The hour was over. She looked at the electric clock. He had given her five minutes extra. This pleased her, and she was ashamed of being pleased over such a small, such a niggardly present. What a pass, indeed, she had come to when the favors of this commonplace little doctor could be treasured, like autumn leaves in a memory book! The knife of terror struck at her, and she saw herself as a transient, and this office with its white walls as the last and bleakest hotel room she would ever lie in. Guests who stay after one P.M. will be expected to pay for the extra day. When she was gone, he would empty the ash tray, smooth out the white cloth on the pillow, open the window for an instant, and the room and he would be blank again, ready for the next derelict.

She put her hat on carefully, trying not to hurry, lest he see how humble and rejected she felt, how willing to be dislodged; and trying, on the other hand, not to take too much time, lest he think her inconsiderate. He picked up her coat from the end of the couch and held it out for her, an attention he rarely paid her. She glanced at him and quickly lowered her eyes. Does he think I am unusually upset today, she wondered. Or was it something else? "My beauty," she murmured to herself. "Well, well!" She slid her arms into the coat. She turned, and he offered her his hand. In slight confusion, she shook it. "Good-by," she said softly. He patted her arm. "Good-by," he said in a rather solicitous voice. He held the door open for her and she slid out awkwardly, half running, not wanting him to see her blush.

On the street, she felt very happy. "He likes me," she thought, "he likes me the best." She walked dreamily down Madison Avenue, smiling, and the passers-by smiled back at her. I look like a girl in love, she thought; it is absurd. And yet what a fine rehabilitation of character that had been! The most dangerous action . . . run a terrible risk. She repeated these phrases to herself, as if they had been words of endearment. I think you can . . . Suddenly, her heart turned over. She shuddered. It had all been a therapeutic lie. There was no use talking. She knew. The mind was powerless to save her. Only a man . . . She was under a terrible enchantment, like the beleaguered princesses in the fairy tales. The thorny hedge had grown up about her castle so that the turrets could hardly be seen, the road was thick with brambles; was it still conceivable that the lucky third son of a king could ever find his way to her? Dr. James? She asked herself the question and shook her head violently. But supposing he should fall in love with her, would she have the strength to remind herself that he was a fussy, methodical young man whom she would never ordinarily have looked at? All at once, she remembered that she had not told him the end of her dream.

She was matriculating at a place called Eggshell College. There was an outing cabin, and there were three tall young men, all of them a sort of dun color, awkward, heavy-featured, without charm, a little like the pictures of Nazi prisoners that the Soviet censor passes. They stumbled about the cabin, bumping their heads on the rafters. She was sorry she had gone there, and she sat down at a table, resolved to take no part in the proceedings. Two other girls materialized, low-class girls, the kind you said "Hello, there" to on the campus. A sort of rude party commenced. Finally one of the men came toward her, and she got up at once, her manner becoming more animated. In a moment she was flirting with him and telling one of the other girls, "Really, he is not so bad as the others. He is quite interesting when you begin to talk to him." His face changed, his hair grew dark and wavy. There was something Byronic about him. He bent down to kiss her; it was a coarse, loutish kiss. "There must be some mistake," she thought. "Perhaps I kissed the wrong one," and she looked up to find that the Byronic air was gone; he was exactly like the others. But in a few minutes it happened again; his skin whitened, his thick, flat nose refined itself, developed a handsome bridge. When he kissed her this time, she kept her eyes shut, knowing very well what she would see if she opened them, knowing that it was now too late, for now she wanted him anyway.

The memory of the dream struck her now, like a heavy breaker. She stopped in the street, gasping. "Oh, my God," she demanded incredulously, "how could I, how could I?" In a moment, she told herself that it was only a dream, that she had not really done that, that this time at least she need feel no remorse. Her thirsty spirit gulped the consoling draft. But it was insufficient. She could not disown the dream. It belonged to her. If she had not yet embraced a captive Nazi, it was only an accident of time and geography, a lucky break. Now for the first time she saw her own extremity, saw that it was some failure in self-love that obliged her to snatch blindly at the love of others, hoping to love herself through them, borrowing their feelings, as the moon borrowed light. She herself was a dead planet. It was she who was the Nazi prisoner, the pseudo-Byron, the equivocal personality who was not truly protean but only appeared so. And yet, she thought, walking on, she could still detect her own frauds. At the end of the dream, her eyes were closed, but the inner eye had remained alert. She could still distinguish the Nazi prisoner from the English milord, even in the darkness of need.

"O my God," she said, pausing to stare in at a drugstore window that was full of hot-water bottles, "do not let them take this away from me. If the flesh must be blind, let the spirit see. Preserve me in disunity. *O di,*" she said aloud, *"reddite me hoc pro pietate mea."*

It was certainly a very small favor she was asking, but, like Catullus, she could not be too demanding, for, unfortunately, she did not believe in God.

Individual Designs for Automobiles Mark the Mode of Today

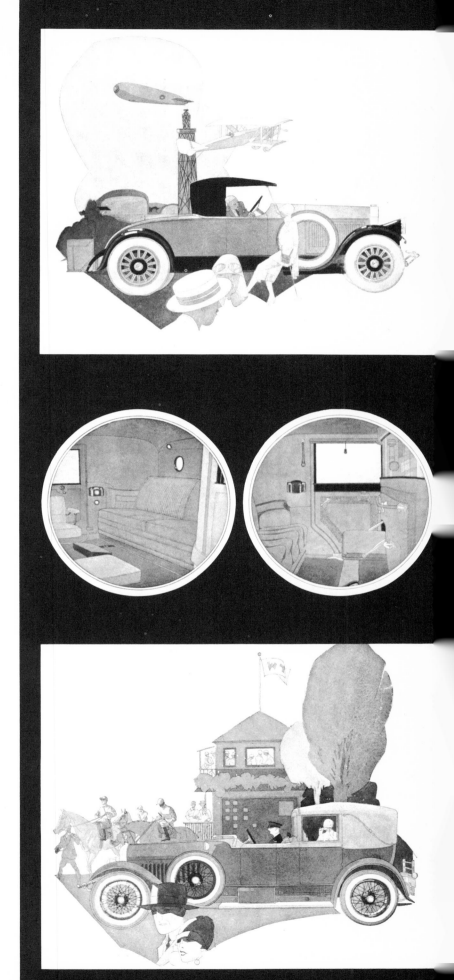

Autos of the twenties became more and more sumptuous, with collapsible tops in the spirit of the open touring car, color schemes made to match ladies' tresses, interiors as plush as the owner could afford. One daring lady was arrested for smoking a cigarette in an open car on Fifth Avenue. "You most certainly can't do that, young lady, not on this street," said the officer.

The Smart Sport of Dude Ranching

G. HART

Dude Ranching, Motor Trekking, and Camping are Typically American Sports, for Which One Dresses in a Special and Often Startlingly Picturesque Fashion

For evening one dresses as at a country club, in a homespun skirt, a Fair Isle sweater, felt hat, and polo coat. She who rides to tea at a neighboring ranch wears a shell skirt over her riding-breeches—a skirt which buttons from belt to hem, both back and front, so that one is properly dressed on one's arrival.

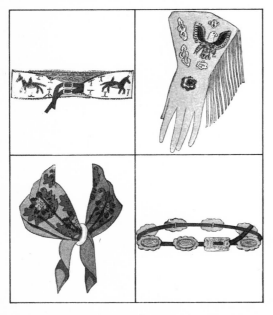

Clockwise:

One way of obtaining the color one craves is in an Indian beaded belt with its gay color and primitive designs.

Buckskin gloves, fringed at the side and gaudily decorated with Indian beadwork, are all the rage on western dude ranches.

Silver hand-beaten conches are much used for belts by the cowboys, and what the cowboy wears the "dude" adopts.

Brilliant silk neckerchiefs slipped through a bone ring are the correct finish to the complete cowgirl costume; from Brooks Brothers.

The Sage Brush of
Western Ranches
Demands Brilliant Color

G. HART

A bit "motion picture" perhaps, but against the sage brush of the plains and the snow of the Rockies, the primitive colors of the aborigines are natural and beautiful. Leather chaps studded with a steel design, a fringed buckskin jacket with a design in Indian beadwork, ditto gloves, and Stetson.

Not the tourist of a few weeks but the dude rancher of long standing may go in for the elaborate equipment of the natives. Goatskin chaps, natural or dyed, fringed leather vest and gloves, beaded belt, bandanna and Stetson, are not only picturesque but thoroughly serviceable for the open spaces.

Ice and Snow and Frosty Air at St. Moritz

During February at St. Moritz and at Lake Placid many international skiing, skating, curling, and hockey events are clicked off. The air is brilliant, cold; the snow never melts. One is always on the toes with vigorous exercise.

MALAGA GRENET

The Bathing Suit Is
Now a Gay Costume

G. HART

This is something that has taken several colorful seasons to develop, this wearing of gorgeous bathing costumes that are neither black nor practical nor inconspicuous. Two or three seasons ago, at Palm Beach, one felt it coming on; last season at Newport it was a definite fact.

Perhaps it was started by the flair for the South Seas, and by the Gauguinesque designs and color that have hung in all of our art galleries, have appeared in our magazines, and have even penetrated to our smart cafés, these last few seasons.

At any rate, it is here. One no longer appears upon the sands of Palm Beach, or Miami, or Nassau (or whatever one's favorite sands are) in something cleverly and not too generously designed of black taffeta or wool jersey. Nor is even the daring "one-piece" suit of the flapper, and those who can wear it, smart. The bathing-suit has achieved the importance of the costume in which one dines or dances. Just as the gossipy bathing hour has spread itself over two full hours or more, and has achieved a new social importance.

The smart woman is making herself look more and more like a vivid Russian poster. Her bathing costume, her hat, her wrap, are all astonishingly gay and form a complete "ensemble," exactly as her evening gown and wrap form a costume complete.

The Technique of
Sports Clothes

*It is easier for a camel to enter a
needle's eye than for one who
breaks the law of correct sports
clothes to look smart.*

MALAGA GRENET

Hermès driving/flying costume of leather

In the Elevator

A supposititious arrangement of contributors to *Harper's Bazar* by Ralph Barton

This is the height of editorial meanness. Here are thirty-one of the sixty-four amiable and versatile writers, artists and couturial advisers who have given the fine fruits of their toil to the development of *Harper's Bazar* during the past three years; yes, and what is their reward? They are thrown to the cruel and cynical Barton. Dastardly! "And that isn't the half of it, dearie!" Next month another elevator load is coming up (of course, precluding the possibilities of murder or arson), including for contrast and good luck G. B. S. and Herman Patrick Tappé!

1. Erté
2. Margery Williams Bianco
3. Pamela Bianco
4. Katherine Sturges
5. Mildred Cram
6. Lady Duff Gordon
7. Henri Bendel
8. Mrs. Fred'k. Y. Dalziel
9. W. L. George
10. Stephen Vincent Benét
11. Gilbert K. Chesterton
12. Etienne Drian
13. George Bellows
14. Dean Cornwell
15. E. F. Benson
16. Arnold Bennett
17. Maurice Bower
18. Rachel Crothers
19. Gertrude Atherton
20. Lord Dunsany
21. Mrs. Larz Anderson
22. Laurids Bruun
23. Acquisitive Connoisseur
24. Lucian Cary
25. Josephine Daskam Bacon
26. Jean Gabriel Domergue
27. Charles Collins
28. Grace Corson
29. George Agnew Chamberlain
30. C. Le Roy Baldridge
31. Ralph (Himself) Barton

Paris Makes of the Raincoat a Very Special Mode

Two of the Smartest
Sports Frocks in Paris

Mary Pickford

Helen Hayes

The Thirties

VERTES

One morning, subscribers to one of America's smartest monthlies realized that the spelling on the masthead of the magazine had changed from Harper's Bazar to Harper's Bazaar. *The few who noticed it probably didn't raise a stir. But shortly after this,* Bazaar *readers were introduced to a new editor, Carmel Snow, and for the next twenty-five years or so, this dynamic female dominated the fashion scene both in America and abroad. The "hautest" of the "haute" held up their showings and collections 'til this petite, smartly and brightly dressed sprite of America's fashion "biz" took her place in the front row. In her own book,* World of Carmel Snow, *Mrs. Snow summed up her philosophy of* Bazaar:

"It is not by chance that Bazaar *publishes fiction and articles on travel and theatre and movies and music in its pages. All these go to make up the climate of fashion and to be in fashion one must be very aware of the weather. You don't have to spend your holidays at the smart resorts; Balenciaga leads a monkish life of retirement. Dior stays in the country and makes the soutanes for the priest.*

"We often speak of fashion influences. Where do they come from? Who sets them in motion? Who, for instance, ruled that tight, bright pants of Pucci would become a ruling passion with American girls? Not Emilio, certainly. He was in his ancestral palace in Florence. He designed those pants for Capri. After the war, Americans began to travel.

They fell in love with Italy. They loved Italian movies, Italian actresses, painting. This was bound to be reflected in fashion. And it was.

"One cannot run fashion by Gallup polls. Play your hunches. Keep flexible. Take off on a new tack at a moment's notice. There is no room for prejudice or cliché. Elegance is good taste plus a dash of daring.

"People said no lady would varnish her fingernails. No man would look twice at a woman with cropped hair. Hussies used hair dyes. The bikini—well. But you can't keep an exciting fashion down. It's no use trying. Fashion is an element mysterious as uranium and just as explosive. Light—lighter than air."

The Once Rich

Top to bottom:

Among Wall Street's four hundred neediest cases, the most pitiful is that of Bettina and Algernon. After expensively collected evidence, there's not a cent left for that Paris divorce.

The slump in the market is nothing compared to the slump in Mrs. Baggs' face when the doctor tells her that the third face-lift will cost her one hundred dollars an inch extra.

Conditions like this are deplorably prevalent among the newly-poor. Mrs. Wyllys has just fluttered in with the surprise: "Darling, we'll keep the cook, and I'll be your secretary."

No ostentatious thrift for Herbert, even if Albertina's money has gone to the bears. "If this is the best you can do," he announces, "I'm afraid our little Romance must end."

Le dernier cri in fashionable economy is doing one's own bootlegging. Decidedly chic this season, but Horace finds it a bit disconcerting under unsympathetic surveillance.

Mademoiselle Chanel

by Jean Cocteau

I have no aptitude for talking about fashion, except in aspects that are not the concern of the couture. But the personality of Mademoiselle Chanel goes singularly beyond such a problem as the length of skirts; beyond the role that she has played in fashion, which is to give women the mysterious order they accept with their eyes closed, even when that order disturbs and displeases them.

In short, Mademoiselle Chanel is a personage, one of those figures without whom the enigma of Paris remains an enigma. To understand our city, it is important to know that its mechanism is not governed by what is noisily current. There are secret forces that assure a continuity of tradition, which might be mistaken from afar as a kind of anarchy.

A startling remark by Mademoiselle Chanel will light our lantern: "What we create in fashion must be beautiful first, then ugly afterward. What is created by art must be ugly first, then beautiful afterward." Such precepts pour from her, revelation of her deep insight, proof that she had far more to bring than simple beauty secrets. Her beauty secrets have a higher aim: the keeping of the *moral* line, rather than the keeping of the line as women ordinarily understand it.

Her long disappearance from the scene where modern publicity brutally pushes about those men and women who invent something re-

sults from the high seriousness with which she undertakes work of the slightest nature, from her refusal to comply with the simple demands of the moment. If Mademoiselle Chanel has reigned over fashion, it is not only because she has cut women's hair, married silk and wool, twined pearls on sweaters, avoided poetic labels for her perfumes, lowered the waistline or raised the waistline, and obliged all women to follow her directives, it is because—outside this gracious and robust dictatorship—there is nothing of her era that she has missed. And she has spent herself as freely in what she has to offer momentarily as on what she has long been meditating in the shadow.

Thanks to a visible splendor, she has aided the secret splendor of artists. Not saying it herself, not wishing it said, she has been companion to all our searchings. Without her, Sergei Diaghilev would never have been able to undertake the revival of *Le Sacre du Printemps*. Without her, Picasso, Erik Satie and I would never have been present to see the triumph of our ballet *Parade*. Everywhere, behind the thinker and the interpreter, one finds her in the modest shadow. Her friendship for Picasso, for Dali, for Stravinsky, for Pierre Reverdy, for myself, in a sense outweighs the extraordinary good fortune of her reign over the couture. One might endlessly apply to her Brummell's famous mot, when he was con-

fronted at Ascot by a young man who complimented him on his elegance: "I cannot be elegant, since you have noticed me."

Because the fashions created by Mademoiselle Chanel have never been extravagant. She has, by a kind of miracle, worked in fashion according to rules that would seem to have value only for painters, musicians, poets. In a way that is uniquely her own she imposes the invisible. In the midst of the social uproar, the nobility of a *silence*.

Her return to the Parisian scene represents far more than the reopening of a great *maison de couture*. She arrives as a sign that we must vanquish the inflation of mediocrity. Her instinct does not deceive her. The time has come when we must break with the fever of improvisation that troubles not only the surface of our city but its very depths. Anybody at all feels entirely capable of doing any task at all. But a weariness has resulted from these excesses. True worth is finding its place again. And I congratulate Mademoiselle Chanel for giving us visible proof of this fact, which the modern tumult hides, alas, from nearly everyone's eyes.

We are happy to see, advancing over the marshes where our pride has been somewhat stagnant, the marvelous little head of a black swan. It belongs to Mademoiselle Chanel, who fully as much as the poets, scorns frivolity and foible.

—Translated by George Davis

en 1937 - Robe du soir

Jean Cocteau
☆ 1937

The Incomparable Coco, Mademoiselle Chanel.

Munkacsi

by Richard Avedon

Martin Munkacsi—to describe his talent in one word, "movement." He took staid sit-it-out studio photography and made it run, walk, frolic, talk to swans, swim, golf, sail. One young man of our time, who also worked for Bazaar *and produced some of its most exciting pictures, wrote how Martin Munkacsi had influenced his work. What better way to show you Munkacsi than through the eyes of the young man, Richard Avedon?*

In 1934 my father lost a business he'd spent a lifetime achieving, and in his middle years tried to sell life insurance that no one could afford to buy. We moved from a long stucco house and six trees in Cedarhurst, Long Island, to a three room apartment on Ninety Eighth Street in New York, a corner of which was called The Dining Alcove. It was there the family ate in silence; it was also my windowless bedroom. I was eleven years old. The walls beside my bed and the ceiling above were my domain, and I covered them with my chosen view: a gleaning of five years' Christmas Tuberculosis seals, three hundred Dixie Cup tops, and the photographs of Martin Munkacsi.

I cared nothing about photography and less about fashion, but the potentialities beyond Ninety Eighth Street filled my waking dreams, and because my family subscribed to *Harper's Bazaar*, it became my window and Munkacsi's photographs my view. There were over twenty of his pictures, buckling from humidity and home-made paste, in my "collection," and the longings of my almost adolescence were focused on them. Photographs of falcons, camels, and women . . . *his women*, striding parallel to the sea, unconcerned with his camera, freed by his dream of them, leaping straight kneed across my bed.

One Sunday evening, my father and I—I was twelve at the time—deep in what he called our "man to man," a walking monologue, never complete without a quote from Theodore Roosevelt about life being a football game and hitting the line hard, arrived at Fifty Ninth Street. We stopped to watch a photographer pose a model. He asked her to lean against a tree, and in that dusk, whispered to her, changing the arch of her throat, the turn of her hand, whispering until her eyes lifted, until he was satisfied, and they left. I stared at the view for a long time, not at all understanding why he had chosen a peeling tree when the park, the fountains, the plaza were so dazzling around him. Ten years later, in Paris, I saw for the first time the great flaking trees of the Champs Elysées; I understood then that he had found the only Proustian bark in New York, and he had photographed it. I knew by that time that the strong, witty, sensitive and anxious face on Fifty Ninth Street ten years before was Munkacsi's. The tree is still alive and I never pass it without remembering. It was my first lesson in photography, and there were many lessons after, all learned from Munkacsi, though I never met him. He brought a taste for happiness and honesty and a love of women to what was, before him, a joyless, loveless, lying art. He was the first. He did it first, and today the world of what is called fashion is peopled with Munkacsi's babies, his heirs.

The Art Department of *Harper's Bazaar* is a particularly enthusiastic place, hell-bent for discovering The New. The morning after Munkacsi's death, bound volumes of vintage *Bazaar* filled the office. His women, laughing out of their pages, dazzled the drawing boards. The breath of his dogwood, the crash of his seas, assaulted the desks, the windowsills, the floor, and the young Art Directors. That morning they discovered Munkacsi! I wish he could have been there. I wish he could have seen their eyes.

He wanted his world a certain way, and what a way! He saw what was free in it, happy in it, and however much he suffered, and he did suffer, his pain never destroyed his dream. Without illusions there would be no art and possibly no life in the world. The art of Munkacsi lay in what he wanted life to be, and he wanted it to be splendid. And it was.

Paris, August 1963

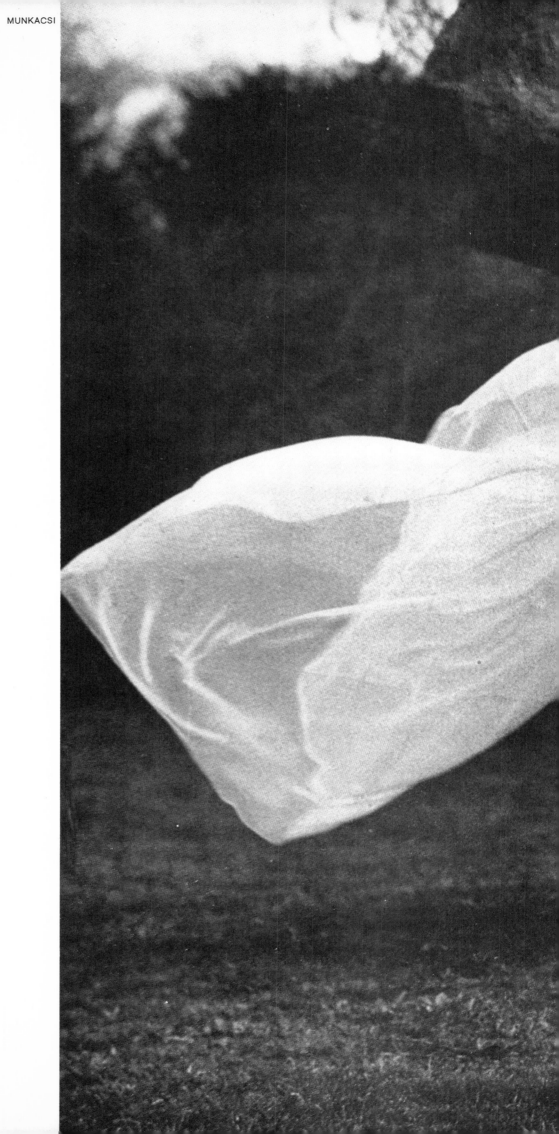

Why Don't You...

by Diana Vreeland

serve individual Pfirsich Bowle *which is a peeled peach in a chilled glass with ice cold Moselle or Rhine wine poured in? Marvelous at tea time!*

put all your dogs in bright yellow collars and leads like all the dogs in Paris?

knit yourself a little scullcap?

whitewash a pair of old linen-closet steps and use on a porch for finger-bowls and jars full of flowers or as a child's bedside table for lamp, books and pencils?

remember how delicious champagne cocktails are after tennis or golf? Indifferent champagne can be used for these.

sweep into the drawing-room on your first big night with an enormous red-fox muff of many skins?

have a furry elk-hide trunk for the back of your car? Hermès of Paris will make this.

tie black tulle bows on your wrists?

turn your child into an Infanta for a fancy-dress party?

rinse your blond child's hair in dead champagne to keep its gold, as they do in France? Or pat her face gently with cream before she goes to bed, as they do in England?

twist her pigtails round her ears like macaroons?

line the pram, hood and all, with white broadcloth?

paint a map of the world on all four walls of your boys' nursery so they won't grow up with a provincial point of view?

The Flying Tigresses

One an airborne beauty queen for real, one a famous actress miming Amelia Earhart.

Jacqueline Cochran

Katharine Hepburn

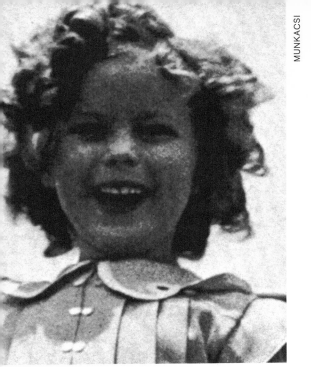

MUNKACSI

The Movie Star Influence

VON HORN

KAY BELL

Top to bottom:
Shirley Temple
Grace Moore
Ginger Rogers

The star syndrome produced the Celluloid queens. They created fashion, started vogues, set a Holly-woodian pace unlike anything this country had known. Adrian and his padded shoulders, Crawford and her ankle straps, Bette Davis and her voice, Shirley Temple and her curls, smoky-eyed Hedy, breathless Katharine Hepburn: they were indeed the goddesses. No one had known anything like their fame since the Greeks created the prover-bial word for them.

Top to bottom:
Joan Crawford
Loretta Young
Bette Davis

Norma Shearer
Elisabeth Bergner
Hedy Lamarr

103

I Have Lived by My Wits

by Elsa Maxwell

They say that I have lived by my wits, but how many people have any wits to live by?

They say that I climbed the ladder hanging to the coat tails of the Duke of Windsor, but I met the "At long last" man just once—and he didn't like me.

They say that not unlike all other San Francisco Irish, the South-of-Market-Street Irish, I am made of pure brass; but I happen to have been born in Keokuk, Iowa, to be exact, of a Scotch father and a French-Dutch mother.

They say that someone is "always" paying for my parties, but the bills that I get and the checks that I write tell a different story.

They say that I specialize in advising Vanderbilt-struck social climbers, but the only advice I have ever given to anyone I gave to the late Jean Patou. He wanted to meet "the really important people," and he wondered what was wrong with him. "Your green suit, for one thing," I said. "Your green socks for another. Get hold of a good tailor and a good haberdasher."

They say that I am a Lesbian because I don't pop into bed with every man I see, but they overlook my fat—and fat is the greatest protection to a woman's virtue.

They say that having spent the first half of my mature life in being snubbed I am trying to spend the second half in turning the tables on my former tormentors, but the truth is that I wouldn't dream of snubbing even a Georgian prince. According to Mr. Maugham, "Life is short, nature is hostile and man is ridiculous." So why snub? I'd rather play bridge, read Cholly Knickerbocker and be merry.

They say that I must be benefiting quite handsomely by my parties because otherwise why would I waste my time in entertaining the jaded rich, but I have no doubt that my parties eventually will land me in the poorhouse.

Why do I give parties if not for money's sake? Because all my life, ever since I was big enough to understand the difference between a filet mignon and a chunk of horsemeat, I wanted to become Number One in some profession or in some line of human endeavor.

I wanted to be a pianist and I was. A fair-to-middling pianist, good enough to accompany a music-hall singer, but not good enough to give a recital at Carnegie Hall.

I wanted to be an actress and I was. A so-so actress, good enough to play the nurse in a stock company's rendition of "Romeo and Juliet," but not good enough to see my name in electric lights on Broadway.

I wanted to be a singer and I was. A mediocre singer, good enough to amuse the soldiers during the war, but not good enough to come within a shouting distance of the Metropolitan.

I wanted to be a song writer and I was. A none-too-gifted songwriter, good enough to write the most patriotic British war song of all ("Carry on, Carry on"), but not good enough to cause any undue jealousy on the part of Cole Porter or Irving Berlin.

I wanted to be an impresario and I was. A more-ambitious-than-capable impresario, good enough to stage benefits and galas, but not good enough to produce hits.

I wanted to be a musical critic and I was. A second-string musical critic, good enough to be entrusted with a matinée at Town Hall, but not good enough to be sent to cover a Wagnerian première.

I wanted to be a Big Hotel Woman and I was. A small Big Hotel Woman, but not good enough to keep the waiters from serving the guests too much butter.

All my life, in everything I touched and in everything I attempted, I have been a dilettante, perhaps a "promising" one, but a dilettante nevertheless. I realize that there is nothing particularly wrong with being a dilettante. Some of my best friends have been known to compose music or to take a crack at writing The Great American Novel . . . But it so happens that by nature and inclination I'm a worshiper of professionals. Given a choice, I'd rather be the best repairer of Shirley Temple dolls the world has ever known than a second-rate builder of dams and bridges. It's provincial of me, I suppose, but it's stronger, oh, so much stronger than my "sound judgment."

That is why when the after-war Society proclaimed me—much to my amazement — as Party-Giver-Extraordinary and the World's-Greatest-Hostess, I accepted the title and the honor only too readily. My sense of humor tried to point out to me that things must be in a pretty rummy state indeed if a former vaudeville performer can become a social leader, but I dealt with my sense of humor harshly and promptly. I gave it the thrashing of its life on that occasion.   *excerpt*

105

MONDAY

TUESDAY

WEDNESDAY

THURSDAY

FRIDAY

SATURDAY

SUNDAY

MONDAY

TUESDAY

The 9-Day Wonder Diet

BREAKFAST	LUNCH	DINNER
Black coffee; grapefruit	Chicken sandwich on rye toast (no butter); raw tomatoes	Stalk of celery; steak, good-sized helping; tomato and endive salad (lemon juice or low-calorie dressing may be used on all salads); half a grapefruit
Black coffee; grapefruit	Jelly omelette or scrambled eggs; three saltines	Two thick lamb chops; stewed tomatoes or carrots or string beans; lettuce and tomato salad; half a grapefruit or sliced pineapple
Black coffee; grapefruit	Minute steak; broiled tomatoes	Minute steak; stewed tomatoes; plain spinach; lettuce and tomato salad
Black coffee; grapefruit	Two lamb chops; stewed tomatoes	Tenderloin steak; stewed tomatoes; plain carrots; one-half head of lettuce; half a grapefruit
Black coffee; grapefruit	French toast	Two lamb chops; any vegetable; stewed celery; two olives; half a raw apple
Black coffee; grapefruit	Ham, cheese or chicken sandwich on rye toast	Chopped meat; tomato and endive salad or mixed vegetable salad; half a grapefruit
Black coffee; grapefruit	Any appetizer; chicken or any meat; any vegetable; one-half helping of dessert	Scrambled eggs; sliced tomatoes
Black coffee; grapefruit	Omelette; three saltines	Two lamb chops; stewed celery and carrots; two olives; half a grapefruit
Black coffee; grapefruit	Scrambled eggs; sliced tomatoes; half a raw apple	Broiled halibut; green salad; celery and olives; any vegetable; sliced oranges

The Miraculous
Madeleine Vionnet

Madeleine Vionnet touched off a French Revolution of her own in the twenties. This great dressmaker created the miracle of the bias cut. At a time when the fashion silhouette was flat, she worked in the round — establishing a relationship between the curves of a woman's body and the hang of a dress that was rhythmic and utterly alluring. Her clothes, rags of intricate cut and infinite chic, had the cling and flow of Greek drapery, without the slightest touch of the archaic. All fashion remembers the hemstitched Vionnet dress, the cowl, the neckline, the halter, the chiffon handkerchief dress, and above all the bias—once a revelation, now a prime principle of dressmaking.

LOUISE-DAHL-WOLFE

108

Elsa Schiaparelli is a Roman, one of the most daring and original fashion talents of the century. She invented clothes that were architecturally as modern as skyscrapers. She brought shoulders into prominence. She made rough peasant textures chic. She gave the world a taste for black and for curious winey combinations of color. She discovered Lastex in America before any other dressmaker would touch it. Who else would have made a glass dress? Who else would have discovered the "boutique," and who else but Schiaparelli would have mixed a color called "shocking pink"?

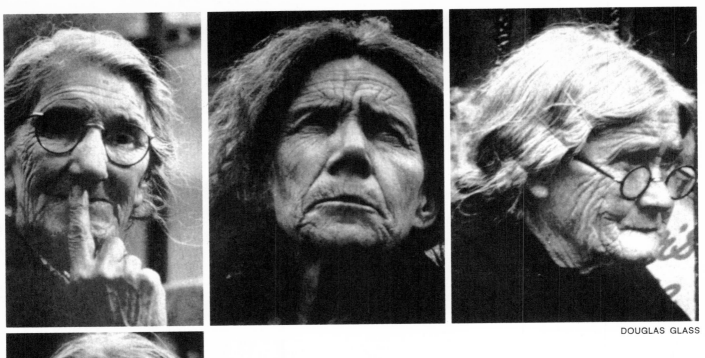

DOUGLAS GLASS

Sweet old Irish hags

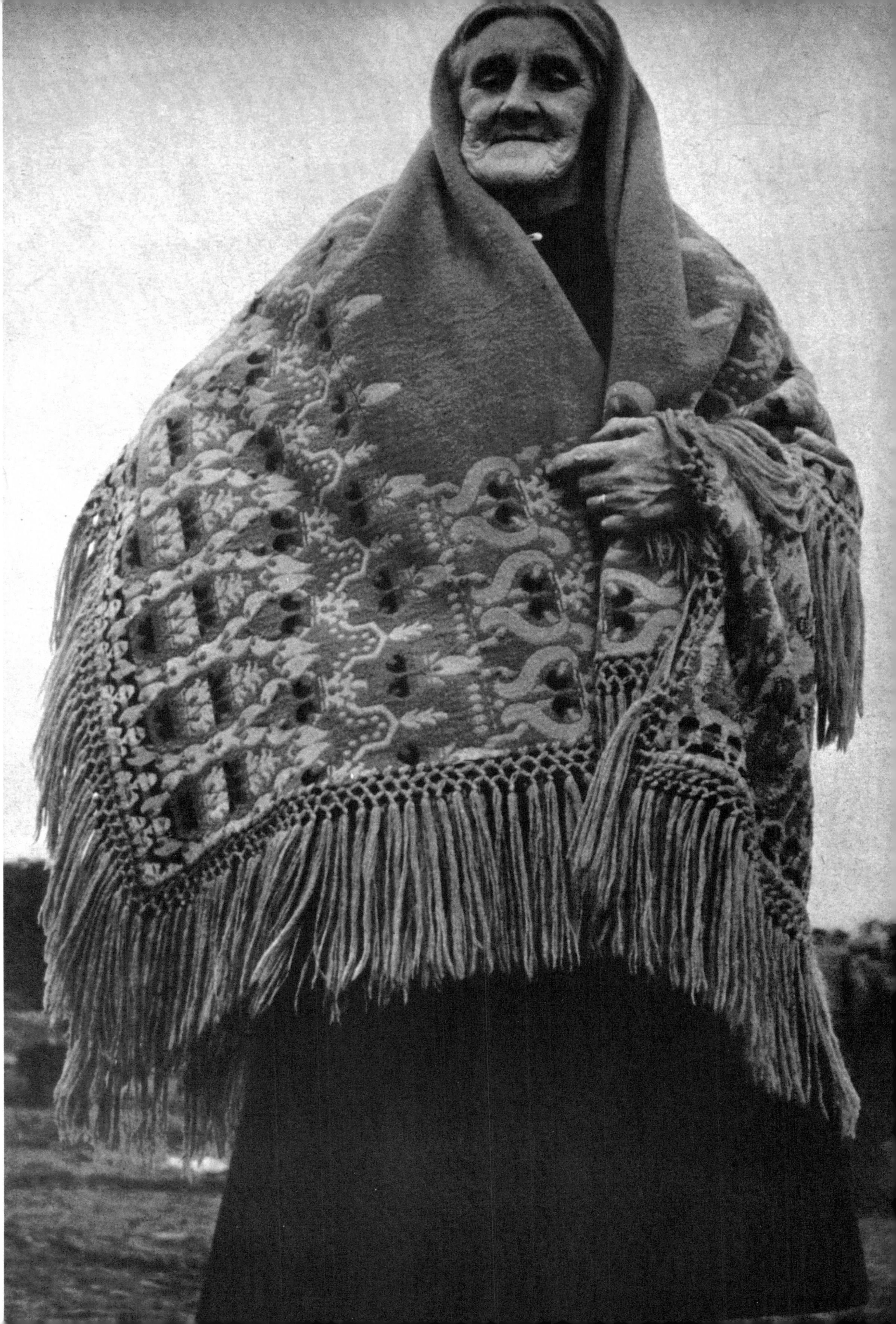

DOUGLAS GLASS

American Beauty Queens

Helena Rubenstein

Elizabeth Arden

113

Her Grace the Duchess of Windsor

114

H. M. Queen Elizabeth II

Fashions by Radio

Sensations of the Paris Collections Transmitted by Radio

Man Ray's photographic impression of a new fashion "coming over" the short waves. In this issue five pages of fashions from the new collections were radioed from Paris to New York.

All collections violently picturesque look 1880 one minute, 1950 the next. The most fantastic modern materials.

Stiff as infantas in the evening. Everyone is cutting whoopsy bangs. Do not believe that derrières are flat. Crowns zoom high as Hussars. Wonderful new shade of violet blue.

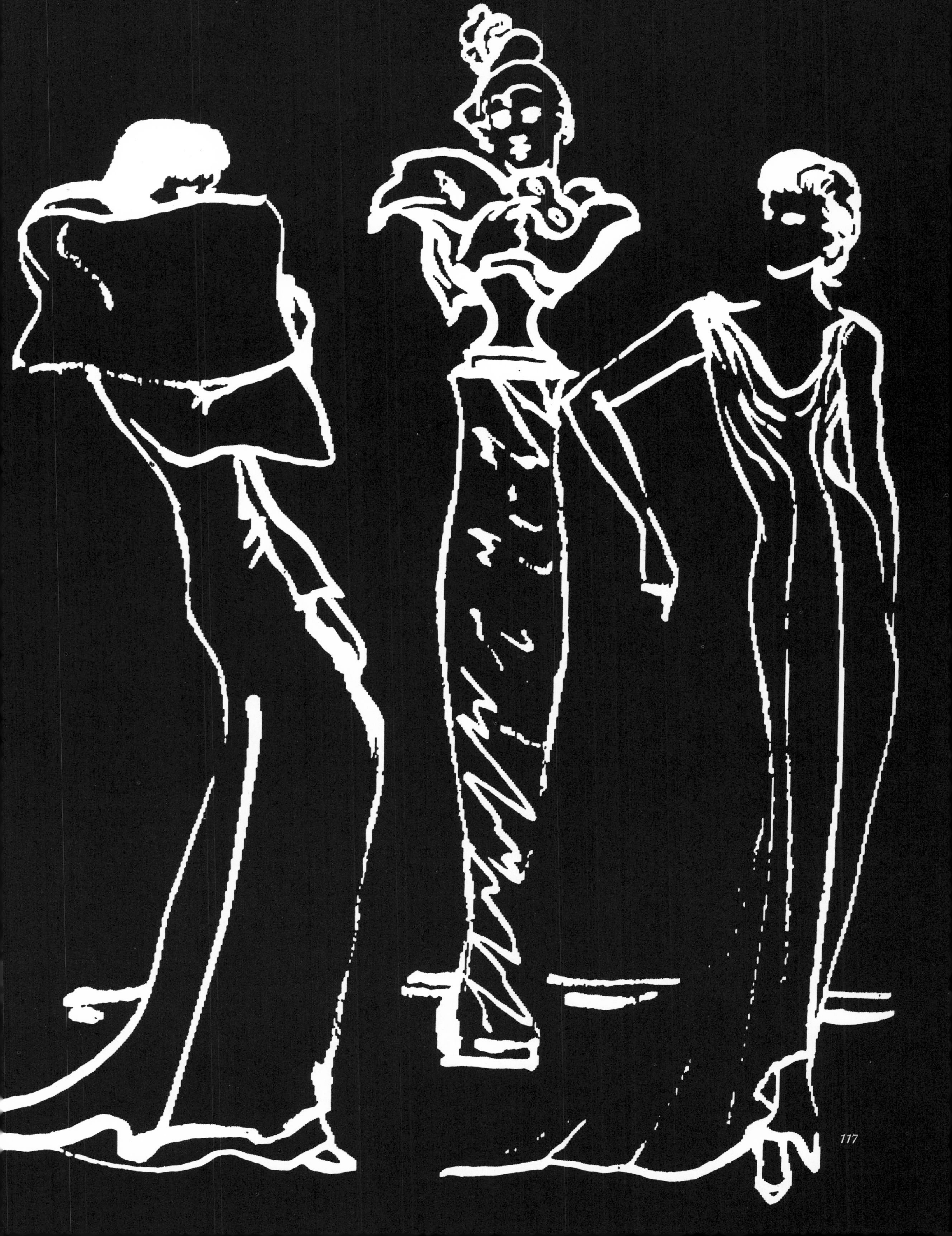
DRAWING BY CHRISTIAN BERARD

Valentina

When the Revue Russe came to town in 1922, it inadvertently gave us one of the great dress designers of our times. Valentina was in the troupe, performing in a pantomime. To her, America seemed the most exciting place in the world. She remained in New York and opened a small dressmaking establishment. Presently, at first nights and at the Ballet, everyone began to ask about the decorative woman with the singular headdresses, the pale white face, the chignon of blond hair, who moved among the conventionally dressed, as timeless as an archaic Greek dancer. Valentina obeys no precedent. She is an architect of dresses, conceiving them in terms of pure form and proportion. Her cut is deceptively simple.

NOGUCHI

119

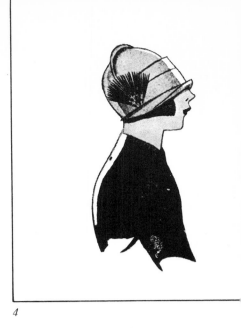

1

2

3

4

5

6

7

8

9

10

11

12

Say When!

1. Say when and who concocted full-panoplied flights of fancy such as this extravaganza.
2. Say when this daring costume became a badge of honor . . . What is it?
3. What now-famous photographer drew this barebacked shift for *Harper's Bazaar* . . . When did this fashion rage?
4. You know its name, but when did it reach this all-time low?
5. At what designer's doorstep would you lay this sort of skulduggery?
6. Remember the days when a lady dressed for a yachting party in a little rag of an ermine cape?
7. AHHHH—the call of the siren suit . . . Say when!
8. This dress had a name and was everybody-who-was-anybody's dish.
9. Ten m.p.h.—No windshield to shield her—The camouflage costume of when?
10. When was this shawl a fad, a furor, a mass hysteria?
11. When did skirts drop to the floor practically overnight?
12. She bobbed, tangoed, maxixed, where is she now?

Answers

1. The French artist Erté, who drew for *Harper's Bazaar* during the twenties, the early thirties.
2. The middy and bloomers were worn by the farmerettes of World War I.
3. Hoyningen-Huene drew this Chanel dress for *Harper's Bazaar* in 1925.
4. The cloche, 1928.
5. Schiaparelli's idea of fun in 1937.
6. This elegancy appeared in June, 1891.
7. A girl dressed by Lucile, 1914.
8. Vionnet's "handkerchief dress," 1921.
9. The linen duster, 1907.
10. Vionnet's Spanish shawl, 1921.
11. Skirts dropped overnight in the 1929 Paris collections.
12. Irene Castle (photograph by Baron de Meyer, 1922).

121

*Bogey's Girl (a Bazaar Discovery)
Lauren Bacall's first magazine cover
appeared in 1943 and a new star
was in orbit. During the next ten
years* Bazaar *followed her sultry
beauty and meteoric career like a
proud mama.*

Humphrey Bogart and Lauren Bacall

The Wanderers

by Eudora Welty

RICHARD AVEDON

"H̲ow come you weren't here yesterday?" old Mrs. Stark asked her maid, looking up from her solitaire board—inlaid wood that gave off pistol-like reports under the blows of her shuffling cards. It was September and here in the hall she imagined she could feel October at her back.

"I didn' get back from my sisters' out in the country."

"And poor Mrs. Rainey dead. What kept you? What were you so busy doing at your sisters'?"

"Showin' my teef."

Mrs. Stark raised her voice. "Only thing I can do for people any more, in joy or sorrow, is send 'em you. Then you disappoint me. You let poor Mrs. Rainey die and keep me from doing a thing about it till here next day. Fix my breakfast and yours and go on down there. Get in the kitchen and clean it up for Miss Virgie but don't pay any attention to her. Start cooking for the funeral, if other people didn't get to it first, yesterday."

"Yes'm."

"Mind you learn to appreciate your own kitchen here when you stand over a hot wood stove all day."

"Sisters' place a place once you get to it—hard time gettin' back."

Mrs. Stark snapped her tiny fingers.

"You and all your sisters! Shoo!"

She rose and walked, with her walk like a girl's, to the front door, looking down over her hill, the burned, patchy grass no better than Mrs. Rainey's, the brown shrubs, but the sweet olive tree was blooming. She called over her shoulder, "I never had cause to set foot in the Rainey house for over five minutes in my life. And no need now. But I hope I know my

duty, Juba, and what any old woman owes another old woman. Do you hear me? Go back and put on a clean apron."

"Means I have to iron me it," Juba said, and after a silent moment withdrew.

The Raineys still held on to the hilltop house at the edge of town, with both men long gone. The tin roof shed the light under the crape myrtle and privet, gone to trees, that edged the porch. The banana plants with their scorched edges, taken together with the well, made the three islands in the whitened grass of the yard. Across and back again, with effort but bobbinlike, had moved Mrs. Fate Rainey in her dress the hard blue of a morning glory.

In old age Mrs. Rainey showed what a neat, narrow head she had, under the thin hair. When she came outdoors, her outthrust head was as silver-looking as a new mailbox. It was out of the autocracy of her stroke—she had suffered "a light stroke" five years ago, "while separating my cows and calves," she would recount it—that she had begun ordering things done by set times. When it was time for her daughter Virgie to come home from work in the afternoon, Mrs. Rainey was afraid she wouldn't get there in time to milk before dark. She still had two Jersey cows. She stood out in the front yard, or moved across it the best way she could, back and forth, waiting for Virgie.

Mrs. Rainey stood in the yard all fair Saturday afternoons and other fair afternoons after five-thirty, when Mr. Nesbitt let Virgie go, looking out for her until she came, barely keeping up with the withdrawing of the shade, which gave her a narrower path to walk. She held up as poorly there, propped by a cane, as the bad well the Negro had made her after she was sick, close to the house. Bleaching down by the roadside was an old chair she had sold things from once, under the borrowed shade of the chinaberry across the road, but she didn't seem to want to sit down now, to be quite that near the trafficking. Clear up where she was, she felt the world tremble, day and night, when the loggers went by. While she lived she was going to wait, and she did wait, standing up, for Virgie her daughter, past forty now and too dressed up, to come home and milk Bossy and Julia the way she should.

As she looked out from her hill, in the creeping sun, it seemed she would like to be argued with and prevailed on to go back in the house, or to suffer contradiction, but from whom? Not even from Virgie.

She reminded the old people in Battle Hill of Snowdie McLain, her neighbor then, watching for King in the old days, her runaway husband who came back again too—in his sixties. They were even reminded vaguely of themselves, the old people, still watching and waiting for something they didn't know or didn't care about or didn't remember any longer.

. . . Mrs. Rainey could not spare her good hand to put up and shade her eyes, yet after you passed you saw her in that position, in your vision if not in your sight, with a hooded stare as though when she saw her daughter she would see *through* her too. But you couldn't be sorry for Raineys, mother or daughter, people said; they would never let you. Even the mother looked ready to ward you off and scare you, there in her gathered, old-lady dress, sometimes in an old bonnety church hat. There's the old lady that watches the turn of the road, thought the old men passing in trucks or wagons on Saturday, going home, lifting their hats. Young people giggled at her, but children and Negroes did not; they took her for granted like the lady on the Old Dutch Cleanser can.

"Have you seen my daughter?"

Mrs. Rainey thought she called to the road, but she didn't; shame drew down her head, for she could still feel one thing if she could feel little else coming to her from the outside world, lack of chivalry. Then, in an odd set way, for she did not know how to lie, she would lie to Virgie when she came. "I asked Passing. And not one of 'em said they could tell me where you were, what kept you so long in town."

Waiting, she heard circling her ears like the swallows beginning, talk about lovers. Circle by circle it twittered, church talk, talk on the post-office steps, vulgar man-talk possibly in barbershops, all she could not get near to, but all coming to her.

"So long as the old lady's alive, it's all behind her back, you reckon?"

"Virgie wouldn't run off and leave her, she's too old and crippled."

"Left once."

"That Mr. Mabry's been taking out his gun and leaving Virgie a bag o' quail every other day. Anybody can see him."

"That's real pitiful."

"He told Virgie the day she got tired of quail just let him know, and he'd quit, that's what I heard."

"Has she let him know?"

"Her? Naw, she ain't let him know to quit. I reckon it would be possible for a human being, a girl—though not young!—to live off them rich birds altogether for a little space of time, especially with her ma to help her eat 'em. Her ma ain't lost her appetite!"

"Virgie's been a high flyer too, has Virgie, hee hee!"

"Guess it wouldn't be polite for neither one of 'em to stop now, on the quails. Even if he heard. Got to keep on now."

"Oh sure. Mr. Mabry's a clean shot, too. A widower from out from Mize."

"But ain't he heard?"

She thought it was over Virgie that people drew their sighs and parted on the square.

But it's my last summer, and she ought to get back here and milk on time, the old lady thought, stubbornly and yet pityingly, the two ways she was.

"Look where the sun is," she called, as Virgie did drive up in the yard in the old coupe Mrs. Rainey kept forgetting she had, the battered thing she had taken in trade for the poor little calf.

"I see it, Mama."

Virgie's long, dark, too heavy hair swung this way and that as she came up in her flowered voile dress, on her high heels through the bearded grass.

"You have to milk before dark, after driving them in, and there's four little quails full of shot for you to dress, lying on my kitchen table."

"Come on back in the house, Mama. Come in with me."

"I been by myself all day."

Virgie bent and gave her mother her evening kiss. Mrs. Rainey knew then that Virgie would drive home and milk and feed the cows and deliver the milk on the road, and come back and cook the little quails. "It's a wonder, though," she thought. "A blessed wonder to see the child do it."

The day Mrs. Rainey died, Virgie was kneeling on the floor of her bedroom cutting out a dress from some plaid material. She was sewing on Sunday.

"There's nothing Virgie Rainey loves better than struggling against a real hard plaid," Mrs. Rainey thought, with a thrust of pain from somewhere unexpected. Whereas there was a simple line down through her own body now, dividing it in half, there should be one in every woman's body; it would need to be the long way, not the cross way—that was too easy—making each of them a side to feel and know, and a side to stop it, to be waited on, finally.

But she wanted to drop to her knees there where Virgie's plaid spread out like a pretty rug for her. Her last clear feeling as she stood there, holding herself up, was that she wanted to be down and covered up, in, of all things, Virgie's hard-to-match-up plaid. But she turned herself around by an act of strength which tore her within and walked, striking her cane, the width of the hall and two rooms and lay down on her own bed.

"Stop and fan me a minute," she called aloud. She was thinking rapidly to herself that Virgie had said, "I aim to get married on my bulb money."

Virgie, who worked in her gown, with the drawstring looped, not tied, came in with pins in her mouth and her thumb marked green from the scissors, and stood over her. She brought a paper up and down over her mother's face. She fanned her with the *Market Bulletin*.

Dying, Mrs. Rainey went rapidly over the list in it, her list. As though her impatient foot would stamp at each item, she counted it, corrected it, and yet she was about to forget the seasons, and the places things grew. Purple althea cuttings, box, four colors of cannas for fifteen cents, moon vine seed by teaspoonful, green and purple jew. Roses: big white rose, little thorn rose, beauty-red sister rose, pink monthly, old-fashioned red summer rose, very fragrant, baby rose. Five colors of verbena, candlestick lilies, milk and wine lilies, blackberry lilies, lemon lilies, angel lilies, apostle lilies. Angel trumpet seed. The

red amaryllis. Some can come from across the road.

Faster and faster, Mrs. Rainey thought: Red salvia, four o'clock, pink Jacob's ladder, sweet geranium cuttings, sword fern and fortune grass, century plants, vase palm, watermelon pink and white crape myrtle, Christmas cactus, golden bell. White star jessamine. Snowball. Hyacinthus. Pink fairy lilies. White. The fairy white.

"Fan me. If you stop fanning, it's worse than if you never started."

And when Mama is gone, almost gone now, she meditated, I can tack onto my ad: the quilts! For sale, Double Muscadine Hulls, Road to Dublin, Starry Sky, Strange Spider Web, Hands All Around, Double Wedding Ring. Mama's rich in quilts, child.

Mrs. Rainey lay there, carelessly on the counterpane, thinking, Crochet tablecloth, Sunburst design, very lacy. She knew Virgie was over her, fanning her in rhythmic sweeps. Presently old Mrs. Rainey's lips shut tight.

She was thinking, Mistake. Never Virgie at all. It was me, the bride with so much. Why, Virgie, go away, it was me. Don't you fan me.

She put her hand up and never knew what happened to it, her protest.

Virgie leaned her head on her arm, her mouth opened and the pins fell out on the floor. She crouched there. She was not much afraid of death, either of its delay or its surprise. As yet nothing came into her head, except something about her dress.

The bed, the headboard dark and ungiving as an old mirror on the wall, to the child a vast King Arthur shield that might have a motto concealed in it, cast its afternoon shadow down, dark as muscadines, to her mother's waist. The old shadow, familiar as sleep the life long, always ran down over the bolster, the warm and knotty medallions of the familiar counterpane—the overworked, inherited, highly personal pattern—from which her mother's black shoes now pointed up.

Behind the bed the window was full of cloudy pressing flowers and leaves in heavy light, like a jar of figs in syrup held up. A hummingbird darted, fed, darted. Under his speed, the window, the house, became something different. But every day he came. He had a ruby throat. The clock jangled as faintly as cymbals struck under water, but did not strike; it couldn't. Yet a torrent of riches seemed to flow over the room, submerging it.

Virgie sent for the doctor. On the front steps she screamed, "Go get Dr. Vernon out of church!" to a passing Negro, who began to sprint in his Sunday clothes.

By midafternoon the house was filling with callers and helpers. . . . Coffee was being kept on the stove and iced tea in the pitcher in the hall. Virgie was dressed and at the front of the house. Moving around her, a lady watered the ferns and evened the shades in the parlor, then watered and evened again. The callers all stayed. Every seat in the parlor and hall was taken, and the porch creaked and the house shook under the men who stood outside.

Sally Howard, her black-stockinged legs seeming to wade through the impeding legs of the other women, crossed the parlor to where Virgie sat on her hands by the closed sewing machine. Sally had chosen the prettiest coffee cup for herself and balanced it serenely.

"Papa sent his deepest sympathy. Let me sit by you, Virgie." She kissed her.

"Excuse me," Virgie was saying. All at once she slept, straight in her chair. When she opened her eyes, she watched and listened to the even bigger roomful as carefully, and as carelessly, as though she were on the point of departure. Through their murmur she heard herself circle the room to speak to them and be kissed. She made the steps of the walk they watched, head, breasts and hips in their helpless agitation, like a rope of bells she started in their ears.

"She can't help it," Sally Howard was saying to the person beside her. "*I know that.*"

The unnaturally closed door led from her mother's room. Behind it, they all knew—waiting as they were for it to open—Mrs. Snowdie McLain was laying Mrs. Rainey out. She washed her and dressed her all alone, tolerating only two Negroes to wait on her, and Mrs. McLain was nearly seventy. Mrs. Willie Stark, whose place everyone felt it to be to supervise the dead being laid out, felt too weak that day, and sent word she had had to lie down.

None of the callers except Miss Snowdie, an old neighbor, had been inside the house since Mr. Fate Rainey's funeral. Nobody had left the Raineys a fresh calling card until today. Only, of course, visiting or not, the Raineys knew their stories all the way as they knew the Raineys', from the beginning and before the beginning, on through, without a break. Virgie leaned her head back against the chair. On some occasions, in some places, always in a house of death, everybody's story came evident, showed forth from the person, became a part of the public domain. It was from gatherings like this that people knew, knew too much.

For she could see Ran McLain, standing at the door, shaking hands. And didn't it show somehow on him that once he had taken advantage of a country girl who killed herself afterward? It showed when he grew middle-aged and ran for mayor. He was deluged with votes, for all was remembered without the opponent's outcry. Ran was still smiling—holding on to a countryman. They had voted for him for his glamour and his story, for being a McLain and the bad twin, for marrying a Stark, and then for ruining a girl and her killing herself for him. Ran knew it every minute, there in her door he stood it.

"Cheer up, now, cheer up," Mr. Nesbitt was saying to her, seeming to lift her to her feet by running his finger under her chin. His eyes—so willed by him, she thought—ran tears and dried. She stood fixed before him. "Come here," he called over his shoulder.

Another businessman was wandering by, close to Mr. Nesbitt—a stranger. "Brought a fella along, Virgie. I'll get him here."

He took hold of them both. "Burt, I want you to meet a lovely girl, a very, very charming young lady! Though today a lady of sorrow, of course. Miss Virgie Rainey. This is Mr. Thisbee from out-of-town."

Mr. Thisbee reached out his hand, Virgie put hers in it.

"Virgie, tell Mr. Thisbee who's your best friend in this town."

"You, Mr. Bitts," Virgie said.

"Tell him who's sorry as hell today about your mother."

"You, Mr. Bitts."

"Everybody in Battle Hill calls me Mr. Bitts, Thisbee, you can too. Now wait. Tell him who hired you when nobody else was in the hiring mood, Virgie. Tell him. And was always kind to you and stood up for you."

"You, Mr. Bitts."

She never turned away until it was finished; today this was somehow easier, a relief.

"Tell him how long you've been working for old Mr. Bitts."

"A long time."

"No, tell him how long it's been—my my my, tell him."

"Since 1920, Mr. Bitts."

"And if you ever made any mistakes in your letters and figgers, who was it stood behind you with the company?"

"I'm very sorry for you in your sorrow," Mr. Thisbee said suddenly, letting go her hand. She almost fell.

"But who? Who?"

Mr. Nesbitt extended his arms overly wide, as he did when asking her to dance with him on rides to Vicksburg. Abruptly he wheeled and went off; he was hurt, disappointed in her for the hundredth time. She saw Mr. Nesbitt's fat, hurt back as he wandered as if lost and stood a long time contemplating the table down the long hall—not set yet.

Food—two banana cakes and a baked ham, a platter of darkly deviled eggs, new rolls—and flowers kept arriving at the back, and the kitchen filled with women as the parlor now filled with men, come farther in. Virgie went back once more to the kitchen, but again the women stopped what they were doing and looked at her as though something—not only today—should prevent her from knowing at all how to cook—the thing they knew. She went to the stove, took a fork and turned over a piece or two of the chicken, to see Missie Spights—whatever her married name was—look at her with eyes wide in a kind of wonder and belligerence.

Then she walked through them and stood on the quiet back porch to feel the south breeze. . . . The cut flowers were plunged stem down and head down in shady water buckets. Virgie had a sudden recollection of recital night at Miss Eckhart's—the moment when she was to be called out. She was thirteen, waiting outside, on guard at a vast calming spectacle of turmoil and saving it. A little drop spilled, she remembered it now: an anxiety which brought her to the point of sickness, that back in there they were laughing at her mother's hat.

She went back into the parlor. Like a forest murmur the waiting talk filled the room.

The door opened. Miss Snowdie stood against it, sideways, looking neither in nor out.

Immediately the ladies rose and filled the doorway; some of them went in. Only the end of the bed and Mrs. Rainey's feet could be seen from within the parlor. There were soft cries. "Snowdie!" "Miss Snowdie! She looks beautiful!" Then the rest of the ladies tiptoed forward and could be seen bending over the bed as they would bend over the crib of a little kicking baby. They came out again.

"Come see your mother."

They pulled peremptorily at Virgie's arms, their voices bright.

"Don't touch me."

They pulled harder, still smiling but in silence, and Virgie pulled back. Her hair fell over her eyes. "Don't touch me."

"Honey, you just don't know what you lost, that's all."

They were all people who had never touched her before who tried now to struggle with her, their faces hurt. She was hurting them all, shocking them. They leaned over her, agonized, pleading with the pull of their hands. It was a lady pulling the hardest who had caught the last breath of her husband in a toy balloon, by his wish, and had it at home still—most of it, until a Negro stole it.

Mrs. Spights's red face looked over their wall. "Your mama was too fine for you, Virgie, too fine. That was always the trouble between you."

In that truth, Virgie looked up at them lightheartedly and they lifted her to her feet and drew her into the bedroom and showed her her mother.

She lay in the black satin. It had been lifted, heavy as a child, out of her trunk, the dress in which the diminished, pea-sized mothballs had shone and rolled like crystals all Virgie's life, in waiting and taken out twice, and now spread out in full triangle. Her head was in the center of the bolster, the widow's place in which she herself had laid it. Miss Snowdie had rouged her cheeks.

They watched Virgie, but Virgie gave them no sign now. She felt their hands smooth down her and leave her, draw away from her body and then give it a little shove forward, even their hands showing sorrow a body did not fall, to give hands back what was broken, to pick up, smooth again. As if people's very touch anticipated the falling of the body, the single watchful body.

Later, she cried when they said, "She used to set out yonder and sell muscadines, see out there? . . . Now the road goes the other way." But though that was like a sad song, it was not true. The road still went the same, to Battle Hill, of course. Only now the wrong people for buying muscadines came by. They were all going away from Bat-

tle Hill, riding trucks and carrying their blades and chains, to haul the big trees to mill. And the vines had dried. She wept because they could not tell it right, while their pointing forefingers moved from the window to her, with her head bowed down.

"Call Mr. Mabry now."

Mr. Mabry, fresh from the barbershop, took Virgie's hand and dropped it, after making a little swing of it a time or two. She withdrew and gave him permission to go into the bedroom. She wondered where she had seen him tiptoe before today. Even old fellows in the hall began to speak of him now, softly, as he looked down at the dead with his face so ruby-like, so recently complimented upon, that in the next moment it would fill with concern for itself.

"He aims to get closer to Mize. Where he don't have to use hoot owls for roosters and fox for yard dogs, is the way he put it to me."

"Then why on earth don't he come to Battle Hill? No nicer place than right here, 's what I think."

"He prefers Mize."

"And see, there's Miss Virgie. He don't want to carry her to the country, don't want her here either, wants to carry her to Mize."

"I declare! It's her chance."

But in the parlor it was now generally felt polite to consider Mrs. Rainey as the center of conversation, since the door was now open. Except Jinny McLain, Ran's wife, who now arrived. With her hand out, she was showing a diamond ring around.

"Look at my diamond. Have you all seen what I bought myself? Four-carat. I deserved me a diamond," she went on to say, taking Virgie's hand and pressing it. "That's what I told Ran. He and I take turns wearing it at night." Softly she kissed Virgie's cheek, whispering, "I don't have to see her—do I, Virgie?"

"Wonder if Katie Rainey wrote a will? Spec' not." An old lady Virgie couldn't place said it half-

way in Virgie's direction, leaning toward her now and then with her full weight. "Virgie might get a little bit of dairy-food savings now, bet she'll spend it, hm? Her pretty quilts, she can't ship those to the fair any more now. What does Virgie care about housekeeping and china plates without no husband, hm? Wonder who Virgie'll give the deer to if she goes away. That picture of the deer Miss Katie hooked with the mistletoe crown over the horns, and the oak leaves, the prettiest thing in the world. The kid doll she used to let any and all play with, once upon a time."

"Oh, I wish I had it now!" cried Sally Howard.

"Her fern stand. Virgie won't stay here to keep care of ferns, I bet. Her begonia, thirty-five years old. Not much older than Virgie, is it, Virgie? She left her recipes to the Methodist Church—I hope."

Mrs. Snowdie McLain had come away from the laying out and taking her praise. Virgie walked out and waited on the porch, for she knew Miss Snowdie would come outside. She had always known Miss Snowdie, an old neighbor, now moved away—moved back to an even older place of the McLains', in McLain Courthouse. She was a gentle lady, with a face as white and folded as a bird dog's, and as gently concerned, but no more. Mr. King McLain, her flyaway husband, had come home a few years ago, at the age of sixty-something, and stayed. They said she had never gotten over it—first his running away, then his running back to her. She never seemed really to feel things now. She walked out on the porch and kissed Virgie almost idly. Her albino's hands were cruelly reddened. Her soft black-and-white-dotted dress smelled as freshly as always of verbena.

"I think she looks all right, Virgie. I saw to her as well as I knew how."

But her eyes went straight past Virgie, across the road, where her old house used to be. The two women stood still in the afternoon light. Beyond them in the yard, the children waiting for their parents stood still too, at that moment, and not knowing where to look, listened—listened to the locusts, which sounded like the sound of the world going around to them when they suddenly beat their cupped hands over their ears.

"Virgie? You know Mrs. Willie Stark and I long ago made up. About Ran and Jinny's trouble; that's over. But do you reckon, at such a time, that kept her from coming? A little delicacy? Knowing we would be face to face over the laying out?"

Miss Snowdie sighed, as if she had forgotten her question with the asking. Across there was where she had lived all those days, the old deserted time, when Virgie had played with Ran and Eugene under her trees, on her porch, under her house, along the river bank and in Cooper's Woods. . . . The old summerhouse was still back there, lattices leaning inward and not matching at the joinings, like a place where long ago something had been kept, that could peep out now. The big chinaberry tree had been cut down some time. There were suckers that sprayed up from the high stump like a fountain. Negroes had carried away most of the sides and roof of the fallen-down house, but had hardly made inroad on the chimney, surprisingly enough; it was mostly still there, visible from here, dove-pink in the dust and green leafiness. . . . Vines had taken the driveway and the front yard and the standing stone steps, and the trees and all.

Virgie removed herself from Miss Snowdie's arm, which had gone around her waist. It seemed to recall her.

"I'd want *her* to lay *me* out," the old lady said.

She was trembling, and said no more. She stood looking out to the road as if she still waited.

Mr. King McLain, treading so lightly they didn't hear him, came out and brushed his wife to one side.

"Katie Blazes, that's what we used to call your mother," and he nodded at Virgie. He had grown a little patch of hair under his lip—not silky—coarse, a pinkish white. It shook in a ruminating way.

"Sir?"

"Katie Blazes, girl. Didn't you ever hear your mother tell how she never took a dare to put a match to her stockings? Whsst! Up went the blazes, up to her knee! Sometimes both legs. Cotton stockings the girls used to wear, fuzzy, God knows they were. Nobody else among the girls would set fire to her legs. She had the neighborhood scared to death she'd go up in flames, at the age of fifteen."

"Sir? Why *was* that?" Miss Snowdie turned to look at him. Virgie watched the black coffee begin to shake in his little cup. There was something terrible about that old man—he was too old.

"In flames!" He turned around and left them.

"I don't know what to do with him," Miss Snowdie said, in a murmur as quiet as the world around them now. She did not know she had spoken.

"Virgie, we've got enough ready to feed an army," Mrs. Spights said in the kitchen door, her arms shining red. "Ham, chickens, potato salad, deviled eggs, and all the cake and foolishness people send besides."

"Does there have to be so much?" Virgie asked.

"Watch. The out-of-town relatives are always hungry."

"If you won't let us sit up with her, we'll all be back early for the funeral, Virgie."

"It's a good thing we brought all our flowers," Missie Spights said, telling her good-by. "Virgie, you haven't a single one."

She saw them all, except Miss Snowdie who stayed to be last, get into their cars in the yard, or walk down the front path and out the gate. As they walked away, they seemed to drag gates and barriers away from her view of the hill, all the little hills. They shimmered, stirred almost invisibly;

cotton fields look busy even on Sunday while they are not being picked. . . .

Down the settling dust of the road came an ancient steaming car, which Virgie saw was a Negro car and then as the one belonging to old Plez's grown grandchildren. It would turn in here. Plez, up until his death, had stopped by, an old man, to milk for Mrs. Rainey on his way to and from Mrs. Stark's. The old car pounded up the hill to her. It was cracked like one of those put-together puzzles of the globe of the world. Its cracks didn't meet from one side across to the other, from their look, and it was all held together with wire straightened out from somewhere else. Next year it would sit in the front yard of Plez's grandchildren for decoration, on its axles, the four wheels gone and the tires divided up between women and children, two for flowerbeds and two for swings.

"I'm so glad to see you," Virgie said.

They had brought the flowers from their dooryard, princess feathers and snow-on-the-mountain. It took them a long time to turn around and get a start back. A little boy ran back with the pan of butterbeans and okra.

"All come to the funeral if you can get away!" she called after them, too late.

Virgie walked down the hill too, crossed the road and made her way through the old McLain place and the pasture and down to the river. She stood on the willow bank. It was bright as midafternoon in the openness of the water, quiet and peaceful. She took off her clothes and let herself into the river.

She saw her waist disappear into reflectionless water; it was like walking into sky, some impurity of skies. All was one warmth, air, water and her own body. All seemed one weight, one matter—until as she put down her head and closed her eyes and the light slipped under her lids, she felt this matter a translucent one, the river, herself, the sky all vessels which the sun filled.

She began to swim in the river, forcing it gently, as she would wish for gentleness to her body. Her breasts around which she felt the water curving were as sensitive at that moment as the tips of wings must feel to birds, or antennae to insects. She felt the sand, grains intricate as little cogged wheels, minute shells of old seas, and the many dark ribbons of grass and mud touch her and leave her, like suggestions and withdrawals of some bondage that might have been dear, now dismembering and losing itself. She moved but like a cloud in skies, aware but only of the nebulous edges of her feeling and the vanishing opacity of her will, the carelessness for the water of the river through which her body had already passed as well as for what was ahead. The bank was all one, where out of the faded September world the little ripening plums started. Memory dappled her like no more than a paler light, which in little agitations came through leaves, not darkening her for more than an instant. The iron taste of the old river was sweet to her, though. If she opened her eyes she looked at bluebottles, the skating water bugs. If she trembled it was at the smoothness of a fish or snake that crossed her knees.

In the middle of the river, whose downstream or upstream could not be told by a current, she lay on her stretched arm, not breathing, floating. Virgie had reached the point where in the next moment she might turn into something without feeling it shock her. She hung suspended in the Big Black River as she would know to hang suspended in felicity. Far to the west, a cloud running finger-like over the sun made her splash the water. She stood, walked along the soft mud of the bottom and pulled herself out of the water by a willow branch, which like warm rain brushed her back with its leaves. . . .

The moon, while she looked into the high sky, took its own light between one moment and the next. A wood thrush, which had begun to sing, hushed its long

moment and began again. Virgie put her clothes back on. She would have given much for a cigarette, always wishing for a little more of what had just been.

She went back to the pasture—the old Cooper's Woods—where the enormous anthills shone, with long shadows, like pyramids on the other side of the world, and drove the cows home. . . .

She went out to milk and came back to the house.

From the hall she looked into her mother's room. The window and the room were the one blue of first dark. Only the black dress, the density of skirt, was stamped on it, like some dark chip now riding midair or on blue lakes.

Miss Snowdie McLain, who had elected to "sit up" the first hours of night, sat sleeping outside the door, the bedroom rocker dragged out to the parlor, in the end. In her powdery dress, her white head hanging and the fan gone from her fingers, it was she at last who bore the appearance of death.

All that were left of Mrs. Rainey's clan came by noon the next day, in plenty of time for the funeral at two—big dark people named Morrison, men and women alike with square chins and blue eyes. A little string of towheaded children in stairsteps made a row behind, eating bananas. Virgie could not remember these Morrisons apart; she found them knocking on the porch. They all moved at once upon her, kissed her, and begged before they got through the door for ice water or iced tea or both. They had ridden in in two trucks, from Walnut and Carthage. The first thing the biggest Morrison did, once in the hall, was to catch up a little Moody girl there swatting flies, and tickle her, speaking soberly over her screams, "Now wait. You don't know who I am."

The same old country Rainey came from Louisiana who had come to Fate's funeral twenty years ago and hadn't sent word since. Again he explained that the Rainey name had been French; he offered to fix the porch floor again that very day, for Virgie, and in

time, but was prevented. He was the only Rainey that came. The Raineys were mostly all died out, or were too far away to buy a ticket.

"But you got in touch," Mrs. Spights told Virgie. It was Mrs. Spights who dispatched telegrams in times of sorrow.

Virgie, waking with the birds, had been driven by something to try to cut down some of the high grass in the yard before people started coming again, for the funeral. After she milked and drove the cows to pasture, she took her sewing scissors outside. She crouched over with them in the pink early light, chewing and sawing the heads off the grass—it had all gone to seed—a handful at a time. The choked out roses surprised and scratched her. She had to come in when Miss Snowdie, the first one, arrived. As though for a long time she had been very angry and had wept, she allowed Miss Snowdie to drive her inside and cook her breakfast.

Then Mrs. Stark's Juba had arrived, followed by a little running Negro bearing curtain stretchers, and had begun taking down all the curtains. In half an hour they were out in the yard, set forth like the tents in the Wilderness of Kadesh engraved on a page of the Bible, in which Virgie, witnessed, had yesterday entered the death of her mother. The ladies soon were everywhere, radiating from the kitchen again. The little McLain children and their nurse had gotten away from old Mrs. Stark, the grandmother, and come over to play in the Rainey yard. The little Morrisons, every time they were gathered up and brought away from the McLains into the house, cried. Blue jays were scolding the whole morning over the roof, and the logging trucks thundered by, shaking their chains and threatening the white curtains with dust.

Mrs. Spights, raising her voice in the bedroom and talking rapidly, was telling one of the Moodys, "Sister couldn't put her good shoes back in the shoe box after *that* funeral, because while she was at the cemetery, Epworth and Wesley made a choo-choo boat out of it—come running to meet her when she got back, with it all lit up so she couldn't give them a scolding." Suddenly Mrs. Spights, rising from her chair by the bed, backed out of the room into the hall: she had heard the coffin come.

"Where are all those Morrisons going to bed down?" asked old Mr. Rainey, indicating with a purpled thumb, like a fig.

"They're striking right out for home after the funeral, sir," Virgie said. "As soon as they've taken some food."

"Pity. Never a chance to really know those." He put a little hooked finger up and touched a string on her father's old banjo, which hung on a nail in the hall, the head faintly luminous by morning light. But he didn't play the note.

Mr. Nesbitt sent word by a Negro in gold spectacles that he had to be out of town during the funeral, and then the Negro handed Mrs. Spights a large, bought cross of gladiolas and ferns which rested on a stand, with Mr. Nesbitt's card tied on. The Morrisons moved upon it and placed it in front of all the other flowers—now steadily being made into wreaths on the back porch—where they could look at it during the service, to remember. The Sunday-school chairs arrived by wagon, and the Morrisons took them at the door and set them in catticornered rows. Had Mrs. Willie Stark been able to come, people said, it wouldn't have happened quite the same way.

Old Mr. King McLain did not appear happy over having to come to the Rainey house again today. He fumed, and went back to visit in the kitchen.

"Little conversation with your mother in '18, or along there," he said to Virgie, who was folding napkins with the Stark "S" on them. "You know in those days I was able to make considerable trips off, and only had my

glimpses of the people back here."

Miss Snowdie had come to stand folding napkins too.

"I'd come and I'd go again, only I ended up at the wrong end, wouldn't you say?" He suddenly smiled, rather fiercely, but at neither woman. He wore the stiffest-starched white suit Virgie had ever seen on any old gentleman; it looked fierce too—the lapels alert as ears. "Saw your mother in a pink sunbonnet. Rosy-cheeked. 'Hello!' 'I declare, King McLain, you look to me as you ever did, strolling here in the road. You rascal.' 'Just for that, what would you rather have than anything? I'm asking because I'm going to get it for you.' 'A swivel chair. So I can sit out front and sell crochet and peaches, if my good-for-nothin' husband'll let me.' Ah, we all knew sweet old Fate, he was a sweet man among us. 'Shucks, that's too easy. Say something else. I'd have got you anything your living heart desired.' 'Well, I told you. And you mischief, I believe you.'

"Three niggers black as dirt daubers up to the house in a wagon, bang-up noon next day. Up to the door, pounding.

"'Oh, King McLain! You brought it so quick-like!'

"But I! I was no telling where by that time! Looked to her, I know, like I couldn't wait long enough to hear her pleasure, so bent, so bent I was on all I did then—to what was next.

"'Watch out! Watch out now, don't set down that thing till I tell you exactly where to put it!' Fussed and fumed. *She* told me how she flew around the yard. Forgot where the shade went. Niggers carrying here, carrying there. Then put it spang by the road, close as she could get.

"Chair always was too big for her, little heels wouldn't touch ground. It was big enough for a man, big enough for Judge McIlderry, 'cause it was his, I prevailed on the widow. Oh, Katie Rainey was a sight, I saw her swing it around many a time, to hear me coming in or starting out,

waving her hand quick. She could see all comings and goings and sell eggs Fate didn't know how to. Oh, then, she could see why Fate Rainey —a real sweet man—had spent all that time trying to find her such a possession and of course failed. I set her on a throne!"

"Mr. King, I never knew the chair came from you," Virgie said, smiling.

He looked all at once inconsolable. She touched his arm, but Miss Snowdie shook her head, guessing food. "He knows he ought to stay off that ham."

"Oh, is there ham?"

The Negroes stood by the table with fly swatters. Virgie laid a little piccalilli with the ham on his plate, which he held for her meekly, even lingeringly, and he went off by himself and ate.

People were gathered now. They sat inside and outside, listening and not listening. Young people held hands, all of them sitting down early to get the back row.

"What are the children up to?" Jinny McLain swept aside a fresh curtain to see out the window. "My daughter has chosen today to catch a pair of green lizards to wear. Lizard earrings! How can she stand those little teeth in her?" Jinny laughed delightedly. "Little King just sits nicely under a bush sucking four-o'clocks—it *is* four o'clock, the way I feel."

Some of the Morrisons carried the coffin into the parlor and placed it over the hearth on the four chairs from around the table. Then the wreaths were stood on edge all across. Miss Snowdie took a place near by and drew her fan deeply through the air, back and forth.

"Sit by me, Virgie," said Sally Howard, who began to put her handkerchief to her eyes.

Brother Dampeer, whose father was the preacher when Mrs. Rainey was a child and baptized her in Cold Creek, arrived just before the funeral. He couldn't let her go without one more visit, he said. Virgie had never seen Brother Dampeer; he kissed her. There was a tuning fork in his shirt pocket that showed when he went back of the coffin and leaned over it to the front and scrutinized the body.

"Come to my crossroads church some pretty Sunday, ever' one of y'all," was all he said, straightening up and addressing the living. Why had he no comment to make on the dead? they felt as a hushed roomful—it was as if he found nothing sufficiently remarkable about the body to give him anything flattering to say. "I guarantee nobody'll bite you if you put in at the collection for the piano, either," he said.

"Common old thing! But of course, he couldn't be turned away," Miss Snowdie whispered. "Coming was his privilege. A perfect stranger, and he handed out fans from Katie's deer horns out there, gave one to everybody."

"It's not time for the Last Look," Mrs. Spights said in her natural voice. But the little Morrisons had to follow right behind Brother Dampeer. They heard Mrs. Junie Morrison say, "Chirren? Want to see your cousin Kate? Go look in, right quick. Take hands and go now, so you'll have her to remember." And they came in dipping their heads low a moment and pulling one another away. The oldest little boy went hopping; it was remembered that at one point during the day he had run a nail in his foot.

"Are we ready?" Dr. Carlyle was facing the room.

Virgie rose, catching her breath. In the pink china jar on the mantel shelf, someone had placed Mrs. Rainey's old stick—like a peach branch—as though it would flower. Virgie looked at it and at Brother Dampeer, as if that were his work. Before his eyes and everybody's she took the stick out and carried it away to the hall, where she placed it in the cane holder on the hat rack. When she was back in her seat, Dr. Carlyle opened the book and held the service.

Every now and then, Mr. King, his tender-looking old head held sidewise, his heels lifted, his right hand out, fingers curved round and delicate over his fan, tiptoed down the hall to the table to pick

at the ham—all as if nobody could see him. While the daughter of Missie Spights ("Oh! Missie married during the oil scare," murmured a voice) played "O Love That Will Not Let Me Go" on the violin, Mr. King sucked a little marrow bone and lifted his wobbly head and looked arrogantly at Virgie through the two open doors of her mother's bedroom. His was the only eye that had not yet wept for Mrs. Rainey. Even the young sweethearts on the back row were crying by now, listening to music. Mr. King pushed out his stained lip. Then he made a hideous face at Virgie, like a silent wildcat yell. It was a yell at everything—including death, not leaving it out—and he did not mind taking his present animosity out on Virgie Rainey. He put a blame on her. He cracked the little bone in his teeth. She felt refreshed all of a sudden at that tiny but sharp sound.

She sat up straight and touched her hair, which sprang to her fingers, as always. Turning her head, looking out of the window through which came the cries of the little McLains playing in the yard, she knew one of those moments of strange alliance—when someone known slightly for years all at once makes known the deepest kinship—an indelible thing which may come without friendship, even despisingly, in rudeness, intruding into the middle of sorrow, and lack future as well as past, but is pure alliance, for whatever it may stand.

"Honey, you just don't *know* how unhappy you *are*," Mrs. Willie Stark—for she had, after all, been able to reach the funeral—said suddenly in Virgie's ear. She waved her own little fan—black chiffon, on a jet chain—at Virgie's cheeks. Mrs. Stark looked very rested, and had exchanged seats with Sally Howard. She let a hand fall plumply on Virgie's thigh, and did not lift it again.

Down the hall, with the blue sky at his back, Mr. King McLain sent for coffee, tasted it, and put

out his tongue in the air to cool it, a bright pink tongue wagging like a child's. He would not on any account go around for a Last Look. No Last Words for Mrs. Rainey were spoken by Mr. McLain. He lay down on the bed in Virgie's room, directly across the hall from the parlor, and snored all through the concluding prayer, while Miss Snowdie, people noticed, pretended he did not; he had to be waked up during "Nearer, My God, to Thee" and then flatly refused to go to the graveyard for the burial.

"Go back," they said to Virgie as they walked out of the parlor. "Be alone with her before you come with us."

"You're the onliest one now," a Morrison said.

Virgie walked back while they waited, and then she was not alone in the parlor. There was little Jinny, shoes and stockings off, quietly bent over the coffin, looking boldly in. Green lizards hung springlike at her ears, their eyes and jaws busy. Jinny looked up wordless at Virgie, but the expression on her face was disappointment.

"How do you first make them open their mouths?" Virgie asked.

"Press their heads until they do," said the child, and ran out on her toes.

"But mainly, Mr. McLain, you're supposed to keep off rich food," Miss Snowdie said, leading her husband down the front steps. Everybody was leaving the house. Virgie watched the mysterious, vulnerable back of the old man who was even now eating, as Miss Snowdie led him away, a white inch of hair in the nape of his neck blowing in the breeze.

Their procession—the coffin passing through them and now going before—marched humped up and awkward, like people waked by night, into the shimmering afternoon.

This was what the children, both the two camps of them, Morrisons and McLains, had been waiting for. Little Jinny, her face bright now, as if she knew she could be in two places at once, any time, stood back with little King. . . . They adored seeing beyond dodging aprons and black protecting arms the sight of grown people streaming tears and having to be held up. They liked coffins carried out because they were liable to be dropped and spill out the dead people. But the chance was slowly fading, no dead people had ever been spilled while any of them watched, just as no freight train had ever wrecked while they prayed for it to, so they could get the bananas.

Virgie again was held by both arms, as if, in the open, she would try to bolt; her body ached from the firm hand of—in the long run—Mrs. Willie Stark. She was escorted to the Stark automobile, where Ran now waited at the wheel, in the line of cars and trucks.

"Poor Mr. Mabry hasn't showed up at all." It was a flushed Mrs. Spights who was the first to tell Virgie that. "But he's home with one of his colds. It came on him yesterday: I saw it coming."

The cemetery was spacious, reaching all the way back to niggertown, yet wherever Virgie looked from the Starks' car window she seemed to see the same gravestones again, like the towers in the Vicksburg Park. . . . Twice she thought she saw Mr. Sissum's grave, the same stone being pulled down by the same vines—the grave into which Miss Eckhart, her old music teacher whom she had loved, had tried to throw herself on the day of his funeral. And more than once—each time across a stretch of little creek—she saw the squat dark stone that marked Miss Eckhart's own grave turn itself from them as they wound near and passed.

Just as a seated angel, first visible from behind with the stone hair spread on the shoulders, turned up later from the side, farther away, showing the steep wings.

"Do you like it?" Sally was asking from the front seat beside Ran—Jinny had had to go home with the children.

So it was Mrs. Howard's angel. After being so gay and flighty always, Sally's mother had gone out of the room one day and killed herself. It was young Loch's death in the war that made her do it, people said. "I was proud of it," said Sally. "It took everything I had."

"Where's Loch's? I don't see it," Ran said.

"Ran, don't you know he's never been brought home?"

He was too young for Virgie ever to know in Battle Hill— Loch, always polite, "too good," "too young," people said, and she remembered him only as going up the wooden staircase to his father's office. He gave a bent, intent nod of the head, too young and already too distant.

"What did you say, Virgie?"

"Nothing, Sally." Yet she must have hurt her some way, if only by imagining what was young all gone—disappeared wholly. No body: no grave—the vision touched her roughly and dreamily with words.

Virgie leaned out to look for a certain blackened lamb on a small hump of earth that was part of her childhood. It was the grave of somebody's stillborn child, the lamb flattened by rains into a little fairy table. There she had entertained all her imaginary company with acorn cups.

"You staying on in Battle Hill?" came Mrs. Spights's deep undertone. Mrs. Stark had not asked yet; perhaps she felt too crowded in her own car to break the silence.

"Going away. In the morning," Virgie was saying.

"Auction off everything?"

Virgie said nothing more; she had decided to leave when she heard herself say so—decided by ear.

The car stopped and Ran lifted the ladies out. Then the group of three fat ones—Ran with Mrs. Stark and Mrs. Spights in arm—moved in front, slowly and self-competing like a worm, under the trees and around. Sally put her fingers in Virgie's, and they followed. . . .

"Thank goodness Snowdie's not here to see that," Mrs. Spights remarked. A little, slicked-up Morrison was astride the white plaster dog that lay on the foot of Eugene McLain's grave. "Ran's here, but nothing bothers Ran."

Virgie, as if nudged, knew they must be near the poor little country girl's grave, with the words on the stone, "Thy Will Be Done." "I hate her," she thought suddenly. "Hate her grave." And she could almost hate Eugene, and him dead too. She kept walking, trembling and yet weary at all their hurts, bumping into Sally now and then. Eugene the good twin—the only McLain man gone since old Virgil, who was buried in the Confederate section—had been a quiet man. "Why is there crossed trumpets on his headstone?" Mrs. Spights had asked Miss Snowdie. "Now I can understand the foot of the grave." Under the little Morrison, kicking its sides, the plaster figure was of Eugene's black dog that died of lonesomeness.

For a long interval Eugene McLain had been away from Battle Hill, learning while he was gone that people don't have to have answers to questions because they ask. He had never noticed Virgie since they had grown up. He never talked about himself, as Ran once did, once did to Virgie. His very wife was not known here; he did not tell about her at all, or make it plain whether he had children somewhere. His wife did not even come to Eugene's funeral, though a telegram had been sent, inviting her. A foreigner? "Why, she could be a dago."

Always his light, tubercular body seemed to hesitate on the street, hold averted, anticipating questions, but when he was back home dying and puttering in his mother's garden, his hands held steady, lifted out a rooted rose cutting from the sand and placed it, every little hair of a root safe, in its pocket of loam. He knew he was dying. Sometimes he looked up on the street and said something strangely spiteful or ambiguous, but he bothered no one.

"He never bothered a soul," they said at his graveside that day. He would never go to a doctor. He had stayed lonely and quiet, until he wasted away.

Mr. Tannyhill passed by, mowing the grass, and reversed his mower and raised his hat significantly. Virgie saw the familiar stone of her father's grave, his name spelled out Lafayette, and the red hole torn out beside it. . . . Her brother was buried on the other side. Perhaps there was nothing there. The box that came back from the other war—who knew what had been sent to the Raineys in that? Somewhere behind her, Virgie could hear the hollow but apologetic coughing of Mr. Mabry. Except that it could not be he, of course; he had not been able to come, after all.

Brother Dampeer was with them still; with his weight thrown to one hip, he stood in front of them all, ahead of the row of Morrisons, and watched the success of the lowering of the coffin, and the filling of the grave.

After Dr. Carlyle's prayer, little crumbs and clods ran down the mound, pell-mell; the earth grew immediately vivacious and wild as a creature. Virgie never moved. People taking their turns went up and scattered the wreaths about and slowly stuck the clods with paper cornucopias of flowers with pins to hold them. The cornucopias were none of them perfectly erect but leaned to one side or the other, edging the swollen pink mound, monstrous, wider than it was long until it should "settle."

As the party moved away, one of the cornucopias fell over and spilled its weight of red zinnias. No one returned to right it. A feeling of the tumbling activity and promptitude of the elements had settled over people and stirred up their dignity; they could not go back now. They left the cemetery without looking at anything, and began to part at the gate. Attrition was their world. Already, tomorrow's rain pelted the grave with loudness, and made hasty streams run down its sides, like a mountain red with

rivers, already settling the patient work of them all; not one little "made" flower holder, but all, would topple over; and so had already; this was the past now.

Brother Dampeer said good-by and climbed on his mount. He had ridden twenty miles on a mule for this.

Four little Morrisons waited for her, perched like birds on the old swivel chair. They put their arms around her knees to go up the path with her. . . .

Smells of ham, banana cake and tuberoses came out to meet them and the children ran ahead. Ferns seemed in the alcoves of twilight to creep, or suddenly to descend like waterfalls in between the rest of the Morrisons and over Old Man Rainey sitting along the edge of the porch, feet dangling. Juba came running forth, humming and moaning, and urging them to come and eat quick.

Virgie had often felt herself at some moment callous over, go opaque; she had seen it happen when her mother changed on the bed while she fanned her. She had felt a moment in life after which nobody could see through her, into her—felt it young. And now Mr. King McLain, an old man, had butted like a goat against the wall he wouldn't agree to or recognize. Virgie's fortress would never come down, indeed, except before hard little horns, a rush and a stampede of the pure wish to live.

The feeling was strong upon her that she had lived the moment before. At the threshold of the shady hall, with the funeral company at her heels, then surrounding her and passing her and now going on to the table without her, she had the feeling of a double coming back.

At seventeen, coming back, she'd jumped from a slowed-down train. She had reached earth dazzled, the first moment, at its unrocked calm. Grass tufted like the back of a dog that had been rolling the moment before shone brown under the naked sprawled-out light of a still-stretching outer world. She heard nothing but the

sigh of the vanished train and the single drumbeat of thunder on a bright July day. Across the field was the square, Battle Hill, the remembered oaks like the counted continents against the big blue. Having just jumped from the endless, grinding interior of the slow train from Memphis, she had come back to something—and she began to run down the field toward it, with her suitcase as light as a shoe box, so little had she had to go away with and now to bring back —the lightness made it easier.

"You're back at the right time to milk for me," her mother said when she got there, and untied her bonnet and dashed it to the floor between them, looking up at her daughter. Nobody was allowed weeping over hurts at her house, unless it was Mrs. Rainey herself first, for son and husband, both her men, were gone.

For Virgie, there were practical changes to begin at once with the coming back—no music, no picture-show job any more, no piano.

But in that interim between train and home, she walked and ran looking about her in a kind of glory.

Virgie never saw it differently, never doubted that all the opposites on earth were close together, love close to hate, living to dying; but of them all, hope and despair were the closest blood—unrecognizable one from the other sometimes, making moments double upon themselves, and in the doubling double again, amending but never taking back.

For that journey, it was ripe afternoon, and all about her was that light in which the earth seems to come into its own, as if there would be no more days, only this day—when fields glow like deep pools and the expanding trees at their edges seem almost to open, like lilies, golden or dark. She had always loved that time of day, but now, alone, untouched now, she felt like dancing; knowing herself not really, in her essence, yet hurt; and thus happy. . . .

Her fingers set, after coming back, set half-closed; the strength in her hands she used up to type in the office but most consciously to pull the udders of the succeeding cows, as if she would hunt, hunt, hunt daily for the blindness that lay inside the beast, inside where she could have a real and living wall for beating on, a solid prison to get out of, the most real stupidity of flesh, a mindless and careless and calling body, to respond flesh for flesh, anguish for anguish. And if, as she dreamed one winter night, a new piano she came and touched had turned, after the one pristine moment, into a calling cow, it was by her own desire.

After she had gone in and fed her company and set the Morrison clan on the right road (they had come clear around by Greenwood), and after Old Man Rainey had gone to bed in the old bedroom up the stairs, Virgie sat down in the uncleared kitchen and ate, herself, while Juba ate near by—a little chicken, at first, then ham, then bacon and eggs. She drank her milk. Then she sent Juba home and turned out the many lights.

After she was in bed and her own light out, there was a peremptory pounding on the porch floor.

"Mr. Bitts?" She first stood and called from the dark window. He had never come. But coming tonight was the liberty he was the likeliest to take. She walked to the open front door, her nightgown blowing about her in the moist night wind. She was trembling, and put on a light in the hall.

From the gleam falling over the transom behind her she could see an old lady in a Mother Hubbard and clayed boots, holding out something white in a dark wrapping.

"Hit's you," the old lady said abruptly. "Child, you don't know me, but I know you and brought you somethin'. Mighty late, ain't it? My nightblooming cereus throwed a flower tonight, and I couldn't forbear to bring you hit. Take it—unwrop it."

Virgie looked at the naked, luminous, complicated flower, large

and pale as a face on the dark porch. For a moment she felt more afraid than she had coming to the door.

"Hit's for you. Keep it—won't do the dead no good. And tomorrow hit'll look like a wrung chicken's neck. Look at it enduring the night."

. . . The old woman declined to come in.

"No, oh no. You used to play the pi-anna in the picture show when you's little and I's young and in town, dear love," she called, turning away through the dark. "Sorry about your mama: didn't suppose anybody make as pretty music as you *ever* have no trouble—I thought you's the prettiest little thing ever was."

Virgie was still trembling. The flower troubled her; she threw it down into the weeds.

She knew that now at the river, where she had been before on moonlit nights in autumn, drunken and sleepless, mist lay on the water and filled the trees, and from the eyes to the moon would be a cone, a long silent horn, of white light. It was a connection visible as the hair is in air, between the self and the moon, to make the self feel the child, a daughter far, far back. Then the water, warmer than the night air or the self that might be suddenly cold, like any other arms, took the body under too, running without visibility into the tactile mouth. As she would drift in the river, too alert, too insolent in her heart in those days, the mist might thin momentarily and brilliant jewel eyes would look out from the waterline and the bank. Sometimes in the weeds a lightning bug would lighten, on and off, on and off, for as long in the night as she was there to see.

Out in the yard, in the coupe, in the frayed velour pocket next to the pistol, was her cache of cigarettes. She climbed inside and, shielding the matchlight, from habit, began to smoke cigarettes. All around her the dogs were barking.

"I'll sell the cows to the first white man I meet in the road," Virgie thought, waking up.

After she had milked them and driven them to pasture and come back, she saw Mrs. Stark's Juba back at the kitchen door.

"Leavin'? One thing, I seen your mama's ghost already," Juba said. She picked up a plate. As she began wrapping the china in newspaper, she explained that Virgie's goods must be packed in papers and locked in trunks before Virgie left, or Mrs. Stark would not think it fitting to the dead or to departure either. Virgie was to come up to the house and bid Mrs. Stark good-by—before noon.

"Still in the house," Juba said. "Ghost be's."

"Well, I don't want to hear about ghosts," Virgie said. They were now crouched together over a shelf in the china closet.

"Don't?"

Juba courteously ignored Virgie's clashing two plates together. Things? Miss Virgie must despise things more than the meanest people, more than any throwing ghosts.

"I don't. I don't like ghosts. Ghosts are terrible."

"Now!" Juba said, by way of affirmation. "However, this'n, your mama, her weren't in two pieces, or floatin' upside down, or any those things yet. No, listen, her weren't upset or cryin'. Her lyin' up big on a stuff davenport like a store window, three four *us* fannin' her."

"I still don't want to hear about it," Virgie said. "Just wrap everything up quick for Mrs. Stark and put it away, then you can go."

"Yes ma'am. Her ghost restin'. Not stren'us minded like some. I sees ghosts go walkin', now and then take their heads off to res', and carry on. But your mama." To be the ghost, Juba laid her hand—which held a cup—on her chest and put her head to one side, fluttering her eyelids tenderly and holding her breath. "Yes'm. Yonder up the wall, is where her was. I says Juba. I says Juba, tell Miss Virgie, her would appreciate word of that."

"Did you come here to make me wrap up and then get in my way?"

Virgie said. "You know I'm in a hurry to shut up this house."

"Goin' off and leave all these here clean curtains?"

"Juba, when I was in my worst trouble, I scared everybody off, did you know that? Now I'm not scary any more. Like Ran McLain; he's not," Virgie said absently as they wrapped together.

Juba laughed in an obscure glee. "You'll scare 'em when you's a ghost."

"Hurry."

"I seen more ghosts than live peoples, 'round here. Black and white. I seen plenty both. Miss Virgie, some is given to see, some try but is not given. I seen that Mrs. Howard from down the road in long white nightgown, no head atall, in her driveway Saddy. Reckanize her freckle arms. You ever see her? I seen her here. She die in pain?"

Juba lowered her lids hypocritically, pretending ignorance of the pain.

"Pain aplenty and I don't ever want to see her." Virgie got to her feet and shooed at Juba with her apron. "Go on, go on back to Mrs. Stark. Tell her I can pack up better without you. Do I have to pack everything?"

"Yes'm. Her idea is," Juba said, "pack 'em up strong for the day the somebody come *unpack*. And I done bent over and stoop best I could. Held all them curlicue plates without spillin' one."

"Do that for Mrs. Stark."

Juba picked herself up. She shook her head at the open cupboard, the dwindled and long-sugared jelly, the rusty cream-of-tartar box, the Mason jar of bay leaves, the spindly and darkened vanilla bottle, all the old confusion. Her eyes fastened and held to the twenty-year-old box of toothpicks, and Virgie, seeing, got it for her.

"Juba, take it all," she said then. "Plates, knives and forks, the plants on the porch, whatever you want, take. And what's in the trunks. You and Minerva divide." Then she had to come out and say something to Juba. "And I saw Minerva." She had seen Minerva's paper sack with her mother's golden hair switch and her own yellow baby clothes in it, sitting on the back porch after the funeral service with Minerva's umbrella, and had let them be carried off. "You tell that Negro. Tell her that I know I was robbed, and that I don't care." She watched the hard words sink in.

Then, "Thank you ma'am for men's clothes," Juba said freshly. "That salt-and-pepper of poor Mr. Rainey."

"Mama kept everything."

"Glory."

"Now you can go."

"Why, it's rainin'!"

Juba left.

"That's it," she called softly, appearing again at the kitchen door in her fedora. "That's right. Cry. Cry. Cry."

"Taking a trip? Think I might come along with you," said Old Man Rainey.

"No, sir, don't you come! Do you want our cows, though?" He gave her a hug before he turned to his coffee.

Virgie went out into the rainy morning and got into her car. She left the place, bumping down the hill. In the road, the McLains' chinaberry tree brushed her window, enjoying the rain like a bird.

On her way through Battle Hill she heard a horn blow from another car; it was Sally Howard. Sally called out, driving abreast.

"I want you to come see Mama's Name in the spring, Virgie. I've been dividing all the bulbs again, and it ought to be prettier than ever!"

"Always see it when I go past your yard," Virgie called back.

"I declare, Virgie, I know how you feel. You'll never get over it, never! I sympathize so!"

They called out from car to car, running parallel along the road with the loose gravel knocking loudly, bounced from one car to the other.

"Well, you come."

"I guess it takes a lot of narcissus to spell Caroline," Virgie called, when Sally still did not pass her.

"Two hundred and thirty-two! And then the hyacinthus all around those, four hundred and twenty-five of them, and I've got it bordered in violets, you know, to tell me where it is in summer!"

Sally's voice, growing louder, grew at the same time more anxious and more reverent. She was not hurt, not suspecting, only anxious.

"Now you come. We were friends that summer——"

Virgie obediently remembered Sally and herself in the revival tent, pulling light bugs off each other's shoulders while singing "Throw Out the Life Line."

"You could come play my piano, nobody does." Then, "Where are you going? Are you going somewhere, Virgie?"

Virgie passed her as Sally turned in at her own house. The Howards' looked the same as always, except, like the old house next to it, where Miss Eckhart had lived, it now had a flylike cluster of black mailboxes at its door, showing it had been all cut up inside for roomers. Across the front yard stretched the violet frame in which Mama's Name was planted against the coming of spring.

Virgie drove the twenty winding miles to McLain and stopped the car in front of the courthouse. She had often done this, if only to turn around and go right back after a rest of a few moments.

McLain pleased her—the water tank, first and last beacon of day—old iron bell in the churchyard looking as heavy as a fallen meteor. The courthouse—space itself—with the columns out from its four faces, and the pea-green blinds, and the stile rising in pepper grass over the iron fence to it, and a quail just now running across the yard, and the trees—trunks flaky black and white now, as if black and white soot, not rain, had fallen from heaven on them, and the wet eyes of cut-off limbs on them, and the whole rain-lighted spread roof of green leaves that moved like children's lips in speech, high up.

Virgie left the car and running through the light drops reached the stile and sat down on it in the open shelter of trees. She touched the treads, worn not by feet so much as by their history of warm, spreading seats. At his distance the Confederate soldier on the shaft looked like a chewed-on candle, as if old gnashing teeth had made him. On past him, pale as a rainbow, the ancient circus posters clung to their sheds, they no longer the defacing but the defaced.

There was nobody out in the rain. The land across from the courthouse used to be Mr. Virgil McLain's park. He was old Mr. King's father; he used to keep deer. Now like a callosity, a cataract of the eye over what was once transparent and bright—for the park racing with deer was an idea strangely transparent and bright to Virgie—was the line of store fronts and the McLain Bijou.

They were sky-colored tin and rosy brick, the doors weathered down to the color and grain of creek water. Caterpillar nets gave the pecan trees over them a domestic look, as if all the old women whiled their time away on them. The vine over the jail hung dead. At the McLain Bijou, directly across from Virgie on the stile, there was a wrinkled blue sheen of rain on the two posters and, deeper in, the square of yellow card ("Deposit Required for Going in to Talk") hung always like a lighted window in a traveler's gloom. She had sometimes come alone to the McLain Bijou after Mr. Nesbitt let her go in the afternoon.

Footsteps sounded on the walk, a white man's. It was Mr. Nesbitt, she thought at first, but then saw it was another man almost like him—hurrying, bent on something, furious at being in the rain, speechless. He was all alone out here. His round face, not pushed out now, away from other faces, looked curiously deep, womanly, dedicated. Mr. Nesbitt's twin passed close to her, and down the street he turned flamboyantly and entered what must have been his own door, splashing frantically through a puddle.

Virgie, picking the irresistible pepper grass, also saw Mr. Mabry, really himself, looking for somebody under his umbrella. How dignified, and not quite yet expectant he looked, and how sad his cold! Mr. Mabry thought he was coming to her eventually, but it was to him that she had come, backward to his protection. She'd had to come backward, to get from the wild spirit of Bucky Moffitt (and where was he? Never under the ground! She smiled, biting the seed in the pepper grass), back past the drunk Simon McDavit that didn't want her, and on, to fearful Mr. Mabry if not to loud, innocent, terrifying Mr. Nesbitt who wanted to stand up for her. She had come to Mr. Mabry, tagged him and left him again, while he was still thinking about things. She sat up tall on the stile, not hiding, feeling that he would look right through her—Virgie Rainey on a stile, bereaved, hatless, in the rain—and he did. She watched him march by. Then she was all to herself.

Was she that? Could she ever be, or would she be? Miss Eckhart—always it turned out to be Miss Eckhart—had had among the pictures from Europe on her walls a certain one. It hung over the dictionary, dark as that book, opposite the piano. It was Perseus with the head of the Medusa. "The same thing as Siegfried and the Dragon," Miss Eckhart had occasionally said, as if explaining second-best. Around the picture, which sometimes blindly reflected the window by its darkness, was a frame covered with enameled flowers, which showed all the time—Miss Eckhart's pride.

The vaunting was what Virgie remembered now, that lifted arm.

Cutting off the head was the heroic act, perhaps, that made visible a horror in life, that was the horror in all love, Virgie thought—the separateness. She might have seen it prophetically when she was young and was afraid of Miss Eckhart. Because Virgie saw things in time, like hearing them—and perhaps because she believed in the Medusa equally with Perseus—she saw the stroke of the sword in three moments, not one. In the three was the damnation—beyond the terror and the beauty and the daring.

Miss Eckhart, whom Virgie loved—for she had instructed Virgie—exhibited the picture on her wall as though she had absorbed that, and then had sat down to the piano with all Beethoven ahead of her. And so it was. With love, she offered Virgie Beethoven—offered, offered, offered—and when Virgie was young, in the strange wisdom of youth that was accepting, she had accepted it too, as with the dragon's blood, and that was the gift she had touched with her fingers that had drifted and left her, "her" music. In Virgie's farthest reach of memory, a melody softly lifted, like a leaf in air. Every time Perseus struck off the Medusa's head, there was the warningly simple melody that began all over again. And again the Medusa, and Perseus again. Whether it was in memory, dream or a kind of despair, Virgie heard and saw.

An old wrapped-up Negro woman with a red hen under her arm came and sat down on the step below her. "Mornin'."

Occasional drops of rain were touching Virgie's hair and her cheek, one drop ran down her arm, like a cool finger; only it was not, never had been, a finger, it was the rain out of the sky. October rain on Mississippi fields. The year's rain, and maybe on the whole South, for all she knew on the everywhere. She stared a moment into its magnitude. It was not only what scared Mr. Bitts and made him go running, just like Mr. Mabry that sneezed, it was the air's and the earth's fuming spreading breath, it could come and go. As if her own modesty could also fall upon her now, freely and coolly, outside herself and on the everywhere, she sat still on the stile.

She smiled once, seeing before her the hideous and delectable face Mr. King McLain had made at the funeral, and when they all knew he was next—even he. Then she and the old beggar woman, the old black thief, sat resting there together in the shelter of the big public tree, listening to the magical percussion, the world beating in their ears.

The Hidden Woman

by Colette

LOUISE DAHL-WOLFE

For a long time he watched the whirl of masqueraders before him, filled with a vague ache from the mixture of colors and the simultaneous blare of two orchestras, set too closely together. His monk's hood pressed against his temples; a nervous pain was starting in the back of his nose. But he was not restless; he rather savored this mingling of malaise and pleasure that permitted the hours to slip by unheeded. He had roamed the corridors of the Opera, drunk the silvery dust that rose from the dance floor, recognized bored friends, and wound around his neck the listless arms of an extremely fat girl, disguised humorously as a sylph. Ill at ease in his domino, stumbling along like all men unused to skirts, this doctor in monk's garb nevertheless did not dare to remove his mask, nor his hood, because of a schoolboy lie.

"I must spend tomorrow night in Nogent," he had told his wife, the night before. "I've just had a call, and I'm afraid that my patient, you know, that poor old lady. . . . When I'd so been look-

ing forward to that ball, like a kid, fancy that. Isn't it silly, a man my age who's never been to an Opera Ball?"

"Very silly, darling, very, very silly! Why, if I'd known, I might not even have married you. . . ."

She laughed, and he gazed admiringly at her narrow face, delicately pink and tapering like a sugared almond.

"You . . . you wouldn't care to go, would you, to the Green-and-Purple Ball? Even without me, if you'd be amused, darling. . . ."

She had shivered, as at the sight of a slug or a repulsively dirty man in the street, a long shiver of distaste that went through her hair, her slender hands, her throat rising from its white dress.

"Oh, not me! Do you see me in a crowd like that, with all those pawing hands. . . . What's there to say, I'm not prudish, I . . . I simply bristle up."

Leaning against the balustrade of the loggia, above the great staircase, he mused on this trembling hind, while he contemplated, directly in front of him, two enormous, square, black-nailed hands clutched against the naked back of a sultana. Sprouting from the lace sleeves of a Venetian nobleman, they dug into the white feminine flesh as though it were dough. . . . Because he was thinking of her, he jumped as he heard beside him a little cough, an odd way his wife had of clearing her throat. . . . He turned and saw, seated astride the balustrade, someone in impenetrable full-length disguise, a Pierrot in a smock with huge sleeves, loose pantaloons, a skullcap, and a white-plaster paint that coated what little skin was visible around the lace-ruffled mask. The fluid fabric of the costume and the skullcap, a weave of dark purple and silver, gleamed like the sea-eel that is fished by night with an iron drag hook from boats with resin-lit lanterns. Struck with astonishment, he waited to hear again that little cough, but it did not come. Pierrot-eel continued to sit, unconcerned, tapping one heel against the balusters, and revealing of his person only two satin slippers and a hand gloved in black and folded on his hip. The two oblique slits in the velvet mask, carefully screened with tulle, let through a smothered fire whose color could not be distinguished.

He almost called, "Irene!" then restrained himself, remembering his own lie. Always clumsy at play-acting, he decided not to try disguising his voice. Pierrot scratched his bottom, with an idle and somewhat common gesture, and the husband breathed again. "Ah, it isn't she!"

But Pierrot pulled from his pocket a flat golden box, opened it to take out a lipstick, and the worried husband recognized an antique snuffbox, his last birthday gift to her. . . . He placed his left hand over the pained region of his heart, with a gesture so abrupt and so involuntarily theatrical that Pierrot-eel remarked him.

"Declaration of love, purple Domino?"

Half stifled by surprise, the suspense, the sensation of living a bad dream, he failed to answer; he was still listening to the barely disguised voice—the voice of his wife. The Eel continued to stare at him, sprawled impudently, head cocked like a bird's; then shrugged her shoulders, swung both feet to the floor and walked away. Her action set free the worried husband, who, restored to an active and normal jealousy, began thinking once more and set out at a leisurely pace to follow his wife.

"She must be here for some one, with some one. In less than an hour, I shall know all."

A hundred hooded monks in purple or green gave sufficient guarantee that he would not be noticed or recognized. Nonchalantly Irene walked ahead of him; he was astonished to observe how indolently she swayed her hips and dragged her feet, as though wearing Turkish sandals. A Byzantine gentleman in emerald and gold brocade seized her as she went past, and she bent backward in his arms, suddenly thin, as though the embrace would cut her in two. The husband ran forward and reached the couple in time to hear Irene's flattering cry, "You big brute!"

She moved on, with the same laggard and relaxed gait, stopping here and there, idling outside the open doors of the boxes, and seldom looking back. She hesitated at the foot of a staircase, swerved, went back toward the entrance to the orchestra, insinuated her way into a noisy group and pressed forward, squeezing through with slithery skill, with the exact motion of a razor sliding into its case. Ten arms held her prisoner, an all but naked wrestler pushed her roughly down on the ledge of the parquet boxes and held her there. She yielded under the weight of the naked man, threw back her head in a laugh that was covered by all the other laughter, and the man in the purple hood saw her teeth gleam under the ruffle of her mask. Then she got away, effortlessly, and sat down on the steps leading down to the dance floor. Standing behind her, an arm's length away, her husband continued to watch. She straightened her mask, brushed her rumpled smock, tightened her skullcap. She seemed as serene as though she were alone, and was on her way again after a few minutes' rest. She put her arms around the shoulders of a knight who wordlessly invited her to dance, and she danced, clinging to him.

"That's he," said the husband to himself.

But she spoke not a word to the armored knight with the moist skin, and left him peaceably after the dance. She drank a glass of champagne at the buffet, a second glass, paid, stood dead still and curious among screaming women as two men started to row. She amused herself by closing her satanic little hands, like black claws, around the white throat of a Dutch girl in a gold cap, who shrieked nervously.

At last the worried man who was following her saw her pause, as though jostled from her path, beside a young man who had collapsed on a bench, out of breath, and was fanning himself with a mask. She leaned over, disdainfully took by the chin his handsome coarse vivid face, and kissed the panting half-opened mouth. . . .

But the husband, instead of leaping forward and wresting apart the two joined mouths, disappeared into the crowd. Dismayed, he no longer feared, he no longer hoped for betrayal. He was sure now that Irene did not know this dance-tipsy boy whom she was kissing, nor the naked strong-man; he was sure that she was waiting for no one, seeking no one, and that, casting aside like a sucked grape the lips that she was now holding under her own, she would be on the move the next instant, prowl further still, pluck another passing stranger, forget him, wanting only to taste, until that time of utter lassitude and the return home, the monstrous delight of being alone, true to her nature as a free animal, of being the unknown woman, to whom a little mask and an all-transforming costume had given back her incurable solitude and her brazen innocence.

—*Translated by George Davis*

The blond streak in the hair—like an errant shaft of sunlight, it strikes across the heads of smart young girls from Maine to Texas. . . . . Blowing back from the temples, framing the face, a crest of light in darker manes, it's a lovely new trick. . . . They learned it from the summer sun, and wisely decided to preserve the flattery of that golden streak through the dead of winter. . . . Off they went to their favorite hairdressers, preferring to trust to competent hands, rather than to indifferent and undependable rays from heaven, for that witching, sun-swiped touch.

On June 22, 1940, France was occupied. In September of the same year, Bazaar sadly announced, "This is the first time in the history of Harper's Bazaar that an issue has appeared without fashions from Paris." From then on American couture had the responsibility of fashion for the world on its smart shoulders.

Bazaar said, "We publish the New York Autumn Openings with pride in the achievements of our American Designers. We have learned from the greatest masters of fashion in the world. Learned, then added something of our own. Such clothes have never been made in America before."

142

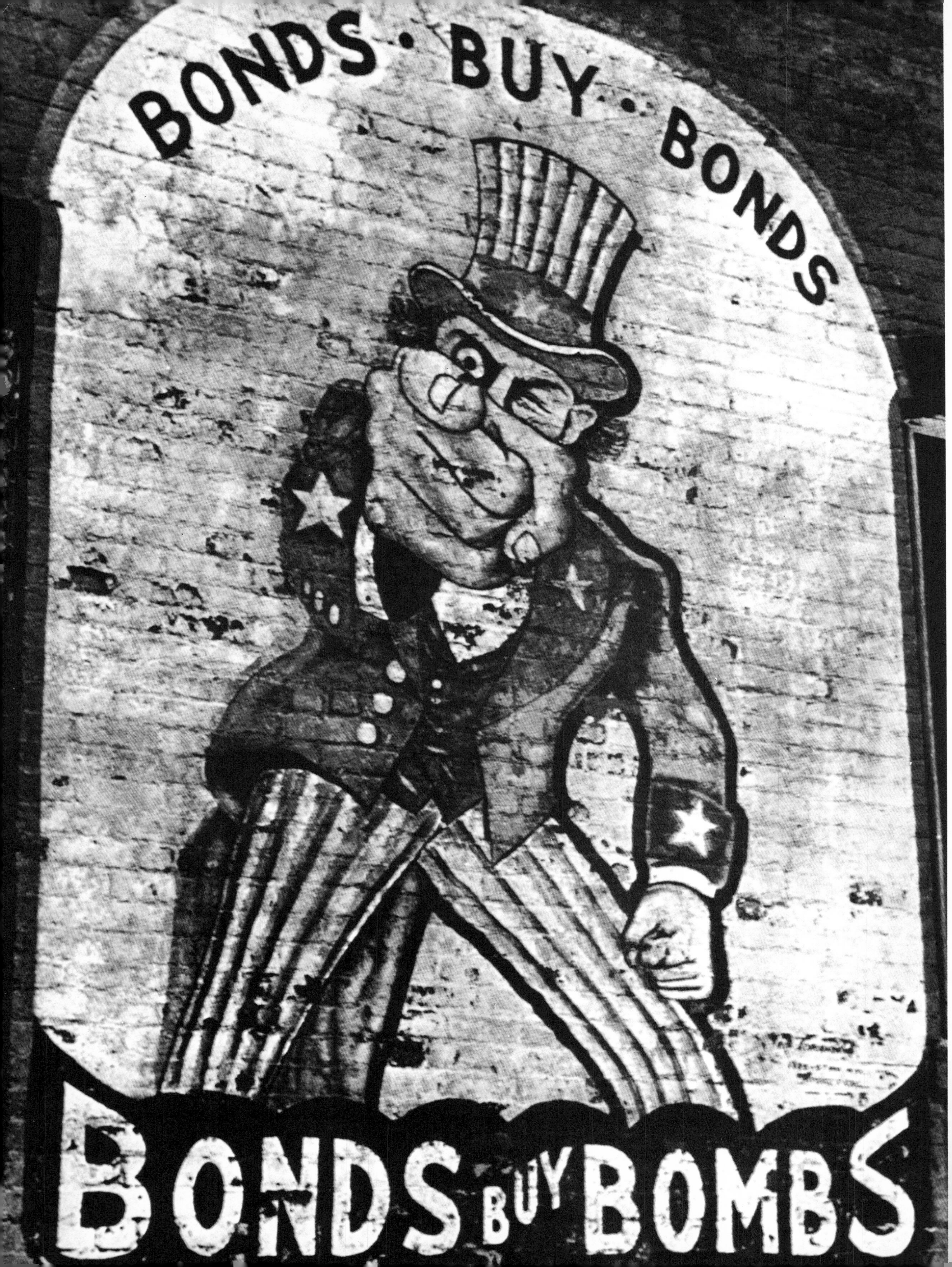
BONDS · BUY · BONDS
BONDS BUY BOMBS

Mrs. Franklin D. Roosevelt

TERRY AND THE PIRATES

A COMIC-STRIP ARTIST
BECOMES A FASHION ARTIST

BURMA: A BODICE OF SLEEK RAYON JERSEY, A WIDE PRINTED SKIRT. ABOUT $85
RAVEN SHERMAN: SILK CHIFFON, WITH A HOOD AND A WIDE CHIFFON BELT. ABOUT $85
NORMANDIE: ORANGE RAYON CREPE, WITH TINY RUFFLES AT SHOULDERS AND HIPS. ABOUT $45

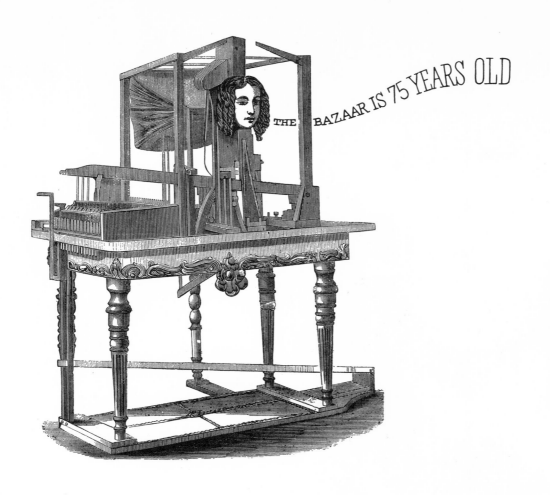

THE BAZAAR IS 75 YEARS OLD

Since the fall of 1867, for seventy-five years of peace and war, prosperity and breadlines, we've seen a lot of water over the dam . . . stereopticon, gaslight, and horse-drawn vehicle give way to film, fluorescent bulb, and flying fortress . . . paletot, pelisse, and bustle change to reefer, slacks and dirndl. Yet we feel our years lightly, looking upon each new issue as a re-birth, a new beginning. Poring back over the old volumes, we are struck by the freshness of the past . . . by the infinite variety and beauty of the changing fashions, and by the consistency of outlook expressed in very different eras.

The talking machine contrived by Professor Faber of Vienna in the 1860's. It could enunciate fourteen alphabetical sounds, emulate laughter and anger, even sing, and had bellows for lungs.

147

Sophie Tucker

Grandma Moses

*Coney Island Today, the Bathing
Paradise of Billions—Where Fun Is
Still on a Gigantic Scale*

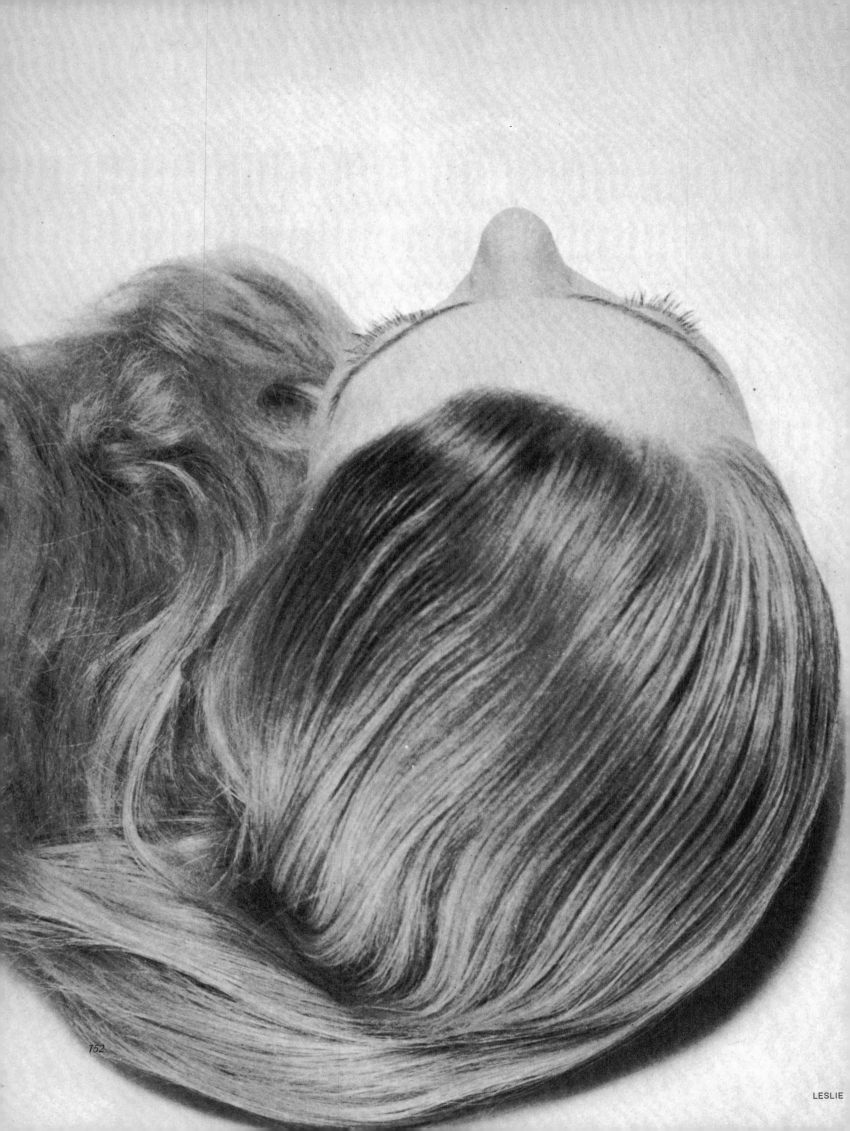

152

LESLIE

Christian Dior

Christian Dior was a mine of inspiration. He was not just another dressmaker. His designs were a milestone in fashion history. Anyone who saw his 1947 spring collection will never forget its dazzling impact. He created a look—a new look—the attractive very full skirt. The phenomenal success and breadth of the Dior skirt did more than upset fashion-conscious women's wardrobes. Dior chose a circuitous route to achieve a larger purpose. His collection set the weaving trade back into motion, with the shuttling of silks in Lyons, of velvets in Saint-Etienne, and the spinning of fine cotton in Roubaix. Le New Look re-established Paris as the metropolis where style was a form of civilization.

Dior's "New Look" created a shape, revolutionized the girdle world. Cinches, Merry Widows, wasp waists, pretend bosoms, padding, basque girdles—all followed with dispatch.

A Blossom Viewing

by Honor Tracy

Toward the end of March, during the year I spent in Japan as correspondent for the London *Observer,* a complete change came over Tokyo and put an end to all meditations of a political kind. Until then the weather had been horrible, with biting winds that screamed round corners, lifting the dust from piles of débris and dashing it into eyes and nose, or with a steady rain pouring implacably down night and day until the battered roads and pavements were studded with deep, dirty pools of water. The people, shivering in their threadbare clothes, moved drearily through the streets in a forest of twirling umbrellas, a menace to the foreigner since the spokes of an open umbrella carried by a Japanese are immediately on a level with his eyes. Many of them wore, as a precaution against the winter air, a gauze mask over the lower part of their faces, which gave them the air of being muzzled and added a touch of its own to the general depression of the scene. But now the sky was clear and the sun was warm

and a faint mist of green went creeping up the boughs of the willows that fringed the Imperial Moat. Kyoko San, the small person who cleaned my room at the Press Club, spent her afternoons arranging sprays of plum blossom in empty beer cans and distributing them to such of the inmates as she thought likely to be appreciative, and the lift girl, who giggled so wildly when anyone said good morning and crouched in a corner in spare moments with a copy of *Anna Karenina* held two inches from her eyes, wore a red camellia behind her ear. Everyone was preparing for the season of cherry blossoms which, with the season of autumn color, is one of the important things of the year. The news-

papers, inclined as a rule to be hazy where information was concerned, all at once became severely factual and issued precise instructions to their readers daily as to where the trees could be found at their best.

The Hibiya Park was crowded with people from morning to evening, enjoying the sun and the flowers. Here the Japanese were to be seen at their most charming and innocent—old men with wrinkled faces and ragged coats walking round and round a tree to get the best view of it, mothers lifting their babies to touch the bloom on the branches and solemn little schoolboys in sailor suits and peaked caps feverishly making sketch after sketch, with their noses to the ground and their bottoms in the air. It was an enchanting scene. The women in gay kimonos, with small children humped upon their backs in a sling and with their slow gliding pace, had the look of huge gaudy snails. The bright, lucent air of the Tokyo spring made each tree, each bough, almost each bud stand out from the background with the beautiful clarity of a Japanese painting. At one end of the park they had prepared an exhibition of dwarf trees—pine, oak and orange—and here, too, was always a crowd filing slowly along before them, lost in admiration. The man in charge of it was a great enthusiast, and no sooner did he catch sight of a foreigner among the spectators than he would dart out and draw attention to the fact that the fruit on the orange trees grew to their full natural size. He seemed very much struck with this, and it seemed remarkable enough to me, as well, the first time he mentioned it, although with constant repetition it rather lost its savor; and I began presently to feel a little piqued that he should never recognize me, although, of course, he must have had trouble in distinguishing one westerner from another.

It is natural for the people of Japan to make much of their blossom in spring and of their maple leaves in autumn, because for the rest of the year, except for a bright stretch in early June when the young rice plants are laid out, the country is monotonous and sad. The pine and maple woods are a dull dark green, the bamboo groves are a dull light green, and the rocks and streams are in melancholy shades of brown and gray. In summer there is a great variety of brilliant butterflies and other winged insects and a profusion of wild flowers, but always flying and growing away from each other, being discovered separately one by one and not striking a note of their own in the picture. But for two weeks in early April or late March everything is gay and colorful; there are clouds of pink and white blossoms whichever way the eye turns; a general excitement prevails; emotional letters are written to the press, poems composed by the dozen; there is copious drinking of *sake* or beer, for even in these times one can manage that much, and then suddenly a wind comes and shakes the bloom down in the very moment

of its pride, not leaving it to fade and wither on the branch; and so, thinking of the warrior cut down in his youth and strength and remembering that life after all is sad, the Japanese can heave a gentle sigh of satisfaction and go back to their work.

In this time my friend Kenichi came to luncheon one day, as he so often did, although not nearly often enough. He belonged to an interesting family. His grandfather was Count Makino, one of the grand old men of Japan, who was now spending a difficult old age in an obscure village across the Bay in what Kenichi referred to bitterly as "the sweet potato country." His father was an astute and successful politician, the leader of the conservatives. Kenichi was a writer of considerable talent and wide culture, who could have had a career if he had been a little more supple in his mind, but he did not get on at all with his father, of whom he would often speak with a frankness rare in a Japanese. He preferred to live penniless and to wear himself out as a literary hack. In his small house by the sea at Kamakura he sat feverishly writing day and night, turning out articles at a horrid pace for literary newspapers and small intellectual reviews. Once or twice a week he traveled up to the city to find new commissions or to collect, if possible, fees that were owing to him. He was getting on for forty now, and was of a most engaging personality. His eyes were still narrower and more tilted than was usual in his race, and there was a markedly ironic curl to his lip. In normal conversation he was gentle and inclined to diffidence, but in his cups he would burst forth in celebration of the glories of Japanese civilization and the Japanese spirit, soaring from one wild fancy to the next in the beautiful precise English he had learned at Cambridge. The next time we met after one of these sessions he would rather sheepishly excuse himself for having talked so much nonsense, and we would speak kindly and en-

couragingly to him and ply him with whisky, and in no time at all the magnificent performance would once more be set in train.

Today he had come on from one of his dunning expeditions through the frowsy editorial offices of the intellectual press, feeling tired and sad. He brought with him Mutsuru Yoshida, a boy of twenty-five with a delicate handsome face and a shock of silky black hair that continually fell down over his eyes, whom he introduced as an interesting new writer. Mr. Yoshida said rapidly and at once: "Please come to my house for a scenery viewing." It was all the English he could find for the time being, and Kenichi explained in his wonderful accent that if it were possible to rake up a car I really should drive out to the place, which was about an hour's trip from the city, and view his friend's peach trees. While we sat down to a meal of glorified hamburgers with French fries, corn mush, grapefruit and raisin salad, and ice cream swimming in chocolate sauce, which both of my guests appeared to enjoy, Kenichi told me more about the young man. He had done his war service in the navy and was aboard the battleship *Yamato* when it put out for Okinawa in the last naval operation of the war. The plan was simply to hold up for a few weeks or days, if possible, the invasion of Japan. There was fuel only for the outward journey, and no air cover at all. The crew sailed, knowing it was not meant to return, and when the ship was finally sunk from the air, only a handful of men were picked out of the water.

"It was a tragedy," Mr. Yoshida threw in, with a peal of laughter. His best friend had been killed on the deck beside him, he told us. When the war was over, the man's fiancée came to him in Tokyo and pressed him for details of how he had looked on the day of the battle and what he had said and how he spent his last minutes. For a whole morning Yoshida talked to her, but she would not be content and kept begging him for more and still more. The mother of the dead sailor had gone out of her mind when the news was broken to her.

"It must have been the same all over the world," he concluded, chuckling. The Japanese of all classes relate a personal misfortune as if it were the funniest thing that ever happened; it is a polite convention, meaning that other people are not to distress themselves, but it sounds very strange until one is used to it. I was by no means used to it yet, and I began to eye Mr. Yoshida with a certain apprehension.

Mr. Yoshida, finding himself alive when most of the others were dead, began casting about for a mystic explanation of his survival. His mind turned toward religion, as he took it that some very special destiny was reserved for him, and in due course he found himself receiving instruction from a Catholic priest. At the present time there was a great drive on the part of Christian missionaries to gather the bewildered and disillusioned young people of Mr. Yoshida's type into their net. A race not always of the most friendly nature was on between the various sects for their salvation, with the Catholics somewhat in the lead. The Catholic ritual perhaps held a greater attraction for the romantic and childlike Japanese than the plain services, bare tabernacles and wheezing harmoniums of the evangelical churches; I had been deeply impressed by the extraordinary gravity and concentration with which Japanese converts followed the Mass, genuflecting and crossing themselves with the precision of clockwork toys and extending to every object in the church, however secular, an impartial reverence, so that they would pass the collection plate around with the same gestures of awed humility as the priest at the altar would use in elevating the Host. Mr. Yoshida was just their man: like St. Francis Xavier before them, they were less concerned to preach among the highways and byways than to build up a spiritual and intellectual elite. He was going to be baptized on Easter Sunday. Kenichi grew a little pensive as he said this. It looked rather as if he himself had had a narrow squeak of this kind at some moment. There seemed, however, to be no doubts at all in the mind of his young colleague, who was bubbling over with the excitement of it all and full of plans for reading Cardinal Newman and Christopher Hollis, and the entire works of St. Augustine and Thomas Aquinas in Latin, a language that he had now been studying for several weeks. There was no drawing back for him now, Kenichi wound up with a sigh; and very likely he knew what he was doing.

"I was always the heaviest drinker on board," smiled Mr. Yoshida at this juncture, possibly having lost the thread of the discussion.

Concerning the tragic history of the *Yamato,* he had written everything down just as it came to him and just as it happened, and the result was much admired. Because, said Kenichi, he had appeared on the literary scene at a moment when the Japanese were beginning to put away the vague, allusive, flowery style of former days and to write frankly and crisply; and what with this new technique, and the color and brutality of his material, Yoshida had produced something fresh and very startling and which pleased immensely the younger generation, even if there were some old fogies down in Kyoto who saw only a further proof of Japan's cultural decadence in it. Then a blow had fallen. The American censor had banned the story as tending "to suggest that heroism was a good thing" and, by its references to the lack of air cover during the battle, to revive the bitterness of the war. And now here was the point, for there is always a point, no matter how suavely and delicately it may be uncovered: the point was could I perhaps help Yoshida to get his story published abroad in order that his light should not be hid and that he might earn foreign currencies with which to purchase the works of Cardinal Newman and Christopher Hollis, and of St. Augustine and Thomas Aquinas in Latin?

I promised to do what I could. Meanwhile time was passing and the sun was streaming down, and we set off to view the peach trees. Kenichi was unable to accompany us, as he was writing a history of English literature, for which the publishers would allow him only a fortnight's time. We drove out along the broken streets of the capital in a northerly direction, past the rows of tiny shacks that the inhabitants were putting up for themselves so fast that they seemed to rise from the ground almost as you watched. Everyone had a vegetable plot no larger than a tablecloth, and a fowl or two kept in a miserable box, but everyone, too, had always one pleasant thing growing beside it— a camellia tree or a bush of sweet-smelling, pink-flowering daphne. Finally the city was left behind and we passed between the dark rice paddies, with farmers up to their knees in mud, guiding their oxen, and through village after village, until at last a long line of ragged blue mountains came into sight. We passed over a high narrow bridge with a torrent twisting and foaming below, and the car stopped.

"Here is my farm," said Mutsuru Yoshida, pointing down a grassy bank to where a neat little house with a tiled roof stood, not far from the river, surrounded by a number of miniature fields. There were about two acres of land, which is quite a respectable amount in Japan nowadays. While the villagers gathered about the car like wasps on a ripe pear and began eagerly questioning the chauffeur, we walked down toward the house where two small feminine figures had pushed back the *shoji,* or outer sliding doors, and were kneeling in devout attitudes to await our approach. These were Mutsuru's mother and his sister, and as we drew near they began bowing with their foreheads to the ground and murmuring the phrases of welcome to which Mutsuru responded with a slight inclination of his head and a rapid flow of instructions. He had changed suddenly, turning from a gentle, modest boy with an inclination to discuss Christian ethics and the Marxist threat to the soul, into the temporary head of a Japanese household. In the evening his father would return from the city and make an end of his brief authority, but for the moment he was in the saddle, his gestures assured and his voice peremptory, at once buoyed up and weighed down by the responsibility of a foreign guest. The ladies scrambled to their feet and disappeared into the kitchen, where they could be heard faintly twittering to each other over their pots and pans, and Mutsuru led the way into the room from which the trees were to be viewed.

It was clear that in spite of the heavy luncheon we had eaten barely two hours ago, a meal was going to be served. Ominous sounds of frying came through the paper wall. The room was beautifully light, two of its walls being entirely of glass enclosed in sliding frames, and simple, with no other ornament than the scroll and the flower vase in the alcove, and no furniture beyond two big square cushions of purple and yellow silk placed side by side. There was an entrancing view of the little valley with the river fretting about the rocks in its bed, the curling feathery tops of the bamboo trees and the gorgeous pink of the peach blossom, but it was not time to look at it yet. Everything must be done properly and in order. We squatted down, each on his cushion. Mutsuru hospitably urged me to be at ease, which meant to loll about in comfort instead of kneeling in the position required on formal occasions—a very arduous and uncomfortable one unless you have been trained to it from childhood. Having seen to this he fell, as he did from time to time, into a profound reverie, and not another word was spoken until his sister

slid back the door and appeared with the first two bottles of *sake*.

A fat little boy put his head round the corner and studied us thoughtfully. It was the sister's child, the son of a warrior killed in the war. Mutsuru, pouring *sake*, explained that the family was being put to a great deal of trouble and inconvenience on his account. They wished the girl to marry again, and to send the small boy away to the dead man's people, to whom he legally belonged and by whom he was being repeatedly claimed. It was true that these people were only poor farmers, living in a province a long way off, but the child must go to them in order, later on, to have a place in the world. Here he could be nothing, because Mutsuru himself would marry soon, and then only his children would count in the household. But to everyone's surprise and annoyance the sister refused to part with her child or to take another husband. In spite of the advice lavished upon her from all sides, she was displaying an unheard-of tenacity.

"My father and I cannot understand the woman's feeling," Mutsuru confessed, shaking his head. Her position seemed natural and straightforward enough: what was strange was only to find that Mutsuru did not think so. I began to fear that even when we had obtained for him Hollis and Newman, Aquinas and St. Augustine, he would find much of their thinking obscure. Dimly one sensed the enormous waste of somebody's time. However, he added, brightening, in the end she doubtless would do what was expected of her. People, and especially women, usually do in Japan: there are so many expecting, and they expect so quietly and ruthlessly, watching and whispering, that the stoutest hearts give up at last under the weight of their courteous disapproval. The little chap watched us stolidly out of button eyes for a while and then, prompted by his mother, performed a shaky reverence and waddled away to the kitchen to be made much of.

The meal was ready: it consisted

of plate after plate of bacon and eggs and a giant crab omelette, served on lacquer trays and laid before us on the floor. Mutsuru overcame the difficulty of eating fried eggs with a pair of chopsticks by raising the plate to his lips and, with a sharp hiss, sucking each egg whole into his mouth. Our cups were filled, emptied and filled again; the women hastened to and fro with fresh bottles of *sake* and further installments of bacon and eggs. *Sake* is a sweetish rice wine which only tastes well when it is hot and must be drunk as soon as poured, or it cools in the wide shallow little cups and grows nasty, and as soon as the cup is empty it must be filled again, or the host is failing in his duty, and thus there is no end to it. Presently orange and crimson flecks were dancing before my eyes, and the sides of the room began wavering as if they were under water. Would the meal never come to a stop? And which was the graver offense against etiquette—to lay one's chopsticks down in the middle of it or to persevere until there was an awful and ignominious collapse? Mutsuru was eating heartily with every sign and sound of enjoyment. The lock of silky black hair had fallen over his eyes, his face was crimson and he was strongly disposed to giggle. At last the supplies of food slackened, fell off and came to an end. Softly as little mice the women crept to and fro, bringing more *sake*, dried persimmons and other sweets, and finally the kettle, scoop, bamboo whisk, and the beautiful porcelain bowls for serving, in decent fashion, the ceremonial tea.

Now Mutsuru consented to display the blossom which he had been keeping up his sleeve until this moment. Carefully he slid back the two outer walls of the room as if he were raising the curtain in a theatre. How lovely it was! The lines of pink blossom flowered out fanwise through the small green beds of bean and spinach, curving gently like the ribs of a shell; the afternoon sun shed a golden blur over the valley, picked out a fantastic boulder in the stream below, brightened the tops of the bamboos as they curled and waved against the far-off blue of the mountain range. Tiny figures of peasant women in shapeless blue trousers and pointed straw hats crouched down in the fields or trotted along with wooden buckets slung seesaw across their backs. It all had a dainty and artificial look about it, as if each tree, each rock and waterfall had been placed deliberately where it would have the greatest effect; a painter could not have come to grips with it, for the work of composition was done. A little breeze sprang up, chased away the fumes of the room, blew sweetly on the bamboo grove, ruffling the branches like the feathers of a bird, and sent a shower of pink petals to the ground.

"Japanese peach blossom!" said Mutsuru softly.

I asked him if the proper thing to do in these circumstances were not to dash off a poem, which was a mistake on my part, for he raised his voice and bawled to the women to come directly, bringing pencil and paper. They fluttered in and out in a trice, as if they had been waiting behind the door with writing materials in their hands. There was nothing for it but to put down whatever came into my poor fuddled head, and accordingly I wrote:

Sitting with my friend Mutsuru
And viewing his peach trees
I drink *sake*
And weep for men in Government offices.

"Now I shall write," said Mutsuru after he had read this over a number of times, but nothing happened. Instead of writing, he groaned and muttered and tossed his dark locks from side to side with an expression of strain on his face. A crisis was taking shape. One must be equal to everything, always, or lose face. Dispassionately considered, my poem was not really formidable as a work of art, but Mutsuru dreaded to produce something that might seem inferior. He closed his eyes and

began tracing Japanese characters in the air with his finger. The muttering grew louder. I wished the question of writing poems had never been raised. Then suddenly his brow cleared and he snatched up a pencil.

Sitting with a foreign woman,

(he read at length, and with pride)

And drinking sweet Japanese *sake* I view the peach trees in flower.

We smiled across the bottles then, and each complimented the other on his literary skill. His mother came in to make the tea, and the poems were at once translated to her and their finer points eagerly pointed out, while she listened, uttering gentle cries of admiration. The afternoon certainly was being spent in a refined and interesting manner. The old lady warmed the tea bowls and put in the powdered tea, which was a bright sage green, poured on the hot water and beat it up with the whisk, an object the size and shape of a shaving brush, but a brush of which the hairs had been carved delicately one by one by a craftsman from a solid stub of bamboo, the outer curling in beautifully over the inner. Many hours of patient work had gone to the making of it. The tea was thick and frothy and tasted faintly bitter, and two cups of it collected our wits very nicely and put us in shape to go away, for the sun was sinking, the entertainment was over, and there was nothing for it but to return to the Club and view once again the corps of distinguished correspondents.

The two ladies now began behaving in a somewhat curious fashion. They made little nervous runs in my direction and then back again, giggling behind their hands, whispering, pulling at each other's sleeves, for all the world like two schoolgirls who cannot decide which is to open the study door first. Mutsuru, looking superior and aloof, said they wanted to go for a drive in the car, as they

had not been in one since before the war, but they were shy of asking. If they might be taken to the first village, they would come home afterward in the bus. Permission was given, and they burst into a stream of thanks and apologies until Mutsuru silenced them with a lordly wave of the hand. Together we bundled into the car and started off. The ladies gave modest little cries of pleasure and further profuse apologies for the trouble they were causing. To have asked something for themselves, to have expressed a definite personal wish, was distinctly a breach of female decorum, and while enchanted by the prospect of a drive, they were also weighed down by a sense of guilt. Mutsuru was looking severe and, as soon as the lamps of the first village came into sight, he at once stopped the car, counted some yen out of his purse for their bus fares home, and hurried them forth into the road; and they stood there as we went on, bowing and waving in the twilight, two courteous, agitated little butterflies.

A faint pink glow had spread over the usually impassive features of the chauffeur, and he was sailing along over the bumpy road with a verve and an abandon most foreign to his style. He had not, apparently, been forgotten in the afternoon's merrymaking. It was evening and work was done, and men strolled casually down the way in twos and threes, deaf to the imperious croak of the horn: children rushed madly from one side of the road to the other; bicycles careened out of side turnings at full speed. Either the Japanese are too engrossed in themselves to watch the traffic, or they do not care whether they live or die; one or the other is true, although it is hard to say which. I sat gasping and wincing, now covering my eyes, now murmuring prayers, telling myself over and over again that we never had accidents but always beautifully missed everyone by inches; and even as I comforted myself, an old peasant shot around a corner on a bicycle straight into our path, wavered, fell, and disappeared under the bonnet of the car.

The chauffeur pulled up and dashed out to see if the man were dead, and I followed him, while Mutsuru, who had been thrown forward and given a nasty crack on the nose, lay back on the cushions, deathly pale, with the tears streaming down his face. The man's companions all jumped off their bicycles and gathered around, and, as if by magic, a crowd of children assembled, all very silent, watching us with beady, unwinking eyes. A policeman, all cap and teeth and spectacles, strode up and began writing in a notebook. The old fellow was alive, and they were helping him to his feet. He was trembling violently, and the blood poured from a gash in his hand. It was my first experience of this kind in Japan and I began to feel nervous. The policeman's face was grim and wooden, and it was impossible to judge if the fast-thickening crowd were hostile or not. The old peasant slowly raised his arm in the air: was he going to attack the chauffeur, who had after all been on his own side of the road, and who was already suffering intensely from the hurt to his prestige? Then carefully and painfully the man took off his cap and made a low bow. The chauffeur returned it, but not so deeply, since he wore the livery of an embassy

and was driving a foreigner. The old peasant bowed half a dozen times again, the chauffeur patiently responding to each until, with a faint hiss and a sigh of "Ah!" he indicated that it was enough. The old man then made a speech, the chauffeur made a speech, and the policeman spoke briefly as well; and finally we helped the wounded man into the car and set off for the hospital. He was still feebly bowing and muttering when the nurses came out to escort him to the surgery.

Mutsuru was feeling a little better, and he presently translated the gist of the conversation for me. "The old man says he has been out this afternoon with some friends from his Agricultural Association, viewing blossom and drinking *sake:* the accident was his fault and he begs to be excused. The chauffeur says he is a wretched driver and asks also to be excused. The policeman says the blossom is wonderfully fine this year."

A few days later, the old man wrote to the chauffeur, saying once more how sorry he was for having given so much trouble and having brought us out of our way.

The whole thing was quite unlike any motoring accident I had witnessed in any other country before. There had been no recriminations, no argument, no unpleasantness of any kind. I found afterwards that this was the usual

way of behaving among the Japanese. Occupation vehicles were often involved in accidents, and there was never any trouble with the people concerned. If there was a death, the authorities paid for the funeral and that was the end of it. I did hear of one case where an American driver had been much to blame, when the victim's son had come to headquarters some days after the funeral, demanding to see the officer in charge and refusing to go away. It was not for the sake of being awkward, however, but simply to get a letter from the authorities expressing their regret, which he could take and read at his father's grave, so that the dead man's spirit could be at rest.

The car ran easily back to Tokyo after this little interlude, narrowly missing a hundred children, and drew up in front of the Club. Mutsuru left at once, to keep a date with some Jesuits. I never saw him again, nor was I able to help get the story of the *Yamato* published abroad, but I often thought of him and hoped that his destiny would turn out to be just as special a one as he anticipated. Kenichi was inside, thirsty, and anxious for an opinion as to whether it was necessary to include Crashaw in a brief history of English literature. He had dealt with a number of the Elizabethans in the course of the afternoon.

The Giveaway

by Phyllis McGinley

Saint Bridget was
A problem child.
Although a lass,
Demure and mild,
And one who strove
To please her Dad,
Saint Bridget drove
The family mad.
For here's the fault in Bridget lay:
She *would* give anything away.

To any soul
Whose luck was out
She'd give her bowl
Of stirabout;
She'd give her shawl,
Divide her purse
With one or all.
And what was worse,
When she ran out of things to give
She'd borrow from a relative.

Her father's gold,
Her grandsire's dinner,
She'd hand to cold

And hungry sinner;
Give wine, give meat,
No matter whose;
Take from her feet
The very shoes,
And when her shoes had gone to
    others,
Fetch forth her sister's and her
    mother's.

She could not quit.
She had to share.
Gave bit by bit
The silverware,
The barnyard geese,
The parlor rug,
Her little niece-
'S christening mug,

Even her bed to those in want,
And then the mattress of her aunt.
An easy touch
For poor and lowly,
She gave so much
And grew so holy
That when she died
Of years and fame,
The countryside
Put on her name,
And still the Isles of Erin fidget
With generous girls named Bride or
    Bridget.

Well, one must love her.
Nonetheless,
In thinking of her
Givingness,
There's no denial
She must have been
A sort of trial
To her kin.
The moral, too, seems rather
    quaint.
Who had the patience of a saint,
From evidence presented here?
Saint Bridget? Or her near and
    dear?

Good Country People

by Flannery O'Connor

Besides the neutral expression that she wore when she was alone, Mrs. Freeman had two others, forward and reverse, that she used for all her human dealings. Her forward expression was steady and driving like the advance of a heavy truck. Her eyes never swerved to left or right but turned as the story turned as if they followed a yellow line down the center of it. She seldom used the other expression because it was not often necessary for her to retract a statement, but when she did, her face came to a complete stop, there was an almost imperceptible movement of her black eyes, during which they seemed to be receding, and then the observer would see that Mrs. Freeman, though she might stand there as real as several grain sacks thrown on top of each other, was no longer there in spirit. As for getting anything across to her when this was the case, Mrs. Hopewell had given it up. She might talk her head off. Mrs. Freeman could never be brought to admit herself wrong on any point. She would stand there

and if she could be brought to say anything, it was something like, "Well, I wouldn't of said it was and I wouldn't of said it wasn't," or letting her gaze range over the top kitchen shelf where there was an assortment of dusty bottles, she might remark, "I see you ain't ate many of them figs you put up last summer."

They carried on their most important business in the kitchen at breakfast. Every morning Mrs. Hopewell got up at seven o'clock and lit her gas heater and Joy's. Joy was her daughter, a large blonde girl who had an artificial leg. Mrs. Hopewell thought of her as a child though she was thirty-two years old and highly educated. Joy would get up while her

mother was eating and lumber into the bathroom and slam the door, and before long, Mrs. Freeman would arrive at the back door. Joy would hear her mother call, "Come on in," and then they would talk for a while in low voices that were indistinguishable in the bathroom. By the time Joy came in, they had usually finished the weather report and were on one or the other of Mrs. Freeman's daughters, Glynese or Carramae. Joy called them Glycerin and Caramel. Glynese, a redhead, was eighteen and had many admirers; Carramae, a blonde, was only fifteen but already married and pregnant. She could not keep anything on her stomach. Every morning Mrs. Freeman told Mrs. Hopewell how many times she had vomited since the last report.

Mrs. Hopewell liked to tell people that Glynese and Carramae were two of the finest girls she knew and that Mrs. Freeman was a *lady* and that she was never ashamed to take her anywhere or introduce her to anybody they might meet. Then she would tell how she had happened to hire the Freemans in the first place and how they were a godsend to her and how she had had them four years. The reason for her keeping them so long was that they were not trash. They were good country people. She had telephoned the man whose name they had given as a reference and he had told her that Mr. Freeman was a good farmer but that his wife was the nosiest woman ever to walk the earth. "She's got to be into everything," the man said. "If she don't get there before the dust settles, you can bet she's dead, that's all. She'll want to know all your business. I can stand him real good," he said, "but me nor my wife neither could have stood that woman one more minute on this place." That had put Mrs. Hopewell off for a few days.

She had hired them in the end because there were no other applicants but she had made up her mind beforehand exactly how she would handle the woman. Since she was the type who had to be into everything, then, Mrs. Hopewell had decided, she would not only let her be into everything, she would *see to it* that she was into everything—she would give her the responsibility of everything, she would put her in charge. Mrs. Hopewell had no bad qualities of her own but she was able to use other people's in such a constructive way that she never felt the lack. She had hired the Freemans and she had kept them four years.

Nothing is perfect. This was one of Mrs. Hopewell's favorite sayings. Another was: that is life! And still another, the most important, was: well, other people have their opinions too. She would make these statements, usually at the table, in a tone of gentle insistence as if no one held them but her, and the large hulking Joy, whose constant outrage had obliterated every expression from her face, would stare just a little to the side of her, her eyes icy blue, with the look of someone who has achieved blindness by an act of will and means to keep it.

When Mrs. Hopewell said to Mrs. Freeman that life was like that, Mrs. Freeman would say, "I always said so myself." Nothing had been arrived at by anyone that had not first been arrived at by her. She was quicker than Mr. Freeman. When Mrs. Hopewell said to her after they had been on the place a while, "You know, you're the wheel behind the wheel," and winked, Mrs. Freeman had said, "I know it. I've always been quick. It's some that are quicker than others."

"Everybody is different," Mrs. Hopewell said.

"Yes, most people is," Mrs. Freeman said.

"It takes all kinds to make the world."

"I always said it did myself."

The girl was used to this kind of dialogue for breakfast and more of it for dinner; sometimes they had it for supper too. When they had no guest they ate in the kitchen because that was easier. Mrs. Freeman always managed to arrive at some point during the meal and to watch them finish it. She would stand in the doorway if it were summer but in the winter she would stand with one elbow on top of the refrigerator and look down on them, or she would stand by the gas heater, lifting the back of her skirt slightly. Occasionally she would stand against the wall and roll her head from side to side. At no time was she in any hurry to leave. All this was very trying on Mrs. Hopewell but she was a woman of great patience. She realized that nothing is perfect and that in the Freemans she had good country people and that if, in this day and age, you get good country people, you had better hang onto them.

She had had plenty of experience with trash. Before the Freemans she had averaged one tenant family a year. The wives of these farmers were not the kind you would want to be around you for very long. Mrs. Hopewell, who had divorced her husband long ago, needed someone to walk over the fields with her; and when Joy had to be impressed for these services, her remarks were usually so

ugly and her face so glum that Mrs. Hopewell would say, "If you can't come pleasantly, I don't want you at all," to which the girl, standing square and rigid-shouldered with her neck thrust slightly forward, would reply, "If you want me, here I am—LIKE I AM."

Mrs. Hopewell excused this attitude because of the leg (which had been shot off in a hunting accident when Joy was ten). It was hard for Mrs. Hopewell to realize that her child was thirty-two now and that for more than twenty years she had had only one leg. She thought of her still as a child because it tore her heart to think instead of the poor stout girl in her thirties who had never danced a step or had any *normal* good times. Her name was really Joy but as soon as she was twenty-one and away from home, she had had it legally changed. Mrs. Hopewell was certain that she had thought and thought until she had hit upon the ugliest name in any language. Then she had gone and had the beautiful name, Joy, changed without telling her mother until after she had done it. Her legal name was Hulga.

When Mrs. Hopewell thought the name, Hulga, she thought of the broad blank hull of a battleship. She would not use it. She continued to call her Joy to which the girl responded but in a purely mechanical way.

Hulga had learned to tolerate Mrs. Freeman who saved her from taking walks with her mother. Even Glynese and Carramae were useful when they occupied attention that might otherwise have been directed at her. At first she had thought she could not stand Mrs. Freeman for she had found that it was not possible to be rude to her. Mrs. Freeman would take on strange resentments and for days together she would be sullen but the source of her displeasure was always obscure; a direct attack, a positive leer, blatant ugliness to her face—these never touched her. And without warning one day, she began calling her Hulga.

She did not call her that in front of Mrs. Hopewell who would have been incensed, but when she and the girl happened to be out of the house together, she would say something and add the name Hulga to the end of it, and the big, spectacled Joy-Hulga would scowl and redden as if her privacy had been intruded upon.

She considered the name her personal affair. She had arrived at it first purely on the basis of its ugly sound and then the full genius of its fitness had struck her. She had a vision of the name working like the ugly sweating Vulcan who stayed in the furnace and to whom, presumably, the goddess had to come when called. She saw it as the name of her highest creative act. One of her major triumphs was that her mother had not been able to turn her dust into Joy, but the greater one was that she had been able to turn it herself into Hulga. However, Mrs. Freeman's relish for using the name only irritated her. It was as if Mrs. Freeman's beady steel-pointed eyes had penetrated far enough behind her face to reach some secret fact.

Something about her seemed to fascinate Mrs. Freeman and then one day Hulga realized that it was the artificial leg. Mrs. Freeman had a special fondness for the details of secret infections, hidden deformities, assaults upon children. Of diseases, she preferred the lingering or incurable. Hulga had heard Mrs. Hopewell give her the details of the hunting accident, how the leg had been literally blasted off, how she had never lost consciousness. Mrs. Freeman could listen to it any time as if it had happened an hour ago.

When Hulga stumped into the kitchen in the morning (she could walk without making the awful noise but she made it—Mrs. Hopewell was certain—because it was ugly-sounding), she glanced at them and did not speak. Mrs. Hopewell would be in her red kimono with her hair tied around her head in rags. She would be sitting at the table, finishing her breakfast, and Mrs. Freeman would be hanging by her elbow outward from the refrigerator, looking down at the table. Hulga always put her eggs on the stove to boil and then stood over them with her arms folded, and Mrs. Hopewell would look at her—a kind of indirect gaze divided between her and Mrs. Freeman—and would think that if she would only keep herself up a little, she wouldn't be so bad-looking. There was nothing wrong with her face that a pleasant expression wouldn't help. Mrs. Hopewell said that people who looked on the bright side of things would be beautiful even if they were not.

Whenever she looked at Joy this way, she could not help but feel that it would have been better if the child had not taken the Ph.D. It had certainly not brought her out any and now that she had it, there was no more excuse for her to go to school again. Mrs. Hopewell thought it was nice for girls to go to school to have a good time but Joy had "gone through." Anyhow, she would not have been strong enough to go again.

The doctors had told Mrs. Hopewell that with the best of care, Joy might see forty-five. She had a weak heart. Joy had made it plain that if it had not been for this condition, she would be far from these red hills and good country people. She would be in a university lecturing to people who knew what she was talking about. And Mrs. Hopewell could very well picture her there, looking like a scarecrow and lecturing to more of the same. Here she went about all day in a six-year-old skirt and a yellow sweat shirt with a faded cowboy on a horse embossed on it. She thought this was funny; Mrs. Hopewell thought it was idiotic and showed simply that she was still a child.

She was brilliant but she didn't have a grain of sense. It seemed to Mrs. Hopewell that every year she grew less like other people and more like herself—bloated, rude and squint-eyed. And she said such strange things! To her own mother she had said—without warning, without excuse, standing up in the middle of a meal with her face purple and her mouth half full—"Woman! do you ever look inside? Do you ever look inside and see what you are *not?* God!" she had cried, sinking down again and staring at her plate, "Malebranche was right: we are not our own light. We are not our own light!" Mrs. Hopewell had no idea to this day what brought that on. She had only made the remark, hoping Joy would take it in, that a smile never hurt anyone.

The girl had taken the Ph.D. in philosophy and this left Mrs. Hopewell at a complete loss. You could say, "My daughter is a nurse," or "My daughter is a schoolteacher," or even, "My daughter is a chemical engineer." You could not say, "My daughter is a philosopher." That was something that had ended with the Greeks and Romans. All day Joy sat on her neck in a deep chair, reading. Sometimes she went for walks but she didn't like dogs or cats or birds or flowers or nature or nice young men. She looked at nice young men as if she could smell their stupidity.

One day Mrs. Hopewell had picked up one of the books the girl had just put down and opening it at random, she read, "Science, on the other hand, has to assert its soberness and seriousness afresh and declare that it is concerned solely with what-is. Nothing—how can it be for science anything but a horror and a phantasm? If science is right, then one thing stands firm: science wishes to know nothing of nothing. Such is after all the strictly scientific approach to Nothing. We know it by wishing to know nothing of Nothing." These words had been underlined with a blue pencil and they worked on Mrs. Hopewell like some evil incantation in gibberish. She shut the book quickly and went out of the room as if she were having a chill.

This morning when the girl came in, Mrs. Freeman was on Carramae. "She thrown up four times after supper," she said, "and was up twict in the night after three o'clock. Yesterday she didn't do nothing but ramble in the bureau drawer. All she did. Stand up there and see what she could run up on."

"She's got to eat," Mrs. Hopewell muttered, sipping her coffee, while she watched Joy's back at the stove. She was wondering what the child had said to the Bible salesman. She could not imagine what kind of a conversation she could possibly have had with him.

He was a tall gaunt hatless youth who had called yesterday to sell them a Bible. He had appeared at the door, carrying a large black suitcase that weighted him so heavily on one side he had to brace himself against the door-facing. He seemed on the point of collapse but he said in a cheerful voice, "Good morning, Mrs. Cedars!" and set the suitcase down on the mat. He was not a bad-looking young man though he had on a bright blue suit and yellow socks that were not pulled up far enough. He had prominent face bones and a streak of sticky-looking brown hair falling across his forehead.

"I'm Mrs. Hopewell," she said.

"Oh!" he said, pretending to look puzzled but with his eyes sparkling. "I saw it said 'The Cedars,' on the mailbox so I thought you was Mrs. Cedars!" and he burst out in a pleasant laugh. He picked up the satchel and under cover of a pant, he fell forward into her hall. It was rather as if the suitcase had moved first, jerking him after it. "Mrs. Hopewell!" he said and grabbed her hand. "I hope you are well!" and he laughed again and then all at once his face sobered completely. He paused and gave her a straight earnest look and said, "Lady, I've come to speak of serious things."

"Well, come in," she muttered, none too pleased because her dinner was almost ready. He came into the parlor and sat down on the edge of a straight chair and put the suitcase between his feet and glanced around the room as if he were sizing her up by it. Her silver gleamed on the two side-boards; she decided he had never been in a room as elegant as this.

"Mrs. Hopewell," he began, using her name in a way that sounded almost intimate, "I know you believe in Chrustian service."

"Well, yes," she murmured.

"I know," he said and paused, looking very wise with his head cocked on one side, "that you're a good woman. Friends have told me."

Mrs. Hopewell never liked to be taken for a fool. "What are you selling?" she asked.

"Bibles," the young man said, and his eye raced around the room before he added, "I see you have no family Bible in your parlor, I see that is the one lack you got!"

Mrs. Hopewell could not say, "My daughter is an atheist and won't let me keep the Bible in the parlor." She said, stiffening slightly, "I keep my Bible by my bedside." This was not the truth. It was in the attic somewhere.

"Lady," he said, "the word of God ought to be in the parlor."

"Well, I think that's a matter of taste," she began. "I think . . ."

"Lady," he said, "for a Chrustian, the word of God ought to be in every room in the house besides in his heart. I know you're a Chrustian because I can see it in every line of your face."

She stood up and said, "Well, young man, I don't want to buy a Bible and I smell my dinner burning."

He didn't get up. He began to twist his hands and looking down at them, he said softly, "Well lady, I'll tell you the truth—not many people want to buy one nowadays and besides, I know I'm real simple. I don't know how to say a thing but to say it. I'm just a country boy." He glanced up into her unfriendly face. "People like you don't like to fool with country people like me!"

"Why," she cried, "good country people are the salt of the earth! Besides, we all have different ways of doing, it takes all kinds to make the world go 'round. That's life!"

"You said a mouthful," he said.

"Why, I think there aren't enough good country people in the world!" she said, stirred. "I think that's what's wrong with it!"

His face had brightened. "I didn't inraduce myself," he said. "I'm Manley Pointer from out in the country around Willohobie, not even from a place, just from near a place."

"You wait a minute," she said. "I have to see about my dinner." She went out to the kitchen and found Joy standing near the door where she had been listening.

"Get rid of the salt of the earth," she said, "and let's eat."

Mrs. Hopewell gave her a pained look and turned the heat down under the vegetables. "I can't be rude to anybody," she murmured and went back into the parlor.

He had opened the suitcase and was sitting with a Bible on each knee.

"You might as well put those up," she told him. "I don't want one."

"I appreciate your honesty," he said. "You don't see any more real honest people unless you go way out in the country."

"I know," she said, "real genuine folks!" Through the crack in the door she heard a groan.

"I guess a lot of boys come telling you they're working their way through college," he said, "but I'm not going to tell you that. Somehow," he said, "I don't want to go to college. I want to devote my life to Chrustian service. See," he said, lowering his voice, "I got this heart condition. I may not live long. When you know it's something wrong with you and you may not live long, well then, lady . . ." He paused, with his mouth open, and stared at her.

He and Joy had the same condition! She knew that her eyes were filling with tears but she collected herself quickly and murmured, "Won't you stay for dinner? We'd love to have you!" and was sorry the instant she heard herself say it.

"Yes mam," he said in an abashed voice, "I would sher love to do that!"

Joy had given him one look on being introduced to him and then throughout the meal had not glanced at him again. He had addressed several remarks to her, which she had pretended not to hear. Mrs. Hopewell could not understand deliberate rudeness, although she lived with it, and she felt she had always to overflow with hospitality to make up for Joy's lack of courtesy. She urged him to talk about himself and he did. He said he was the seventh child of twelve and that his father had been crushed under a tree when he himself was eight years old. He had been crushed very badly; in fact, almost cut in two and was practically not recognizable. His mother had got along the best she could by hard working and she had always seen that her children went to Sunday School and that they read the Bible every evening. He was now nineteen years old and he had been selling Bibles for four months. In that time he had sold seventy-seven Bibles and had the promise of two more sales. He wanted to become a missionary because he thought that was the way you could do most for people. "He who losest his life shall find it," he said simply and he was so sincere, so genuine and earnest that Mrs. Hopewell would not for the world have smiled. He prevented his peas from sliding onto the table by blocking them with a piece of bread which he later cleaned his plate with. She could see Joy observing sidewise how he handled his knife and fork and she saw too that every few minutes, the boy would dart a keen appraising glance at the girl as if he were trying to attract her attention.

After dinner Joy cleared the dishes off the table and disappeared and Mrs. Hopewell was left to talk with him. He told her again about his childhood and his father's accident and about various things that had happened to him. Every five minutes or so she would stifle a yawn. He sat for two hours until finally she told him she must go because she had an appointment in town. He packed his Bibles and thanked her and prepared to leave, but in the doorway he stopped and wrung her hand and said that not on any of his trips had he met a lady as nice as her and he asked if he could come again. She had said she would always be happy to see him.

Joy had been standing in the road, apparently looking at something in the distance, when he came down the steps toward her, bent to the side with his heavy valise. He stopped where she was standing and confronted her directly. Mrs. Hopewell could not hear what he said but she trembled to think what Joy would say to him. She could see that after a minute Joy said something and that then the boy began to speak again, making an excited gesture with his free hand. After a minute Joy said something else at which the boy began to speak once more. Then to her amazement, Mrs. Hopewell saw the two of them walk off together, toward the gate. Joy had walked all the way to the gate with him and Mrs. Hopewell could not imagine what they had said to each other, and she had not yet dared to ask.

Mrs. Freeman was insisting upon her attention. She had moved from the refrigerator to the heater so that Mrs. Hopewell had to turn and face her in order to seem to be listening. "Glynese gone out with Harvey Hill again last night," she said. "She had this sty."

"Hill," Mrs. Hopewell said absently, "is that the one who works in the garage?"

"Nome, he's the one that goes to chiropracter school," Mrs. Freeman said. "She had this sty. Been had it two days. So she says when he brought her in the other night he says, 'Lemme get rid of that sty for you,' and she says, 'How?' and he says, 'You just lay yourself down acrost the seat of that car and I'll show you.' So she done it and he popped her neck. Kept on a-popping it several times until she made him quit. This morning," Mrs. Freeman said, "she ain't got no sty. She ain't got no traces of a sty."

"I never heard of that before," Mrs. Hopewell said.

"He ast her to marry him before the Ordinary," Mrs. Freeman went on, "and she told him she wasn't going to be married in no office."

"Well, Glynese is a fine girl," Mrs. Hopewell said. "Glynese and Carramae are both fine girls."

"Carramae said when her and Lyman was married Lyman said it sure felt sacred to him. She said he said he wouldn't take five hundred dollars for being married by a preacher."

"How much would he take?" the girl asked from the stove.

"He said he wouldn't take five hundred dollars," Mrs. Freeman repeated.

"Well we all have work to do," Mrs. Hopewell said.

"Lyman said it just felt more sacred to him," Mrs. Freeman said. "The doctor wants Carramae to eat prunes. Says instead of medicine. Says them cramps is coming from pressure. You know where I think it is?"

"She'll be better in a few weeks," Mrs. Hopewell said.

"In the tube," Mrs. Freeman said. "Else she wouldn't be as sick as she is."

Hulga had cracked her two eggs into a saucer and was bringing them to the table along with a cup of coffee that she had filled too full. She sat down carefully and began to eat, meaning to keep Mrs. Freeman there by questions if for any reason she showed an inclination to leave. She could perceive her mother's eye on her. The first roundabout question would be about the Bible salesman and she did not wish to bring it on. "How did he pop her neck?" she asked.

Mrs. Freeman went into a description of how he had popped her neck. She said he owned a '55 Mercury but that Glynese said she would rather marry a man with only a '36 Plymouth who would be married by a preacher. The girl asked what if he had a '32 Plymouth and Mrs. Freeman said what Glynese had said was a '36 Plymouth.

Mrs. Hopewell said there were not many girls with Glynese's common sense. She said what she admired in those girls was their common sense. She said that reminded her that they had had a nice visitor yesterday, a young man selling Bibles. "Lord," she said, "he bored me to death but he was so sincere and genuine I couldn't be rude to him. He was just good country people, you know," she said, "—just the salt of the earth."

"I seen him walk up," Mrs. Freeman said, "and then later—I seen him walk off," and Hulga could feel the slight shift in her voice, the slight insinuation, that he had not walked off alone, had he? Her face remained expressionless but the color rose into her neck and she seemed to swallow it down with the next spoonful of egg. Mrs. Freeman was looking at her as if they had a secret together.

"Well, it takes all kinds of people to make the world go 'round," Mrs. Hopewell said. "It's very good we aren't all alike."

"Some people are more alike than others," Mrs. Freeman said.

Hulga got up and stumped, with about twice the noise that was necessary, into her room and locked the door. She was to meet the Bible salesman at ten o'clock at the gate.

She had thought about it half the night. She had started thinking of it as a great joke and then she had begun to see profound implications in it. She had lain in bed imagining dialogues for them that were insane on the surface but that reached below to depths that no Bible salesman would be aware of. Their conversation yesterday had been of this kind.

He had stopped in front of her and had simply stood there. His face was bony and sweaty and bright, with a little pointed nose in the center of it, and his look was different from what it had been at the dinner table. He was gazing at her with open curiosity, with fascination, like a child watching a new fantastic animal at the zoo, and he was breathing as if he had run a great distance to reach her. His gaze seemed somehow familiar but she could not think where she had been regarded with it before. For almost a minute he didn't say anything. Then on what seemed an insuck of breath, he whispered, "You ever ate a chicken that was two days old?"

The girl looked at him stonily. He might have just put this question up for consideration at the meeting of a philosophical association. "Yes," she presently replied as if she had considered it from all angles.

"It must have been mighty small!" he said triumphantly and shook all over with little nervous giggles, getting very red in the face, and subsiding finally into his gaze of complete admiration, while the girl's expression remained exactly the same.

"How old are you?" he asked softly.

She waited some time before she answered. Then in a flat voice she said, "Seventeen."

His smiles came in succession like waves breaking on the surface of a little lake. "I see you got a wooden leg," he said. "I think you're real brave. I think you're real sweet."

The girl stood blank and solid and silent.

"Walk to the gate with me," he said. "You're a brave sweet little thing and I liked you the minute I seen you walk in the door."

Hulga began to move forward.

"What's your name?" he asked, smiling down on the top of her head.

"Hulga," she said.

"Hulga," he murmured, "Hulga. Hulga. I never heard of anybody name Hulga before. You're shy, aren't you, Hulga?" he asked.

She nodded, watching his large red hand on the handle of the giant valise.

"I like girls that wear glasses," he said. "I think a lot. I'm not like these people that a serious thought don't ever enter their heads. It's because I may die."

"I may die too," she said suddenly and looked up at him. His eyes were very small and brown, glittering feverishly.

"Listen," he said, "don't you think some people was meant to meet on account of what all they got in common and all? Like they both think serious thoughts and all?" He shifted the valise to his other hand so that the hand nearest her was free. He caught hold of her elbow and shook it a little. "I don't work on Saturday," he said. "I like to walk in the woods and see what Mother Nature is wearing. O'er the hills and far away. Pic-nics and things. Couldn't we go on a pic-nic tomorrow? Say yes, Hulga," he said and gave her a dying look as if he felt his insides about to drop out of him. He had even seemed to sway slightly toward her.

During the night she had imagined that she seduced him. She imagined that the two of them walked on the place until they came to the storage barn beyond the two back fields and there, she imagined, things came to such a pass that she very easily seduced him and then, of course, she had to reckon with his remorse. True genius can get an idea across even to an inferior mind. She imagined that she took his remorse in hand and changed it into a deeper understanding of life. She took all his shame away and turned it into something useful.

She set off for the gate at exactly ten o'clock, escaping without drawing Mrs. Hopewell's attention. She didn't take anything to eat, forgetting that food is usually taken on a picnic. She wore a pair of slacks and a dirty white shirt, and as an afterthought, she had put some Vapex on the collar of it since she did not own any perfume. When she reached the gate no one was there.

She looked up and down the empty highway and had the furious feeling that she had been tricked, that he had only meant to make her walk to the gate after the idea of him. Then suddenly he stood up, very tall, from behind a bush on the opposite embankment. Smiling, he lifted his hat which was new and wide-brimmed. He had not worn it yesterday and she wondered if he had bought it for the occasion. It was toast-colored with a red and white band around it and was slightly too large for him. He stepped from behind the bush still carrying the black valise. He had on the same suit and the same yellow socks sucked down in his shoes from walking. He crossed the highway and said, "I knew you'd come!"

The girl wondered acidly how he had known this. She pointed to the valise and asked, "Why did you bring your Bibles?"

He took her elbow, smiling down on her as if he could not stop. "You can never tell when you'll need the word of God, Hulga," he said. She had a moment in which she doubted that this was actually happening and then they began to climb the embankment. They went down into the pasture toward the woods. The boy walked lightly by her side, bouncing on his toes. The valise did not seem to be heavy today; he even swung it. They crossed half the pasture without saying anything and then, putting his hand easily on the small of her back, he asked softly, "Where does your wooden leg join on?"

She turned an ugly red and glared at him and for an instant the boy looked abashed. "I didn't mean you no harm," he said. "I only meant you're so brave and all. I guess God takes care of you."

"No," she said, looking forward and walking fast, "I don't even believe in God."

At this he stopped and whistled. "No!" he exclaimed as if he were too astonished to say anything else.

She walked on and in a second he was bouncing at her side, fanning with his hat. "That's very unusual for a girl," he remarked, watching her out of the corner of his eye. When they reached the edge of the wood, he put his hand

on her back again and drew her against him without a word and kissed her heavily.

The kiss, which had more pressure than feeling behind it, produced that extra surge of adrenalin in the girl that enables one to carry a packed trunk out of a burning house, but in her, the power went at once to the brain. Even before he released her, her mind, clear and detached and ironic anyway, was regarding him from a great distance, with amusement but with pity. She had never been kissed before and she was pleased to discover that it was an unexceptional experience and all a matter of the mind's control. Some people might enjoy drain water if they were told it was vodka. When the boy, looking expectant but uncertain, pushed her gently away, she turned and walked on, saying nothing as if such business, for her, were common enough.

He came along panting at her side, trying to help her when he saw a root that she might trip over. He caught and held back the long swaying blades of thorn vine until she had passed beyond them. She led the way and he came breathing heavily behind her. Then they came out on a sunlit hillside, sloping softly into another one a little smaller. Beyond, they could see the rusted top of the old barn where the extra hay was stored.

The hill was sprinkled with small pink weeds. "Then you ain't saved?" he asked suddenly, stopping.

The girl smiled. It was the first time she had smiled at him at all. "In my economy," she said, "I'm saved and you are damned but I told you I didn't believe in God."

Nothing seemed to destroy the boy's look of admiration. He gazed at her now as if the fantastic animal at the zoo had put its paw through the bars and given him a loving poke. She thought he looked as if he wanted to kiss her again and she walked on before he had the chance.

"Ain't there somewheres we can

sit down sometimes?" he murmured, his voice softening toward the end of the sentence.

"In that barn," she said.

They made for it rapidly as if it might slide away like a train. It was a large two-story barn, cool and dark inside. The boy pointed up the ladder that led into the loft and said, "It's too bad we can't go up there."

"Why can't we?" she asked.

"Yer leg," he said reverently.

The girl gave him a contemptuous look and putting both hands on the ladder, she climbed it while he stood below, apparently awestruck. She pulled herself expertly through the opening and then looked down at him and said, "Well, come on if you're coming," and he began to climb the ladder, awkwardly bringing the suitcase with him.

"We won't need the Bible," she observed.

"You never can tell," he said, panting. After he had got into the loft, he was a few seconds catching his breath. She had sat down in a pile of straw. A wide sheath of sunlight, filled with dust particles, slanted over her. She lay back against a bale, her face turned away, looking out the front opening of the barn where hay was thrown from a wagon into the loft. The two pink-speckled hillsides lay back against a dark ridge of woods. The sky was cloudless and cold blue. The boy dropped down by her side and put one arm under her and the other over her and began methodically kissing her face, making little noises like a fish. He did not remove his hat but it was pushed far enough back not to interfere. When her glasses got in his way, he took them off of her and slipped them into his pocket.

The girl at first did not return any of the kisses but presently she began to and after she had put several on his cheek, she reached his lips and remained there, kissing him again and again as if she were trying to draw all the breath out of him. His breath was clear and sweet like a child's and the kisses were sticky like a child's. He mumbled about loving her and about knowing when he first seen her that he loved her, but the mumbling was like the sleepy fretting of a child being put to sleep by his mother. Her mind, throughout this, never stopped or lost itself for a second to her feelings. "You ain't said you loved me none," he whispered finally, pulling back from her. "You got to say that."

She looked away from him off into the hollow sky and then down at a black ridge and then down farther into what appeared to be two green swelling lakes. She didn't realize he had taken her glasses but this landscape could not seem exceptional to her for she seldom paid any close attention to her surroundings.

"You got to say it," he repeated. "You got to say you love me."

She was always careful how she committed herself. "In a sense," she began, "if you use the word loosely, you might say that. But it's not a word I use. I don't have illusions. I'm one of those people who see *through* to nothing."

The boy was frowning. "You got to say it. I said it and you got to say it," he said.

The girl looked at him almost tenderly. "You poor baby," she murmured. "It's just as well you don't understand," and she pulled him by the neck, face-down, against her. "We are all damned," she said, "but some of us have taken off our blindfolds and see that there's nothing to see. It's a kind of salvation."

The boy's astonished eyes looked blankly through the ends of her hair. "Okay," he almost whined, "but do you love me or don'tcher?"

"Yes," she said and added, "in a sense. But I must tell you something. There mustn't be anything dishonest between us." She lifted his head and looked him in the eye. "I am thirty years old," she said. "I have a number of degrees."

The boy's look was irritated but dogged. "I don't care," he said. "I don't care a thing about what all you done. I just want to know if

you love me or don'tcher?" and he caught her to him and wildly planted her face with kisses until she said, "Yes, yes."

"Okay then," he said, letting her go. "Prove it."

She smiled, looking dreamily out on the shifty landscape. She had seduced him without even making up her mind to try. "How?" she asked, feeling that he should be delayed a little.

He leaned over and put his lips to her ear. "Show me where your wooden leg joins on," he whispered.

The girl uttered a sharp little cry and her face instantly drained of color. The obscenity of the suggestion was not what shocked her. As a child she had sometimes been subject to feelings of shame but education had removed the last traces of that as a good surgeon scrapes for cancer; she would no more have felt it over what he was asking than she would have believed in his Bible. But she was as sensitive about the artificial leg as a peacock about his tail. No one ever touched it but her. She took care of it as someone else would his soul, in private and almost with her own eyes turned away. "No," she said.

"I known it," he muttered, sitting up. "You're just playing me for a sucker."

"Oh no no!" she cried. "It joins on at the knee. Only at the knee. Why do you want to see it?"

The boy gave her a long penetrating look. "Because," he said, "it's what makes you different. You ain't like anybody else."

She sat staring at him. There was nothing about her face or her round freezing-blue eyes to indicate that this had moved her; but she felt as if her heart had stopped and left her mind to pump her blood. She decided that for the first time in her life she was face to face with real innocence. This boy, with an instinct that came from beyond wisdom, had touched the truth about her. When after a minute, she said in a hoarse high voice, "All right," it was like surrendering to him completely. It was like losing her own life and

finding it again, miraculously, in his.

Very gently he began to roll the slack leg up. The artificial limb, in a white sock and brown flat shoe, was bound in a heavy material like canvas and ended in an ugly jointure where it was attached to the stump. The boy's face and his voice were entirely reverent as he uncovered it and said, "Now show me how to take it off and on."

She took it off for him and put it back on again and then he took it off himself, handling it as tenderly as if it were a real one. "See!" he said with a delighted child's face. "Now I can do it myself!"

"Put it back on," she said. She was thinking that she would run away with him and that every night he would take the leg off and every morning put it back on again. "Put it back on," she said.

"Not yet," he murmured, setting it on its foot out of reach. "Leave it off for a while. You got me instead."

She gave a little cry of alarm but he pushed her down and began to kiss her again. Without the leg she felt entirely dependent on him. Her brain seemed to have stopped thinking altogether and to be about some other function that it was not very good at. Different expressions raced back and forth over her face. Every now and then the boy, his eyes like two steel spikes, would glance behind him where the leg stood. Finally she pushed him off and said, "Put it back on me now."

"Wait," he said. He leaned the other way and pulled the valise toward him and opened it. It had a pale blue spotted lining and there were only two Bibles in it. He took one of these out and opened the cover of it. It was hollow and contained a pocket flask of whiskey, a pack of cards, and a small blue box with printing on it. He laid these out in front of her one at a time in an evenly spaced row, like one presenting offerings at the shrine of a goddess. He put the blue box in her hand. "This product to be used only for the prevention of disease," she read, and dropped it. The boy was unscrewing the top of the flask. He stopped and pointed, with a smile, to the deck of cards. It was not an ordinary deck but one with an obscene picture on the back of each card. "Take a swig," he said, offering her the bottle first. He held it in front of her, but like one mesmerized, she did not move.

Her voice when she spoke had an almost pleading sound. "Aren't you," she murmured, "aren't you just good country people?"

The boy cocked his head. He looked as if he were just beginning to understand that she might be trying to insult him. "Yeah," he said, curling his lip slightly, "but it ain't held me back none. I'm as good as you any day in the week."

"Give me my leg," she said.

He pushed it farther away with his foot. "Come on now, let's begin to have us a good time," he said coaxingly. "We ain't got to know one another good yet."

"Give me my leg!" she screamed and tried to lunge for it but he pushed her down easily.

"What's the matter with you all of a sudden?" he asked, frowning as he screwed the top on the flask and put it quickly back inside the Bible. "You just a while ago said you didn't believe in nothing. I thought you was some girl!"

Her face was almost purple.

"You're a Christian!" she hissed. "You're a fine Christian! You're just like them all—say one thing and do another. You're a perfect Christian, you're . . ."

The boy's mouth was set angrily. "I hope you don't think," he said in a lofty indignant tone, "that I believe in that crap! I may sell Bibles but I know which end is up and I wasn't born yesterday and I know where I'm going!"

"Give me my leg!" she screeched. He jumped up so quickly that she barely saw him sweep the cards and the blue box back into the Bible and throw the Bible into the valise. She saw him grab the leg and then she saw it for an instant slanted forlornly across the inside of the suitcase with a Bible at either side of its opposite ends. He slammed the lid shut and snatched up the valise and swung it down the hole and then stepped through himself.

When all of him had passed but his head, he turned and regarded her with a look that no longer had any admiration in it. "I've gotten a lot of interesting things," he said. "One time I got a woman's glass eye this way. And you needn't to think you'll catch me because Pointer ain't really my name. I use a different name at every house I call at and don't stay nowhere long. And I'll tell you another thing, Hulga," he said, using the name as if he didn't think much of it, "you ain't so smart. I been believing in nothing ever since I was born!" and then the toast-colored hat disappeared down the hole and the girl was left, sitting on the straw in the dusty sunlight. When she turned her churning face toward the opening, she saw his blue figure struggling successfully over the green speckled lake.

Mrs. Hopewell and Mrs. Freeman, who were in the back pasture, digging up onions, saw him emerge a little later from the woods and head across the meadow toward the highway. "Why, that looks like that nice dull young man that tried to sell me a Bible yesterday," Mrs. Hopewell said, squinting. "He must have been selling them to the Negroes back in there. He was so simple," she said, "but I guess the world would be better off if we were all that simple."

Mrs. Freeman's gaze drove forward and just touched him before he disappeared under the hill. Then she returned her attention to the evil-smelling onion shoot she was lifting from the ground. "Some can't be that simple," she said. "I know I never could."

Jacques Fath and One of
His Dreams

"There is no such thing as a frigid woman, Miss Abernathy."

Marlene Dietrich

Edith Sitwell

Mae V

LOUISE DAHL-WOLFE

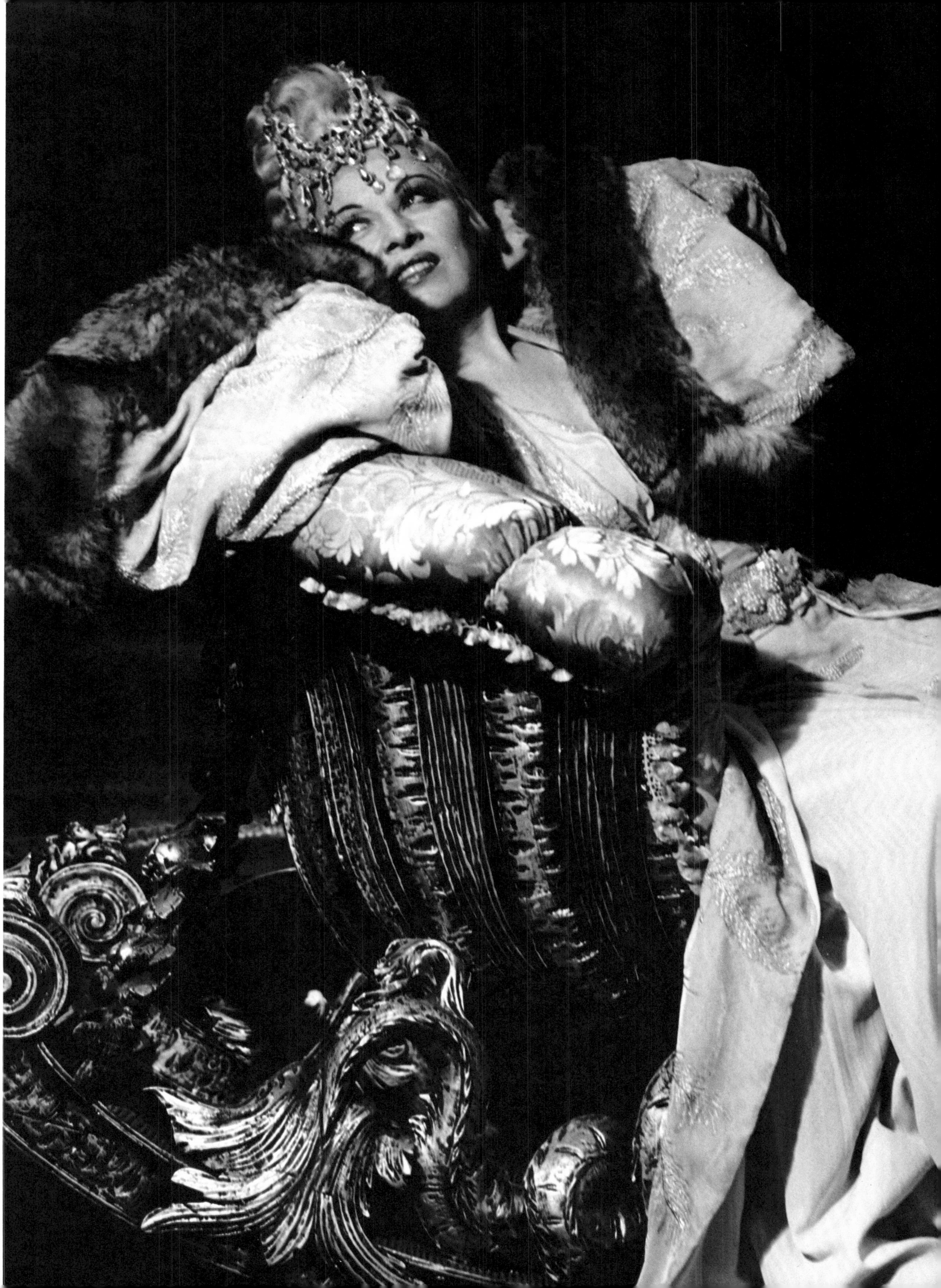

Merle Oberon

178

Judy Garland

Gloria Swan

RICHARD AVEDON

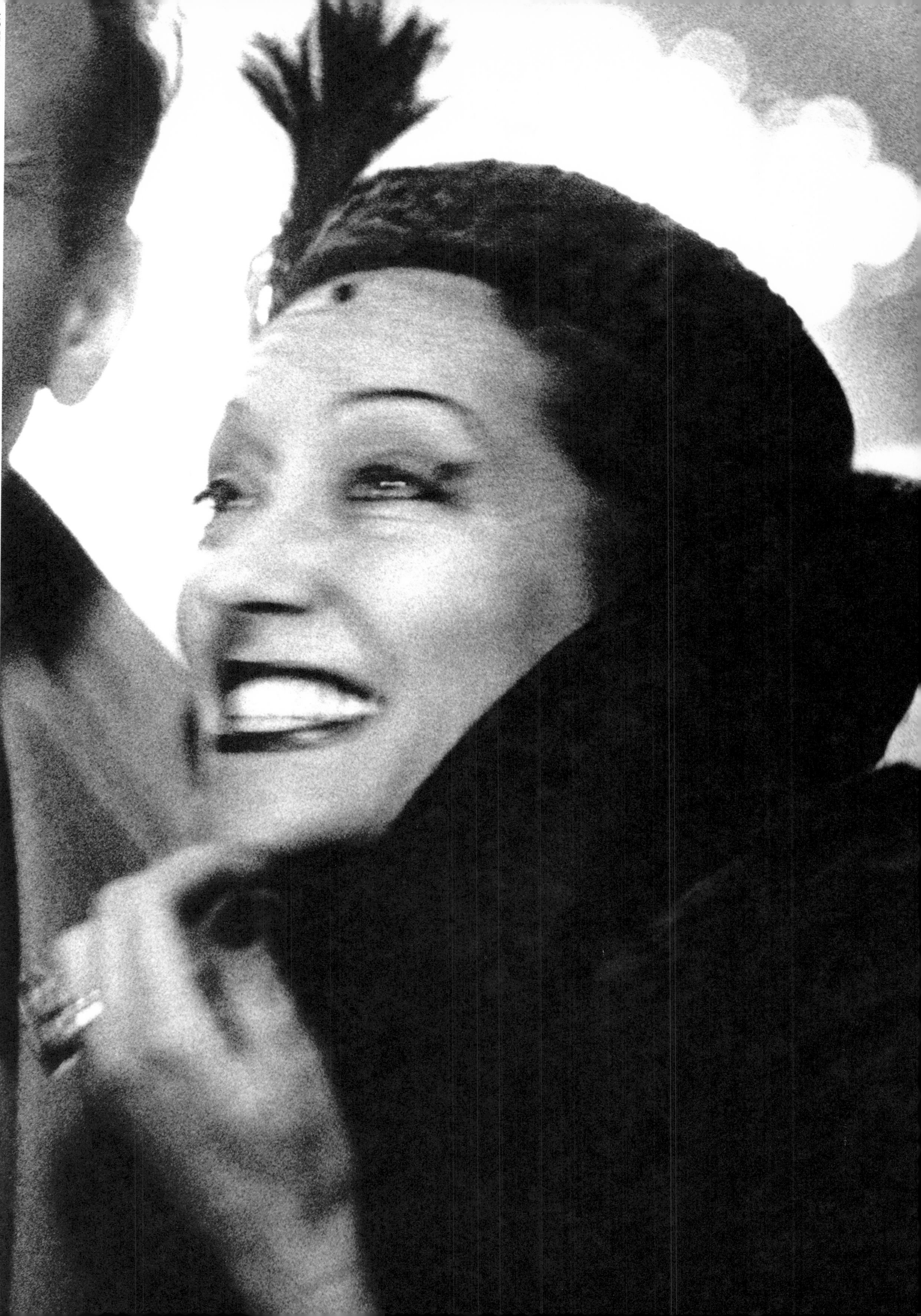

PAUL RADKAI

Grace Kelly

183

RICHARD AVEDON

Detail from Botticelli's *Primavera*

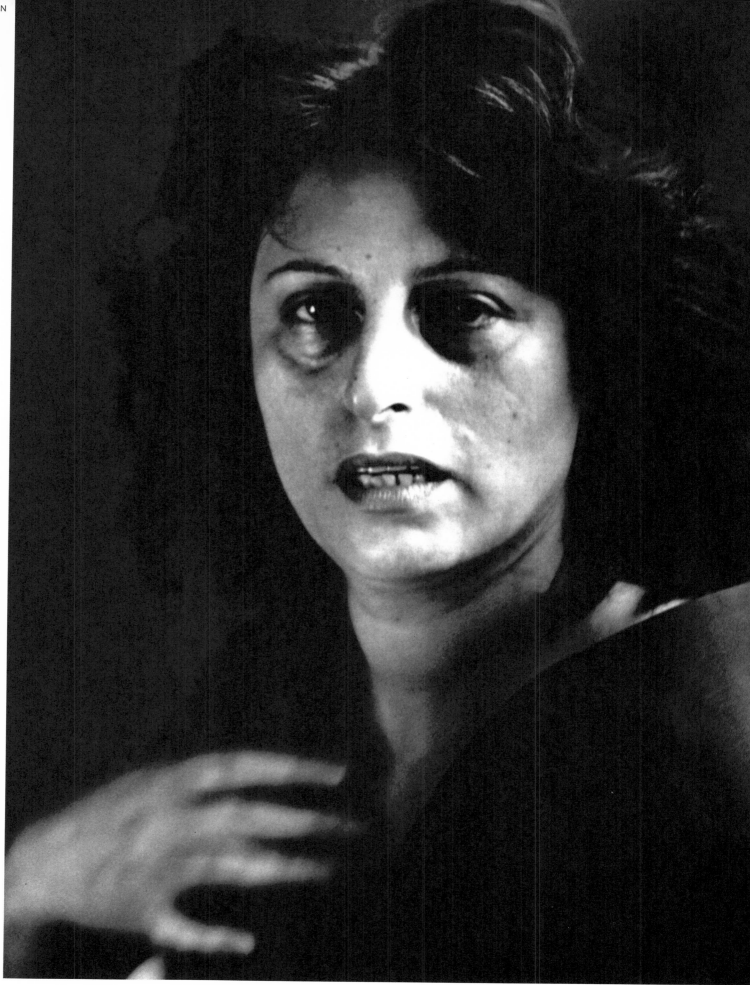

Anna Magnani

Suzy Parker, "the" model of the 50's.

RICHARD AVEDON

Marianne Moore

Gloria Vanderbilt

190

Audrey Hepburn

Kay Kenda

Katharine Hepburn

Little Girl Alias Femme Fatale

by Cecil Beaton

● Miss Marilyn Monroe calls to mind the bouquet of a fireworks display, eliciting from her awed spectators an openmouthed chorus of wondrous ohs and ahs. She is as spectacular as the silvery shower of a Vesuvius fountain; she has rocketed from obscurity to become our postwar sex symbol—the pin-up girl of an age. And whatever press agentry or manufactured illusion may have lit the fuse, it is her own weird genius that has sustained her flight.

Transfigured by the garish marvel of Technicolor and Cinemascope, she walks like an undulating basilisk, scorching everything in her path but the rosemary bushes. Her voice has the sensuality of silk or velvet.

But the real marvel lies in the paradox—somehow we know that this extraordinary performance is pure charade, a little girl's caricature of Mae West. The puzzling truth is that Miss Monroe is a make-believe siren, unsophisticated as a Rhine maiden, innocent as a sleepwalker. She is an urchin pretending to be grown up, having the time of her life in mother's motheaten finery, tottering about in high-heeled shoes and sipping ginger ale as though it were a champagne cocktail. There is an unwordly, a winsome naïveté about the child's eyes that, quick as a flash, will screw up into a pair of sexy, smoldering slits and give you a synthetic "come-hither" look. Just as obligingly, the delicate, flexible mouth, half-parted in springtime ecstasy, will burst into a generous grimace, displaying flawless seed-pearl teeth while the surrounding lips quiver nervously and seem almost shocking in their mobile suggestiveness.

Behind this brilliant, pseudo-fatal façade is the real Marilyn Monroe. She might be the latter-day incarnation of a Greuze portrait, the quintessence of partridge-plump prettiness with full, high breasts, eighteenth-century rump and a delicately modeled face—eyes felicitously wide apart, chin appealingly small, putty-like nose created expressly for wrinkling up with delight, or for photography (though in profile the urchin is apt to gain the ascendancy).

Passing across these enviable features, like blips on a radar screen, is an incredible display of inspired, narcissistic moods. With the possible exception of a Scotch landscape, there has seldom been such an everchanging subject for the photographer. He may miss recording one mood, but a dozen others will assault him with machine-gun recompense.

In her presence, you are startled, then disarmed, by her lack of inhibition. What might at first seem like exhibitionism is yet counterbalanced by a wistful incertitude beneath the surface. If this star is an abandoned sprite, she touchingly looks to her audience for approval. She is strikingly like an overexcited child asked downstairs after tea. The initial shyness over, excitement has now gotten the better of her. She romps, she squeals with delight, she leaps onto the sofa. She puts a flower stem in her mouth, puffing on a daisy as though it were a cigarette. It is an artless, impromptu, high-spirited, infectiously gay performance. It may end in tears.

Equally impromptu is her general appearance. This canary blond nymph has been so sufficiently endowed by nature as to pay no attention to the way she looks. Her hair, her nails, her make-up, have a makeshift, spontaneous attractiveness. It is all very contemporary: Marilyn Monroe conjures up two straws in a single soda, juke boxes, sheer nylons and drive-in movies for necking (does she not project a hypnotized nymphomania?).

This, then, is the wonder of the age — a dreaming somnambule, a composite of Alice in Wonderland, Trilby and a Minsky artist. Perhaps she was born the postwar day we had need of her. Certainly she has no knowledge of the past. Like Giradoux' Ondine, she is only fifteen years old; and she will never die.

Marilyn Monroe

Mrs. Patrick Guinness

Lady Sarah Crichton-Stuart

198

Greta Garbo

Ethel Merman

200

Brigitte Bar

204

HIRO

SILANO

HIRO

207

Children of the Bolshoi Ballet
with teacher

209

LOUIS FAU

Ten years before they became big
time, *Bazaar* showed the big boot.

Phyllis Diller

214

Maya Plisetska

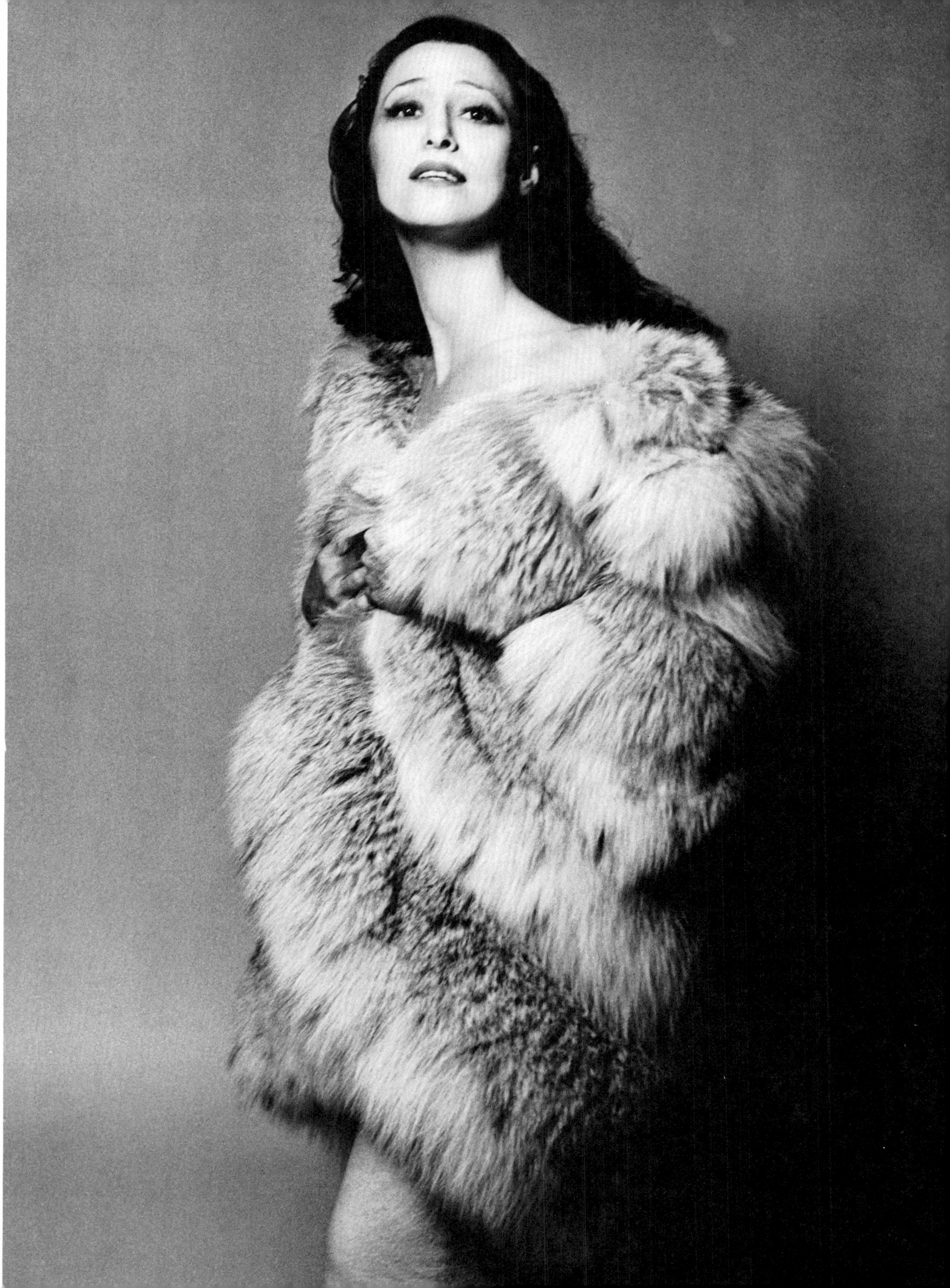

RICHARD AVEDON

218

Mai Britt

Tallulah Bankhead, the American
theatre's *grande dame terrible,*
who has scattered legends about her
like land mines. When Tallulah
Bankhead was made, the mold
was broken: her personality
overwhelms the idea of mere talent
or beauty.

219

My Clothes and I

An Interview with Edith Sitwell

SANFORD R. ROTH

The great English poetess, Edith Sitwell—that "throwback to the Plantagenets" as she likes to put it—sat bonelessly erect in the corner of a cretonne sofa in a London ladies' club. Her face seemed as alien to the conventional human face as the moon is to electric light bulbs.

"I always think the resemblance to a portrait of King Henry VII really remarkable," said her secretary.

"Well, my grandmother and his mother could have been sisters," said Dame Edith, "but I never think he was a very nice man. He was mean with his money. Not at all like me, and it's been my downfall."

She was wearing four enormous chunks of aquamarine on her famous hands and her nails were enameled deep brown-red. Her plain satin dress was cut with a low U-neck, and the brooch pinned there was a huge, clear, pale blue stone set in engraved gold that her brother Osbert brought her from China.

The fur coat she wears "like an animal," summer and winter, indoors and out of doors, was a chestnut brown jacket and her black hat was a cap of beaded feathers with a great sheaf of stiffened net shooting from the crown.

"I get all my hats at Whiteleys these days," she said. "They've got a wonderful hat department. The buyer is a Miss Pery. When I bought this one there, she pointed straight at it: 'There she is!' she said, 'there she is!' I always wear a hat—my hair is so fine and thin you see—except for dinner.

"I never think about clothes: I've got so few. It's only when I suddenly realize I'm all in rags that I consider them at all.

"When I get up, a sort of peacock instinct tells me what to put on. In the country it's a plain black dress. They're all the same but I've got four of them, for cleanliness.

"I couldn't possibly wear tweeds. It would be like dressing a lion in rabbit's clothes. People would follow me on bicycles if I did. I'd look so extraordinary. When I was a girl my mother forced me to wear them, and navy blue and fawn. She herself was a woman of astonishing Roman beauty, but she had a perverse way of suppressing it. I've seen people with beautiful carriage, but her head was set on her neck and her neck was set on her shoulders more wonderfully than you can imagine. In the summer she used to keep me bundled in thick tweeds as a kind of insurance for fine weather.

"I didn't really wear what I wanted until I was about twenty-five. I used to have to wear pale colors like other girls for dances. You can imagine what I looked like in pink—underwear pink. I can remember the dress I had to wear for my coming-out dance: white tulle with spangles and water lilies on the skirt.

"I've only ever bought one thing off-the-peg, and it caused a scandal. I was about twenty at the time and I went out to one of those places, not Debenham and Freebody, but somewhere like it, and bought a black velvet dress.

"Now all my clothes are made for me by a dressmaker, but when I was thinner—I used to be very thin and my waist was twenty-four inches—it was easier and they used to be made at home. Usually I design them, but they are all the same. I wouldn't dream of following fashion. How could one be a different person every three months?

"I have to get a new evening dress now. I shall go to Liberty first and look at their brocades, and it will be made quite straight and go to the ground. I think frills very pretty on other people, and those dresses that go straight to the knees and then flounce out, but not for me. I've had my reciting clothes—which I take great care over: it's my job—made the same way for years. It's the stuff that is important.

"Of course I've made mistakes, but I like to forget about them, pretend they never happened. I've got a gold-and-white brocade cloak made out of stuff from the furnish-ing people, Burnet's, in Garrick Street. It was made before the Second World War. And I wear green velvet and red velvet.

"Tchelitchew designed my red velvet gown. He's painted six or seven portraits of me, and he designed me a black dress out of very soft woolen stuff when I lived in Paris. It had immense skirts and long, pointed sleeves.

"I feel undressed without my rings. These aquamarines I love, but I've got a beautiful topaz like a sunflower—and when I've worn these too much I feel it's being neglected. I haven't worn it for a month or so now, since I was in Italy. I've got red and green and black amber: amber bracelets and a ring I call tiger-into-grape. It's yellow, veined with blue and red, but when it snows it turns blue.

"This gold collar was made for me by an American woman called Millicent Rogers. She was one of my greatest friends, though I only met her once. She sent it to me, and the British Museum kept it four days and thought it was pre-Columbian, undoubtedly from the tomb of an Inca—though they couldn't make out how the gold could be stiffened in a way that wasn't in existence in those days. But I have to be careful of the clanking when I am reciting, and don't often wear it for that.

"I am entirely unself-conscious always, but when I am reciting it's like a bird flying or a fish swimming. Nobody has ever criticized my clothes. They wouldn't dare. I'd look at them. . . .

"But of course I am pleased if they admire anything, pleased to give them pleasure. And I admire what other people wear when it is unusual.

"I take very great care of my hands and put cream on them—Peggy Sage and other things. I always go to Peggy Sage to have them done, except in Italy, where I have to do them myself because it means going into Florence.

"I wear fur gloves all the winter. In the morning I put cream on my face, and I make up my eyebrows and put on lipstick. When I was much younger I wore rouge too, but it wasn't really me.

"I do all my writing in bed. I sit there reading and knitting bed jackets to wear when I'm writing. They are white with intricate work down the front. I found the pattern before the First World War and I know it by heart now.

"I'm not beautiful, but I wouldn't look any other way. My hands are my face!"

The Ring

by Isak Dinesen

CECIL BEATON

On a summer morning a hundred and fifty years ago a young Danish squire and his wife went out for a walk on their land. They had been married a week. It had not been easy for them to get married, for the wife's family was higher in rank and wealthier than the husband's. But the two young people, now twenty-four and nineteen years old, had been set on their purpose for ten years; in the end her haughty parents had had to give in to them.

They were wonderfully happy. The stolen meetings and secret, tearful love letters were now things of the past. To God and man they were one; they could walk arm in arm in broad daylight and drive in the same carriage, and they would walk and drive so till the end of their days. Their distant paradise had descended to earth and had proved, surprisingly, to be filled with the things of everyday life: with jesting and railleries, with breakfasts and suppers, with dogs, haymaking and sheep. Sigismund, the young husband, had promised himself that

from now there should be no stone in his bride's path, nor should any shadow fall across it. Lovisa, the wife, felt that now, every day and for the first time in her young life, she moved and breathed in perfect freedom because she could never have any secret from her husband.

To Lovisa—whom her husband called Lise—the rustic atmosphere of her new life was a matter of wonder and delight. Her husband's fear that the existence he could offer her might not be good enough for her filled her heart with laughter. It was not a long time since she had played with dolls; as now she dressed her own hair, looked over her linen press and arranged her flowers she again lived through an enchanting and

cherished experience: one was doing everything gravely and solicitously, and all the time one knew one was playing.

It was a lovely July morning. Little woolly clouds drifted high up in the sky, the air was full of sweet scents. Lise had on a white muslin frock and a large Italian straw hat. She and her husband took a path through the park; it wound on across the meadows, between small groves and groups of trees, to the sheep field. Sigismund was going to show his wife his sheep. For this reason she had not brought her small white dog, Bijou, with her, for he would yap at the lambs and frighten them, or he would annoy the sheep dogs. Sigismund prided himself on his sheep; he had studied sheep-breeding in Mecklenburg and England, and had brought back with him Cotswold rams by which to improve his Danish stock. While they walked he explained to Lise the great possibilities and difficulties of the plan.

She thought: 'How clever he is, what a lot of things he knows!'

and at the same time: 'What an absurd person he is, with his sheep! What a baby he is! I am a hundred years older than he.'

But when they arrived at the sheepfold the old sheepmaster Mathias met them with the sad news that one of the English lambs was dead and two were sick. Lise saw that her husband was grieved by the tidings; while he questioned Mathias on the matter she kept silent and only gently pressed his arm. A couple of boys were sent off to fetch the sick lambs, the while master and servant went into the details of the case. It took some time.

Lise began to gaze about her and to think of other things. Twice her own thoughts made her blush deeply and happily, like a red rose, then slowly her blush died away, and the two men were still talking about sheep. A little while after their conversation caught her attention. It had turned to a sheep thief.

This thief during the last months had broken into the sheep-folds of the neighborhood like a wolf, had killed and dragged away his prey like a wolf and like a wolf had left no trace after him. Three nights ago the shepherd and his son on an estate ten miles away had caught him in the act. The thief had killed the man and knocked the boy senseless, and had managed to escape. There were men sent out to all sides to catch him, but nobody had seen him.

Lise wanted to hear more about the horrible event, and for her benefit old Mathias went through it once more. There had been a long fight in the sheep house, in many places the earthen floor was soaked with blood. In the fight the thief's left arm was broken; all the same, he had climbed a tall fence with a lamb on his back. Mathias added that he would like to string up the murderer with these two hands of his, and Lise nodded her head at him gravely in approval. She remembered Red Riding-hood's wolf, and felt a pleasant little thrill running down her spine.

Sigismund had his own lambs in his mind, but he was too happy in himself to wish anything in the universe ill. After a minute he said, "Poor devil."

Lise said, "How can you pity such a terrible man? Indeed Grandmamma was right when she said that you were a revolutionary and a danger to society!" The thought of Grandmamma, and of the tears of past days, again turned her mind away from the gruesome tale she had just heard.

The boys brought the sick lambs and the men began to examine them carefully, lifting them up and trying to set them on their legs; they squeezed them here and there and made the little creatures whimper. Lise shrank from the show and her husband noticed her distress.

"You go home, my darling," he said, "this will take some time. But just walk ahead slowly, and I shall catch up with you."

So she was turned away by an impatient husband to whom his sheep meant more than his wife. If any experience could be sweeter than to be dragged out by him to look at those same sheep, it would be this. She dropped her large summer hat with its blue ribbons on the grass and told him to carry it back for her, for she wanted to feel the summer air on her fore-head and in her hair. She walked on very slowly, as he had told her to do, for she wished to obey him in everything. As she walked she felt a great new happiness in being altogether alone, even without Bijou. She could not remember that she had ever before in all her life been altogether alone. The landscape around her was still, as if full of promise, and it was hers. Even the swallows cruising in the air were hers, for they belonged to him, and he was hers.

She followed the curving edge of the grove and after a minute or two found that she was out of sight to the men by the sheep house. What could now, she wondered, be sweeter than to walk along the path in the long flower-ing meadow grass, slowly, slowly, and to let her husband overtake her there? It would be sweeter

still, she reflected, to steal into the grove and to be gone, to have van-ished from the surface of the earth from him when, tired of the sheep and longing for her company, he should turn the bend of the path to catch up with her.

An idea struck her; she stood still to think it over.

A few days ago her husband had gone for a ride and she had not wanted to go with him, but had strolled about with Bijou in order to explore her domain. Bijou then, gamboling, had led her straight into the grove. As she had followed him, gently forcing her way into the shrubbery, she had suddenly come upon a glade in the midst of it, a narrow space like a small alcove with hangings of thick green and golden brocade, big enough to hold two or three people in it. She had felt at that moment that she had come into the very heart of her new home. If today she could find the spot again she would stand perfectly still there, hidden from all the world. Sigismund would look for her in all directions, he would be unable to understand what had become of her and for a minute, for a short minute—or, perhaps, if she were firm and cruel enough, for five—he would realize what a void, what an unendurably sad and horrible place the universe would be when she was no longer in it. She gravely scrutinized the grove to find the right entrance to her hiding-place, then went in.

She took great care to make no noise at all, therefore advanced ex-ceedingly slowly. When a twig caught the flounces of her ample skirt she loosened it softly from the muslin, so as not to crack it. Once a branch took hold of one of her long golden curls; she stood still, with her arms lifted, to free it. A little way into the grove the soil became moist; her light steps no longer made any sound upon it. With one hand she held her small handkerchief to her lips, as if to emphasize the secretness of her course. She found the spot she sought and bent down to divide the foliage and make a door to her sylvan closet. At this the hem of her dress caught her foot and she stopped to loosen it. As she rose she looked into the face of a man who was already in the shelter.

He stood up erect, two steps off. He must have watched her as she made her way straight toward him.

She took him in in one single glance. His face was bruised and scratched, his hands and wrists stained with dark filth. He was dressed in rags, barefooted, with tatters wound round his naked ankles. His arms hung down to his sides, his right hand clasped the hilt of a knife. He was about her own age. The man and the woman looked at each other.

This meeting in the wood from beginning to end passed without a word; what happened could only be rendered by pantomime. To the two actors in the pantomime it was timeless, according to a clock it lasted four minutes.

She had never in her life been exposed to danger. It did not occur to her to sum up her position, or to work out the length of time it would take to call her husband or Mathias, whom at this moment she could hear shouting to his dogs. She beheld the man before her as she would have beheld a forest ghost: the apparition itself, not the sequels of it, changes the world to the human who faces it.

Although she did not take her eyes off the face before her she sensed that the alcove had been turned into a covert. On the ground a couple of sacks formed a couch, there were some gnawed bones by it. A fire must have been made here in the night, for there were cinders strewn on the forest floor.

After a while she realized that he was taking her in as she had taken in him. He was no longer just run to earth and crouching for a spring, but he was wondering, trying to know. At that she seemed to see herself with the eyes of the wild animal at bay in his dark hiding-place: her silently approaching white figure, which might mean death.

He moved his right arm till it hung down straight before him between his legs. Without lifting the hand he bent the wrist and slowly raised the point of the knife till it pointed at her throat. The gesture was mad, unbelievable. He did not smile as he made it, but his nostrils distended, the corners of his mouth quivered a little. Then slowly he put the knife back in the sheath by his belt.

She had no object of value about her, only the wedding ring which her husband had set on her finger in church, a week ago. She drew it off, and in this movement dropped her handkerchief. She reached out her hand with the ring toward him. She did not bargain for her life. She was fearless by nature, and the horror with which he inspired her was not fear of what he might do to her. She commanded him, she besought him to vanish as he had come, to take a dreadful figure out of her life, so that it should never have been there. In the dumb movement her young form had the grave authoritativeness of a priestess conjuring down some monstrous being by a sacred sign.

He slowly reached out his hand to hers, his finger touched hers, and her hand was steady at the touch. But he did not take the ring. As she let it go it dropped to the ground as her handkerchief had done.

For a second the eyes of both followed it. It rolled a few inches toward him and stopped before his bare foot. In a hardly perceivable movement he kicked it away and again looked into her face. They remained like that, she knew not how long, but she felt that during that time something happened, things were changed.

He bent down and picked up her handkerchief. All the time gazing at her; he again drew his knife and wrapped the tiny bit of cambric round the blade. This was difficult for him to do because his left arm was broken. While he did it his face under the dirt and suntan slowly grew whiter till it was almost phosphorescent. Fumbling with both hands, he once more stuck the knife into the sheath. Either the sheath was too big and had never fitted the knife, or the blade was much worn—it went in. For two or three more seconds his gaze rested on her face; then he lifted his own face a little, the strange radiance still upon it, and closed his eyes.

The movement was definitive and unconditional. In this one motion he did what she had begged him to do: he vanished and was gone. She was free.

She took a step backward, the immovable, blind face before her, then bent as she had done to enter the hiding-place, and glided away as noiselessly as she had come. Once outside the grove she stood still and looked round for the meadow path, found it and began to walk home.

Her husband had not yet rounded the edge of the grove. Now he saw her and helloed to her gaily; he came up quickly and joined her.

The path here was so narrow that he kept half behind her and did not touch her. He began to explain to her what had been the matter with the lambs. She walked a step before him and thought: All is over.

After a while he noticed her silence, came up beside her to look at her face and asked, "What is the matter?"

She searched her mind for something to say, and at last said, "I have lost my ring."

"What ring?" he asked her.

She answered, "My wedding ring."

As she heard her own voice pronounce the words she conceived their meaning.

Her wedding ring. "With this ring"—dropped by one and kicked away by another—"with this ring I thee wed." With this lost ring she had wedded herself to something. To what? To poverty, persecution, total loneliness. To the sorrows and the sinfulness of this earth. "And what therefore God has joined together let man not put asunder."

"I will find you another ring," her husband said.

The Schedule

by Françoise Mallet-Joris

This is my schedule: Six o'clock, get up. Suzanne is still asleep. (I can't very well complain about my wife's sleeping soundly. My mother also used to surprise me by her capacity for sleep as well as by the quantities of medicines she took. That too was quite a schedule: injections, followed by pills, followed by drops.) Then setting-up exercises. Since even a writer has to take care of his body, I do setting-up exercises. Suzanne is still asleep. Aniouta also. (I'll explain about Aniouta later; she doesn't fit in here.)

Six-thirty, get dressed.

Seven o'clock, walk through the streets of Paris. This serves a dual purpose: I have something to look at and some fresh air to breathe. Only I question whether this is really an advantage. Too often the critics have commented on "Serge Brenner's interest in the poor, which is so reminiscent of Dostoevsky. . . ." I blame all this on my mother who loves the unusual, on my Russian grandfather whom I never knew, on the first critic who stuck (and stick she did,

like a burr) that description on one of my books. Dostoevsky indeed! If I were to rewrite Paul Bourget's *Blue Duchess* (I think it was Bourget's) the critics would still find that it smacks of Dostoevsky. My morning walk is ruined whenever I think of him. How I loathe Dostoevsky! I'd cross myself at the very sound of his name if I thought that would exorcise him, but I know that I should continue to be haunted by a procession of icons and samovars. Might as well give up.

Normally I take advantage of a free Saturday afternoon to visit museums, for they are a good source of comparisons for descriptive passages. On one of these I decided to be unfaithful to my

wife. As this is most unusual for me I shan't linger on the incident. She was naturally much less attractive than Suzanne—a meaningless fact and besides I only half liked the woman. In the first plush hotel where we stopped there was no room free: hotels of that kind are usually full on Saturdays. I suggested another, inferior one and, since she liked me, she did not demur. I hadn't been near the place in five years; from second-rate it had turned into a flea-trap.

"You're sure you don't mind?"

"Not a bit. It makes me feel like a character in one of your novels; it's so Dostoevsky-like."

What a blow! We spent the afternoon at a movie.

This is not really a digression. Seven to eight, walk and meditate.

Eight o'clock, go home. Aniouta gets up. My daughter is five years old. Her name is really Anne, but her grandmother, who cannot resist the unusual, calls her that and Suzanne and I weakly follow suit. Weak-minded as I am, if in twenty years my mother is still living, we'll gather around a samovar,

Anne will get married in the Russian quarter and when she is unfaithful to her husband, people will blame it on her Russian background. Poor child.

Eight-thirty, breakfast. Suzanne is up. Enter Mina, the maid.

"What a cold morning. How can Mr. Brenner . . ."

One would think that my morning walk (like everything else I do, for that matter) is a personal insult. She hovers over Suzanne.

"Will there be anything else? Good Lord! It's quarter to nine already! Here are your things."

Suzanne drops Aniouta at the kindergarten on her way to the advertising agency where she works. Mina feels sorry for her and makes an outrageous fuss over her: I can find my own overcoat. (Yesterday I had the cheek to ask to have a button sewn on.) I can look for my own brief case, Mina couldn't care less. I don't have an office; I don't have set hours. I can wait until she has time to sew that button back on. (She couldn't do it yesterday, what with all the work she has to do in the apartment—three rooms—and all those papers lying about!) I can wait until she happens to stumble over my brief case—it can't possibly be lost. I have no office, Mina, but I do have a schedule. She snorts.

Actually my schedule allows for all this. In the face of her manifest ill will, I have added a heading which rather pleases me: Nine to nine-thirty, commotion. In this manner I reach, at nine-thirty, the café where I work undisturbed until twelve forty-five.

"Mr. Brenner is at a café." Mina scornfully tells any chance visitor. She never says, "Mr. Brenner is working."

And at one o'clock when I go home for lunch: "The butcher saw you at a café."

What's so surprising about that? I've gone there every day for the past ten years. At first, when I was still living with my mother, I went there to get away from the sound of her voice. Then, when I was first married, it was to get away from Aniouta's. And now I go there from force of habit. (Mina's handling of the vacuum cleaner effectively replaces my mother's and the baby's sound effects.) So what is so surprising about my being seen there? Yet Mina never fails to mention this as though she had found me out in some shameful secret. I spend my life in a café. Poor Mrs. Brenner! That I unaccountably earn my living in this deplorable manner only makes matters worse. Furthermore, Mina is not going to be bribed into keeping her thoughts to herself simply because this is my means, albeit modest, of livelihood. Halfhearted protests from Suzanne, laughter or tears from Aniouta—a typically Russian atmosphere.

I look at my watch. From two to two-twenty I rest. After I have finished my coffee I stretch out for twenty minutes with my eyes closed. I must lie down before dealing with my correspondence (two-thirty to three-thirty), the reading of manuscripts (three-thirty to five-thirty) and a visit to the Art Editions, in which I have an interest (six to six-thirty). This is an afternoon sufficiently well filled to satisfy even the most carping critic. Not Mina. She has a genius for whittling down my twenty minutes. She brings the coffee in late with the excuse that I'll be undisturbed after my wife has gone. She then blows in like a gale with an urgent letter which turns out to be an advertisement for Nescafé. She runs the vacuum cleaner, breaks a plate and, when she runs out of ideas, sings. When she suddenly stops, the house has never seemed so quiet. I look at my watch: only nine more minutes. How can I relax for nine minutes? I can't insert another heading of "Commotion" to my afternoon schedule, there isn't room. I leave the house, quivering.

I have been feeling tired for some time. One of my books has just come out and I have already sketched out the next one in my mind. I do this sort of thing automatically without having to think about it—I suppose it's my subconscious at work; it's very convenient. After that all I need to do is put my schedule into operation: five hours of work per day for one year; seven hours for six months; ten hours for three months. Then I have it typed, and there it is.

But not this time. I have the outline and the schedule as usual but I can't seem to put it into operation. I just cannot settle down to work. My daily walk is haunted more and more by Dostoevsky. How can I manage to keep all traces of him out of my novel so that no one will accuse me of having imitated him and of having finally overdone it? How can I get the point across that I detest him, that I can't keep his characters straight, that I don't even read Russian and that I make it a point never to read a translation? Incidentally, my plot calls for a beggar. I can't have a beggar! Why not simply a drunk named Nicholas Arcadovitch, or something of the sort? "This is super-Dostoevsky, my dear Serge Brenner, and just as we were about to congratulate you, too; you must steer clear of him." I hear them even at night.

Nonetheless I continue to follow my schedule. Walk, meditate, Aniouta, the Café des Sports five hours a day. But I produce not one single sentence, not even the title. Instead, I draw pictures of cats. I can't draw anything else, although I used to do water colors. One morning I drew two hundred and fifty cats each with a different expression. I am also becoming increasingly sensitive to Mina's insinuations. "The painter saw you at the café." I can see the day when she will add "drawing cats." I am sure she wouldn't be a bit surprised if I were paid for drawing pictures of cats . . . there are so many queer things going on nowadays. But I am not going to sink to the level of a paid cat artist. I must do something. I have decided to go to the country.

Suzanne thinks this quite natural. Writers need to immerse themselves in nature every so often. Everybody knows that. They also need solitude. Go, my darling, and don't worry about anything. "Why should he?" Mina asks aggressively, pulling out of a scrap basket a sheet of paper which I had absent-mindedly thrown there. "May I give this to Aniouta? Then it won't be wasted." It's time for me to go; I am about to be found out.

I leave on the thirtieth, which allows me to arrive on the first and to take a rest cure of thirty days exactly. I like round figures. The most important thing is that I must do no writing. But in the country, what is there to do? I'll surely be bored to death unless I give some direction to my life. Therefore I make up the following schedule: Eight o'clock, get up; setting-up exercises, of course—I mustn't let myself go. Breakfast (Mina's absence will be beneficent). Nine to twelve, walk. I must drink in nature, fill my lungs with oxygen, collect a few comparisons, my constant preoccupation. Noon, lunch (still without Mina). I shall then have twenty minutes of relaxation without losing a single second.

All I have left to do now is to organize the afternoon. Write? No. Letters? Perhaps. Yes. I am glad to have hit upon that. There are so many friends one loses sight of, so many civilities one regrets not having paid, and a postcard can make up for a dinner invitation that was refused. This will be a profitable occupation without undue mental strain. Let's say from two to three. At three I'd like something else. A variety of occupations is essential, but when I am not working I always feel that I am wasting time. Perhaps I could take up painting again. I might even be able to do something other than cats. The thought appeals to me. Very well, painting from three to five. Then reading. I shall at last be able to get to all those books with the wonderful titles which I keep buying but which I never find time to read. Reading from five to seven; then dinner, and I shall plan to stay until nine in the dining room which also serves as a bar and where I can study local types.

There, that's done. The first week slips by without a hitch. The new schedule works as smoothly as a well-oiled machine. My long walks unquestionably do me good; my friends are delighted to receive my thoughtful letters and I like writing them for I have been losing touch. My bright water colors are a pleasant distraction and Aniouta likes them; I have finally read the novels written by my friends M, R, X—all those novels, with their dedications, whose gloomy bindings used to look at me reproachfully from the shelves of my library. I have read the book on China and the one about Victorian England which I bought three years ago. All would be well if only. . . . I must have written too enthusiastically, for my friend R, on the ninth day, announces his forthcoming visit. Fortunately I have read his novel. In Paris I always managed to avoid the subject, but here in the country it would be more difficult. Who knows, the main purpose of his visit may be to corner me on that score. But this is not my real objection.

He is due to arrive at one o'clock. By that time I ought to be having my dessert. And what about my twenty minutes' rest? Let's assume that I'll sacrifice them to him. Let's even assume, since he is a friend, that his visit can take the place, in my country schedule, of the heading "Letter writing to friends." A bit of rationalization, true, but it will do. Will he be gone by three? Probably not. He must be looking forward to a pleasant afternoon in the country until at least five. What about my painting? This throws everything off again. I am obsessed by this question until his arrival.

He is late. One-thirty! I ought to be taking my nap by now. It isn't that I'm sleepy; it's the principle of the thing. I try hard to relax. I manage a smile. We have lunch. He is pleasant, lively, warm. René likes me and I like him. But the thought that he is making me waste time obsesses me, gnaws at me, deafens me to the point that I cannot hear his well-intentioned conversation. This is absurd since I came here for the express purpose of doing nothing! But this nothing has become organized, has turned into something in which René has no place. I ought to have allowed for his visit, to have set aside one day a week for "visits from friends." Then I should have been perfectly relaxed.

René is eating with maddening deliberateness. It is already two-forty. My worst fears are realized: he will not leave until five. I try to adjust myself to this thought, to rid myself of my obsession. I'm turning into a maniac. At last he is through. I am very fond of René. I keep repeating to myself: "friendly chat until five o'clock." After I have repeated this heading two or three times, it begins to seem natural and I view him more kindly; I even start to say to him, "Your novel is really . . ." when he gets up and says guilelessly, "Why don't we go for a walk?" Walk? But walking is from nine to twelve! It isn't that I'm tired. But something within me rebels, becomes frantic again. Despite my efforts to remind myself that I'm being absurd, I have to make a superhuman effort to follow him, gnashing my teeth as I go.

And this goes on until evening. We walked, drank tea, talked, dined, smoked. He didn't leave until nine, delighted with his "day in the country," and I answered, smiled, walked, talked, smoked with an all-consuming hatred in my heart. And when he had finally gone, I went back to my room where I collapsed sobbing on the bed. Sobbing.

I had been proud to take my father's place, to have responsibilities; proud, at the age of twelve, to answer the invitations of my friends with, "I can't; I have to look after Mother." Proud to work for her, proud of my good marks, of my discipline. I loved my life, the hours spent at school, the hours I spent in the evening writing, filled as I was with the hope (a well-grounded one as it turned out) of earning my living by it some day. And all through the years I loved having a schedule for injections, pills, drops. I had been a model pupil, a model teacher. My first book sold well. I would become a model writer, a model father. The essential was discipline. We can make what we want of life if we are sufficiently determined. But one single false step, one single slip, one minute's delay can make everything disappear, like Aladdin's palace.

I looked at my watch, at the alarm clock. I was exactly halfway through my first novel. I had to stop in one minute to give some drops to my mother who was so ill that she often gasped for breath. I loved my mother. I didn't dislike my profession as a teacher; I should have to remain one if these notebooks did not turn into a book. Or if this book went by unnoticed. I daydreamed. The clock showed one minute past nine. Mother was already waiting on the floor below. I must remember her schedule. Drops now. I wondered why I wanted to write. I had no real taste for risks—or did I? I had no need to escape; I loved my life—or did I?

It was nine-thirty by the clock.

These notebooks which were the very essence of my life were suddenly, with all their questions, like hostile strangers. Since I loved my life, my mother, her schedule, my profession, since I loved my wife, my daughter, unquestioningly, why this urge to write?

I began to feel rebellious against the tyranny of this work which now seemed meaningless. Why another profession? Why more questions? Weren't there enough unanswered ones already? I had started to write for pleasure; the writing had turned into a quest for advancement, for change, for a pleasanter profession with a more varied landscape. Would it never be more than that? Wouldn't there always be interruptions for medicines, for letters? Had I become a prisoner of my own handiwork? Ought not these notebooks to answer some of my questions?

I found I was tired. Tired from so much effort and too weak to do anything about it. Automatically my eyes turned to the large alarm clock. I leapt up.

When I came into her room she had turned blue. She was revived with the greatest difficulty. Thank heaven she is still alive.

I don't know what made me think of this incident. In any event there is nothing to be learned from it. It is far too reminiscent of Dostoevsky. But René's visit has put me on my guard. I watch myself very closely and find I am a little queer. For example, when I have decided to walk fifteen kilometers, nothing would induce me to walk an extra one. But I am not going to start inquiring into the reasons for this. There are too many uncertainties when one ventures along unknown paths. The only time I ever tried to question the world I nearly killed my mother. I am not going to risk any more deaths; the game isn't worth the candle. I am quite pleased to have found the title of my next novel, *The Schedule*. And there will be no beggars. Not even a little one. It will be quite Kafka-like. I must have a German grandfather somewhere in my background.

—*Translation from the French by C. J. Richards*

The Snake

by Maria Dermoût

EDITH VISSER

The old house still stood there in the old garden on the sugar plantation, deep in the interior of Java—the 'big house,' as it was called.

Each family that had lived here, each of a long succession, had built away at it, adding something here, altering something there. The garden too had suffered change. There was now a brick-lined lotus pool, an orchid shed, a guest pavilion. The paths had been diverted, to wind among flower-beds and clumps of flowering shrubs. Eventually little of the original scene was left, aside from a few trees—the two banyans on each side of the house, the kanari trees along the drive. And a large stone vase standing on a pedestal in the center of the kitchen garden, where once the rose garden had been.

But to the left of the house, behind the deer park, in that corner of the garden that sloped away to the river, nothing had been changed. There, there were no more lawns, no paths, no flower-beds, but just coconut palms, planted in rows like the trees of an orchard. And instead of a wall there was a hedge of thorny bamboo, taller than a man. And beyond it, though sealed off from the main garden and, like it, enclosed by a bamboo hedge, lay another, a small garden.

A long—a very long—time ago, a man had lived in the 'big house,' with two women. One in the big house—she had a child—and one in the small house, hidden away behind the thorn hedge of the small garden, close to the river-side.

In the beginning everything went well. The woman in the big house was proud, she held her child stiffly by the hand and uttered never a word.

The woman in the small house did not speak much either, not in the beginning. She was happy when the man visited her. He visited her often. Sometimes he would come early in the morning: she made such good coffee, really strong coffee, and he always drank it as black and bitter as he could get it, with only a little milk and almost no sugar. She drank hers weak, with lots of milk and lots of sugar. Sometimes he would come in the afternoon. Sometimes he would come to her in the evening after the light had gone. Or at night. But the man *lived* in the big house.

Slowly, gradually, a change began to come over the woman who lived in the small house. To begin with it was only a soft whisper playing about his ear: wouldn't he like to come and live with her in the small house? Only that. She asked nothing more. Then she began to say it out loud. In the end she was saying almost nothing else. Sometimes she grew furious, stamped her foot, wept, and threatened to jump into the river . . . just like that!

But all the man said was: "I live in the big house."

Then the woman in the small house did something she had never done before. She put on her best raiment, and, instead of taking the little path that followed the line of the river down to the village, down to the market, she walked into the garden of the big house. She did not dare to enter by one of the two drives. She crawled through the hedge of thorny bamboo and made her way cautiously through the garden until she had approached close to the big house. Neither did she come out into the open but kept to the undergrowth, kept under the trees, and waited near the rose garden. For every morning the other woman, the woman from the big house, would come here to gather roses.

And, after a time, this she did.

She was fair-haired, and very pale. In her one hand she held a pair of scissors, on her arm hung a small basket. She had a child with her, the boy was as slim and pale as she was.

Before long she began to pick her roses, bending down over the flowerpots that stood ranged in rows on their pedestals, forming squares round an empty stone vase. And she looked neither to left nor to right.

Again and again the scissors rang out with a sharp snip-snap and she laid one rose after the other in the little basket. Sometimes she would pause and hold one in her hand and smell the scent—they were still wet with the dew and fragrant. And now and then she would also pause to call out to the child.

But he didn't want to come to her side. He was wandering about among the flowerpots, looking around him in all directions, as though he were searching for something: first on the ground, then higher up in the flowerpots, then higher still, all round him—and suddenly he saw the other woman standing there among the bushes, in the shadow of the trees. She stood at a distance, motionless, and fixed the boy with her eyes. She had round, black, glittering eyes. The boy stared back at her too. Then he

gave a shriek and raced back to his mother and hid his head against her side.

"O, mamma!" he cried.

The woman was startled, what is it? what is it? and looked about her, everywhere, to see what could have made the child so scared.

Then she, too, saw the other woman, only a glimpse, for at the same moment, the other woman had turned away and begun to walk back to the small house. She had a strange, swift, sinuous way of walking and was gone in no time.

The woman threw her basket and scissors, all her roses, on the ground and clasped the child more tightly in her arms. He was shivering as though he had caught a fever and despite his size she carried him through the garden, into the big house, and to her own dressing room, put him down a moment, closed all the doors and windows and bolted them too, then took him in her arms again and went and sat down with him.

"Hush now, hush," she kept repeating. "We'll be going now, hush!" And she went on rocking him to and fro until he ceased to shiver and fell asleep. When he was fast asleep, she laid him down on the sofa, fetched a blanket to cover him, opened the door cautiously, took the key with her, locked the door again on the far side, and called out softly to the older servants, the spèn (that is, the butler), the coachman, the woman cook, the nursery maid, her personal maid—the oldest five.

"Of course, you'll understand that we'll be leaving now," she said. And all five nodded their heads to signify that of course they understood. She discussed everything with them, calmly, rapidly, settled everything item by item, as if she had thought it all out long before: those trunks, those clothes for the boy, those for herself, toys. That carriage and those horses. "Now, think of this, Kokkie, and that too!" The spèn received the keys. "You'll remember this, won't you? And don't forget that. There are some roses still lying in the garden and a basket and a pair of

scissors. The roses must be put in water." She picked up the folding slate, on which in those days they used to write little messages for the neighbors, and inside it she wrote: 'We're leaving now,' and placed her name and her son's underneath it. On the outside she wrote the address.

"You must give this to the master, when the master arrives." And she handed the slate to the spèn. Then she opened up the dressing room again to get to the cupboards. For each of the five servants she searched out a souvenir, no rubbish: a silver box and a watch that had belonged to her father; a golden bangle, a ring, a brooch she had worn when a young girl. All the costly things the man had given her she left in the cupboard. The spèn uttered a brief blessing, make haste! make haste!

Before the man arrived home, at the hottest moment in the forenoon, in broad daylight, the woman rode away from the big house, in the carriage and four, with the coach driver and the groom on the box, with her trunks, and a hatbox, with her child on her lap. He was still half asleep and only woke up properly later on, looking around him then, surprised, and at once anxious once more: "Where, where was . . . ?" His mother smoothed a hand over his hair.

"We've left," she said. "Did you hear me? Left! Now you must come and sit next to me for we're off on our travels together now." And the boy scrambled off her lap and sat upright at her side.

When the man arrived home at the big house, the spèn gave him the little slate.

Later on he went to the woman in the small house and told her the news. She drew him to her. Never had he known a woman so radiant, so full of fire. And tenderness.

"Well, are you now coming to live with me in the small house?"

"No," said the man. "I live in the big house."

And so for her nothing had actually changed. The man lived on his own in the big house, the woman never made any attempt to join him there, neither did he ever invite her to. He visited her in the small house, but he did not live there.

What then happened no one can say precisely.

One morning, shortly afterwards—they had drunk a cup of coffee together—the man became ill at the woman's place, in the small house. She did not call for help. She laid him in her bed and waited at his side. He was dead before nightfall.

It was the cholera season, said the one. But the other said the woman had put some white powder instead of sugar in his bitter, black coffee. They sold it at the market, to sharpen the blades of their krises with, and for the rats.

So the man died in the small house, just as if he had always lived in it. For, after all, a person does usually die in the house where he has lived, doesn't he?

Cholera or rat poison, who was there now to tell? It had all been forgotten.

The small house had tumbled into ruins. The ruins had been cleared away.

The big house had been rebuilt, time after time. Rebuilt, changed. The garden changed too. And a succession of new people had come here to live, with other children, other servants, other animals.

Only a few of the trees were still the same.

And now once again a man, a woman and a child lived in the big house, as they had done long ago.

This child was a little girl, thin, agile, with black hair, as talkative, as inquisitive, as a magpie. In the afternoons, when she should have been sleeping, she would crawl through the window of her bedroom and play in the garden with the two little Javanese girls, nieces of her nurse.

They had the run of the garden. There was not a spot they hadn't explored, not a fruit they hadn't tasted. But when they were playing at the far end of the garden, near the river, under the coconut palms, and she went to creep through the bamboo hedge—"Come on, you cowards! Let's go and have a peep at that other garden!"—the other two grew scared and cried, "No, no, we're not allowed to, you know we're not, you know it's forbidden!" And they held her back and tugged at her dress as hard as they could, or ran off and told on her. And the nurse or the old spèn would always turn up at the last minute and fetch her away and talk really crossly to her.

Afterwards she'd call the two nieces 'nasty tell-tales,' but they acted as though they did not care in the least what she called them.

Then, one afternoon, when they were away somewhere else and everyone was asleep, she went there all the same. On her own. She wanted to take just one look. She was always one for taking just one look.

It was a bitter disappointment—what was there to look at? There was nothing at all to be seen. The stone foundations of a house, covered in moss, weeds everywhere, and one tree. A banyan tree, not even a big one.

Trees are beautiful but this tree wasn't. It was different, too, from the other trees, different from the two banyans on each side of the big house, so tall and spreading, of such a brilliant green, with all those decorative, pale brown roots dangling in the air. Swarms of chattering birds would settle among their leaves to guzzle the fat, dark red berries or take a brief rest in their shade. Different from the stately old kanari trees along the drive, their trunks like tall, moss-grown columns. Different from the row of mango trees next to the coach house, the sunlight a glitter of bright green and yellow shining right through their tender young leaves. Different from the sturdy broad rubber trees against the garden wall, the wunggu's, with their purple—pale purple, dark purple—clusters of blossom, the flame trees, with the red. Different from all the fruit trees in the garden, the tamarinds along the great highway, with leaves as small as sequins, trembling and twinkling at the wind's slightest sigh. Different from the stately palm trees, the majestic king palms, the areca palms, with a leaf like a flame curled round the younger leaves to protect them, the coconut palms, rattling and creaking in the wind, or the tall swaying fronds of bamboo, which stood silhouetted against the sky as fine, as delicate, as curly feathers.

This tree was different. It was very old, it was still alive, but it stood there as though drained of all its strength, sapless, with a trunk full of cracks and crevices, its dangling air-roots shriveled, its leaves all spottled. Yet it stood erect, erect and full of menace. An old, an evil tree.

Between its roots, which stuck up high out of the ground, lay freshly picked flowers and the ash of spent incense. Could it be a sacred tree? Oh, was *that* why this garden was 'forbidden'?

It seemed so quiet here. Why were there no flowers, no berries, no fruits? No animals, not one bird, not a butterfly, not even a tiny lizard?

Nothing that moved, that had color, fragrance.

It was as though the silence was a glass bell that had closed down over everything here. There was no air inside . . . however was she to breathe? She could not move either, but stood, and stared, and waited, and did not know what she was waiting for.

Suddenly she heard the sound of someone crawling through the hedge at her back. It was the spèn. He gave her a terrible fright, she had never seen him looking like this before. He, who was always so immaculately attired, in long, white, starched trousers, a long, white, starched jacket, with a waistband of batik-work and a batik-work headcloth wound impeccably smooth round his head . . . why, he was not even dressed! He was wearing short blue underpants, held up by a white shoelace tied round his waist, the upper half of his body was naked, he wasn't even wearing a headcloth—his long hair tied in a slovenly knot, with a comb thrust into it, as though he were a woman. He must have run all the way, he was panting badly.

He ran past her without stopping and placed a saucer he was carrying down among the high projecting roots of the tree, where the flowers lay and the incense had burned. There was milk in the saucer, but colored brown with something, such as coffee, cocoa, or was it perhaps Javanese sugar? Then he came and stood at her side. "Stand still!" he said. He was very angry. And she *had* been standing still, all this time.

So there they stood, side by side.

After a while she saw that in one of the cracks in the trunk, close to the ground, something—something slow, something sinuous—was moving, was crawling out into the open. It was a snake, an ordinary snake, not a poisonous snake all black and white ringed, not a snake green all over its body, but a large brown snake with black markings, a perfectly ordinary snake.

At first it seemed it would come straight at her. With lightning-swift movements, it slithered forward, lifted its flat head off the ground, and stared at her. It really was fixing her with its small, black, glittering eyes. And she in turn had to look back at it. She hunched up her shoulders, bent her head, and went cold to the very core of her being.

Then the snake turned aside and slid up to the saucer of milk. But it did not drink from it. It just inspected it, curled itself round the saucer, and then, swift

and sinuous, disappeared into the crack from which it had come.

"Come along, quickly now!" The spèn bent the thorny fronds of the hedge aside for her, pulling them to carefully again when she had passed through. She walked behind him, silent and submissive, walked slowly, shuddering every now and again, and feeling sick. In the big garden, under the coconut palms, she came to a halt.

"Spèn," she said, "you must kill that snake!"

Then the spèn spoke to her—he who otherwise would rarely utter a word, he who was now not even properly dressed and who looked like some queer old, flat-breasted woman clad in short blue knickers—spoke to her fiercely, in reprimand: "Will you just hold your tongue! Just take care that you never say that again! That snake lives there. It is its home, and you are not allowed to go there! You know perfectly well it is forbidden!" And he repeated: "You must never go there again!"

The little girl stared at him. "*I shall never go there again,*" she said obediently. "But what if the snake should come to *us,* in the big house? What then?"

"This snake will never come to the big house. It will never leave its home there." And the spèn spoke with such conviction that she believed him without hesitation, and uttered a great sigh of relief. But at the same moment she was forced to think how the snake must live there, close to them, in the crack in the trunk of the old banyan tree, near the river, with

the flowers, the incense, the saucer of milk in front of its cave. She could see it all clearly before her.

"But now you've forgotten your saucer. And the snake didn't even drink one drop of that milk!"

"No, it didn't," snapped the spèn. "The snake refuses to drink when strangers are present. The snake will drink later on. And now that's enough from you! Come along! Get ahead with you!"

"But, but do you always take it something to drink then, *and* flowers, *and* incense?" she asked, astonished. "But why, why?"

"So that the snake will not become angry with the people in the big house."

Yes. Yes, she could understand that.

"But don't you ever take it anything else besides milk?" (She was not too fond of milk herself.)

"Milk, with a little coffee in it, and sugar."

"But why coffee and sugar?" she asked, for she was one for always wanting to know all the details.

"Because the snake likes coffee, and lots of sugar! And now you can stop all that chatter and hold your tongue. Come along!"

But shortly afterwards, the spèn spoke again. "You'd better not talk about that snake. Not to anyone. Do you understand? Or are you too stupid to understand why?"

Of course she was not stupid. Of course she understood why.

—Translated from the Dutch by James Brockway

The Dummy

by Susan Sontag

Since my situation is intolerable, I have decided to take steps to resolve it. So I have constructed a perfectly life-like dummy, made of various brands of Japanese plastic simulating flesh, hair, nails and so forth. An electronics engineer of my acquaintance, for a sizeable fee, set up the interior mechanism of the dummy: it will be able to talk, eat, work, walk and copulate. I hired an important artist of the old realistic school to paint the features; after twelve sittings the job was done to my entire satisfaction. Needless to say, this dummy perfectly resembles me. My broad nose is there, my brown hair, the lines on each side of my mouth. Even I could not tell the dummy and myself apart, were it not for the fact that from my peculiar vantage point it is quite obvious that he is he and that I am I.

All that remains is to install the dummy in the center of my life. He will go to work instead of me, and receive the approval and censure of my boss. He will bow and scrape and be diligent. All I require of him is that he bring me

HARRY HESS

the check every other Wednesday; I will give him carfare and money for his lunches, but no more. I'll make out the checks for the rent and the utilities, and pocket the rest myself. The dummy will also be the one who is married to my wife. He will make love to her on Tuesday and Saturday night, watch the television with her every evening, eat her competent dinners, quarrel with her about how to bring up the children. (My wife, who also works, pays the grocery bills out of her salary.) I will also assign the dummy Monday night bowling with the team from the office, the visit to my mother on Friday night, reading the newspaper each morning, and perhaps buying my clothes (two sets—one

for him, one for me). Other tasks I will assign as they come up, as I wish to divest myself of them. I want to keep for myself only what gives me pleasure.

A grandiose plan, you say? But why not? The problems of this world are only truly solved in two ways: by extinction, or by duplication. Former ages, less advanced than ours, had only the first choice. But I see no reason not to take advantage of the marvels of modern science and technology for the liberation of man. I have a choice. And, not being the suicidal type, I have decided to duplicate myself.

On a fine Monday morning I wind the dummy up and set him loose, after making sure he knows just what to do—that is, he knows just how I would behave in any familiar situation. (The unprecedented situations I leave him to decide for himself.) The alarm goes off. He rolls over, pokes my wife, who wearily gets out of the double bed and turns the alarm off. She puts on her slippers and robe, then limps, stiff-ankled, into the bathroom. The dummy lies in bed a few more minutes. When she comes out and heads for the kitchen, he gets up and takes her place in the bathroom. He urinates, washes out his mouth, shaves, comes back into the bedroom and takes his clothes out of the dresser and closet, returns to the bathroom, dresses, then joins my wife in the kitchen. My children are already at the table. The younger girl didn't finish her homework last night, and my wife is writing a note of excuse to the teacher. The older girl sits haughtily, munching the cold toast. "Morning, Daddy," they say to the dummy. The dummy pecks them each on the cheek in return. Breakfast passes without incident, I observe with relief. The children leave. They haven't noticed a thing. I begin to feel sure my plan is going to work. Only now do I notice, by my excitement, that I had greatly feared it would not—that there would be some mechanical failure on the dummy's part, so that he would not recognize his cues. But no, everything is going right, even the way he folds *The New York Times* is correct; he reproduces exactly the amount of time I spend on the foreign news, and it takes him just as long to read the sports pages as it took me.

The dummy kisses my wife, he steps out the door, he enters the elevator. (Do machines recognize each other, I wonder?) Into the lobby, out the door, on the street walking at a moderate pace—the dummy has left on time, he doesn't have to worry—into the subway he goes. Steady, calm, clean (I cleaned him myself Sunday night), untroubled, he goes about his appointed tasks. He will be happy as long as I am satisfied with him. And so I will be, whatever he does, as long as others are satisfied with him. Meanwhile, I have myself to myself.

Nobody notices anything different in the office, either. The secretary says hello, he smiles back as I always do; then he walks to my cubicle, hangs up his coat and sits at my desk. The secretary brings him my mail. After reading it, he calls for some dictation. Next, there is a pile of papers—my unfinished business left from last Friday—to attend to. Phone calls are made, an appointment is set up for lunch with a client from out of town. There is only one irregularity that I notice: the dummy smokes seven cigarettes during the morning; I usually smoke between ten and fifteen. But I set this down to the fact that he is new at his work, and has not had time to accumulate the tensions which I feel after working six years in this office. It occurs to me that he will probably not have two martinis —as I always do—during the lunch, but only one; and I am right. But these are mere details, and will be to the dummy's credit if anyone notices them, which I even doubt. His behavior with the out-of-town client is quite correct, perhaps a shade too eager and deferential, but this too I put down to inexperience. Thank God, no simple matter tripped him up. His table manners were as they should be. He didn't pick at his food, but ate with appetite. And he knew he should sign the check, rather than pay with cash; for the firm has an account at the restaurant which he chose.

In the afternoon there is a sales conference. The vice-president is explaining a new promotional campaign for the Midwest. The dummy makes a couple of suggestions. The boss nods. The dummy taps his pencil on the top of the long mahogany table and looks thoughtful. I notice he is chainsmoking. Could he be feeling the pressure so soon? I feel a moment's solicitude for him. What a hard life I led! After less than a day of it, even a dummy shows some wear and tear. The rest of the afternoon passes without incident. The dummy makes his way home to my wife and children, eats his dinner appreciatively, plays Monopoly with the children for an hour, watches a Western on TV with my wife, bathes, makes himself a ham sandwich in the kitchen, and then retires to bed. I don't know what dreams he dreamt, but I hope they were restful and pleasant. If my approval could give him an untroubled sleep, he had it. I am entirely pleased with my creation.

The dummy has been on the job for several months now. What can I report? A greater degree of proficiency? But that's impossible. He was fine the first day. He couldn't be any more like me than he was at the very beginning. So he does not have to get better at his job, but only stick at it contentedly, unrebelliously, without mechanical failure. My wife is happy with him, at least no more unhappy than she was with me. My children call him Daddy and ask him for their allowance. My fellow-workers and my boss continue to entrust him with my old job at the office.

Lately, though—just the past week, really—I have noticed something that worries me. Only slightly. It is the attention that the dummy is paying to the new secretary, Miss Love. I hope it isn't her name that arouses him, somewhere in the depths of that complicated machinery; I imagine machines can be awfully literal-minded. Anyway, it isn't anything serious. Just a slight lingering at her desk when he comes in in the morning, a second's pause, no more, when she says hello; whereas I—and he until recently—used to walk by that desk without breaking my stride. And he does seem to be dictating more letters lately. Could it be an increased zeal on behalf of the firm? I remember how, the very first day, he spoke up at the sales conference. Or could it be the desire to detain Miss Love a few minutes more? Are all those letters really necessary? I could swear he thinks so. But then you never know what goes on behind that imperturbable dummy's face of his. I'm frankly afraid to ask him. Is it because I don't want to know the worst? Or because I'm afraid he'll be angry at my violation of his privacy? In any case, I have decided to wait until he tells me.

Then one day it comes. The news I had dreaded. At eight in the morning the dummy corners me in the shower, where I had been spying on him while he was shaving—really just marveling how he remembered to cut himself every once in a while, as I do. He unburdens himself to me, confesses all. I am astonished at how much he is moved. Astonished, and a little envious. I never dreamed a dummy could have so much feeling, that I would see a dummy weep. I try to quiet him, I admonish him, then I reprimand him. It's no use. His tears become sobs. He, or rather his passion, whose mechanism I cannot fathom, begins to revolt me. I'm also terrified my wife and children will hear him, rush to the bathroom, and there find this berserk creature who would be incapable of normal responses. (Might they find both of us here in the bathroom? That, too, is possible.) I run the shower, open both the sink faucets, and flush the toilet to drown out the painful noises he is making. All this for love! All this for the love of Miss Love! He has barely spoken to her, except in the way of business. Certainly, he hasn't slept with her, of that I am sure. And yet he is madly, desperately in love. He wants to leave my wife. I explain to him how impossible that is. First of all, he has certain duties and responsibilities. He is the husband and father to my wife and children. They depend on him; their lives would be smashed by his selfish act. And second, what does he know about Miss Love? She's at least ten years younger than he is, has given no particular sign of noticing him at all, and probably has a nice boyfriend her own age whom she's planning to marry.

The dummy refuses to listen. He is inconsolable. He will have Miss Love or—here he makes a threatening gesture—he will destroy himself. He will bang his head against the wall, or jump out of a window, disassembling irrevocably his delicate machinery. Now I become really alarmed. I see my whole marvelous scheme, which has left me so beautifully at my leisure and in peace the last months, ruined. I see myself back at the job, making love again to my wife, fighting for space in the

subway during the rush hour, watching television, spanking the children. If this was intolerable to me before, you can imagine how unthinkable it is now. Why, if only you knew how I had spent these last months, while the dummy was administering my life. Without a care in the world, except for an occasional spurt of curiosity as to the fate of my dummy, I had slid to the bottom of the world. I slept anywhere now: in flophouses, on the subway (which I only boarded very late at night), in alleys and doorways. I didn't bother to collect my paycheck from the dummy any more, because there was nothing I wanted to buy. Only rarely did I shave myself. My clothes were torn and stained.

Does this sound very dreary to you? It was not, it was not. Of course, when the dummy first relieved me of my own life, I had grandiose plans for living the lives of others. I wanted to be an Arctic explorer, a concert pianist, a great courtesan, a world statesman. I tried being Alexander the Great, then Mozart, then Bismarck, then Greta Garbo, then Elvis Presley—in my imagination, of course. I imagined that, being none of these people very long, I could have only the pleasure of their lives, none of the pain; for I could escape, transform myself, whenever I wanted. But the experiment failed, for lack of interest, from exhaustion, call it what you will. I discovered that I am tired of being a person. Not just tired of being the person I was, but any person at all. I like watching persons, but I don't like talking to them, dealing with them, pleasing them or offending them. I don't even like talking to the dummy. I am tired. I would like to be a mountain, a tree, a stone. If I am to continue as a person, the life of the solitary derelict is the only one tolerable to me. So you will see that it was quite out of the question that I should allow the dummy to destroy himself, and have to take his place and live again my old life.

I continue my efforts of persuasion. I get him to dry his tears and

go out and face the family breakfast, promising him that we will continue the conversation in the office, after he dictates his morning batch of letters to Miss Love. He agrees to make the effort, and makes his red-eyed, somewhat belated appearance at the table. "A cold, dear?" says my wife solicitously. The dummy blushes and mumbles something. I pray that he will hurry up. I am afraid he will break down again. I notice with alarm that he can hardly eat, and leaves his coffee cup two-thirds full.

The dummy makes his way sadly out of the apartment, leaving my wife somewhat perplexed and apprehensive. I see him hail a cab instead of heading for the subway; matters are really critical. In the office, I eavesdrop as he dictates his letters, sighing between every sentence. Miss Love notices, too. "Why, what's the matter," she says cheerfully. There is a long pause. I peep out of the closet, and what do I see! The dummy and Miss Love in a hot embrace. He is stroking her breasts, her eyes are closed, with their mouths they wound each other. The dummy catches sight of me, staring from behind the closet door. I signal wildly, trying to make him understand that we must talk, that I'm on his side, that I'll help him. "Tonight?" whispers the dummy, slowly releasing the ecstatic Miss Love. "I adore you," she whispers. "I adore you," says the dummy in a voice above a whisper, "and I must see you." "Tonight," she whispers back. "My place. Here's the address."

One more kiss and Miss Love goes out. I emerge from the closet and lock the door of the little office. "Well," says the dummy. "It's Love or death." "All right," I say sadly, "I won't try to talk you out of it any more. She seems like a nice girl anyway. And quite attractive. Who knows, if she had been working here when I was here. . . ." I see the dummy frowning angrily, and don't finish the sentence. "But you'll have to give me a little time," I say. "What are you going to do? As far as I can see, there's nothing you can do," says the dummy. "If you think I'm going home to your wife and kids any more, after I've found Love!" I plead with him for time.

What do I have in mind? Simply this. The dummy after all is now in my original position. His present arrangements for life are intolerable to him. But having more appetite for a real, single life than I ever had, he doesn't want to vanish completely from the world. He just wants to replace my admittedly second-hand wife and two noisy daughters with the delightful, childless Miss Love. Well then, why shouldn't my solution—duplication—work for him as it did for me? Anything is better than suicide. The time I needed of him was to make another dummy, one to stay with my wife and children and go to my job while this dummy (the true dummy, I must now call him) eloped with Miss Love.

We agree to conclude our conference a little later that day. I borrow some money from him to go to a Turkish bath and get cleaned up, to get a haircut and shave at the barber's, and to buy myself a suit like the one he is wearing. On his suggestion, we are to meet for lunch at a small restaurant in Greenwich Village, where it is impossible that he should meet anyone who might recognize him. I'm not sure what he is afraid of. Of having lunch alone, and being seen talking to himself? Of being seen with me? But I am perfectly presentable now. And if we are seen as two, what could be more normal than a pair of identical adult male twins, dressed alike, having lunch together, and engaged in earnest conversation? The lunch takes place. We both order spaghetti *al*

burro and baked clams. After three drinks, he comes round to my point of view. In consideration of my wife's feelings, he says—not mine, he insists several times in a rather harsh tone of voice—he will wait. But only a few months, no more. I point out that in this interim I will not ask that he not sleep with Miss Love, but only that he be discreet in his adultery.

Making the second dummy was a little harder than making the first. My entire savings were wiped out. Prices of humanoid plastic and the other materials, the fees of the engineer and the artist, had all gone up within just a year's time. The dummy's salary, I might add, hadn't gone up at all, despite the evidence of the boss's increased appreciation of the dummy's value to the firm. The dummy is annoyed that I insist that he, rather than I, sit for the artist when the facial features are being molded and painted. But I point out to him that if the second dummy is drawn from me again, there is a chance it would be a somewhat faded or blurred copy. Undoubtedly, there are some disparities between the appearance of the first dummy and my own, even though I cannot detect them. I want the second dummy to be like him, wherever there is the slightest difference between him and me. I shall just have to take the risk that the second dummy might also reproduce the unforeseen human passion that robbed the first dummy of his value to me.

Finally, the second dummy is ready. Also on my insistence, and very reluctantly since he wanted to have all his spare time to spend with Miss Love, the first dummy takes charge of his training and indoctrination period, lasting several weeks. Then the great day ar-

rives. The second dummy is installed in the first dummy's life in the midst of a Saturday afternoon baseball game, during the seventh inning stretch. It has been arranged that the first dummy will go out to buy hot dogs and Cokes for my wife and children. It is the first dummy who goes out, the second who returns laden with the food and drinks. The first dummy then leaps into a cab, and races off to the waiting arms of Miss Love.

That was nine years ago. The second dummy is living with my wife in no more exalted or more depressed a fashion than I had managed with her. The oldest girl is in college, the second in high school; and there is a new child, a boy, now six years old. They have moved to a new co-op apartment in Forest Hills; my wife has quit her job; and the second dummy is assistant vice-president of the firm. The first dummy went back to college nights while working as a waiter during the day; Miss Love also went back to college and got her teacher's license. He is now an architect with a growing practice; she teaches English at Julia Richmond High School. They have two children, a boy and a girl, and are remarkably happy. From time to time, I visit both my dummies. Never without sprucing myself up first, you understand. I consider myself a relative, and the godfather, sometimes the uncle, of all their children. I notice neither are ever too happy to see me, perhaps because of my shabby appearance, but they haven't the courage to turn me out. I never stay long, but I wish them well, and congratulate myself for having solved the problems of this one poor short life that is allotted me in so equitable and responsible a manner.

Camp Cataract

by Jane Bowles

Beryl knocked on Harriet's door and was given permission to enter. She found her friend seated near the window, an open letter in her hand.

"Good evening, Beryl," said Harriet. "I was just reading a letter from my sister." Her fragile, spinsterish face wore a canny yet slightly hysterical expression.

Beryl, a stocky blond waitress with stubborn eyes, had developed a dogged attachment to Harriet and sat in her cabin whenever she had a moment to spare. She rarely spoke in Harriet's presence, nor was she an attentive listener.

"I'll read you what she says; have a seat." Harriet indicated a straight chair and Beryl dragged it into a dark corner where she sat down. It creaked dangerously under the weight of her husky body.

"Hope I don't bust the chair," said Beryl, and she blushed furiously, digging her hands deep into the pockets of the checked knickers she habitually wore when she was not on duty.

" 'Dear Sister,' " Harriet read. " 'You are still at Camp Cataract

visiting the falls and enjoying them. I always want you to have a good time. This is your fifth week away. I suppose you go on standing behind the falls with much enjoyment like you told me all the guests did. I think you said only the people who don't stay overnight have to pay to stand behind the waterfall . . . you stay ten weeks . . . have a nice time, dear. Here everything is exactly the same as when you left. The apartment doesn't change. I have something I want to tell you, but first let me say that if you get nervous, why don't you come home instead of waiting until you are no good for the train trip? Such a thing could happen. I wonder of course how you feel about the apartment once you are by the waterfall.

Also, I want to put this to you. Knowing that you have an apartment and a loving family must make Camp Cataract quite a different place than it would be if it were all the home and loving you had. There must be wretches like that up there. If you see them, be sure to give them loving because they are the lost souls of the earth. I fear nomads. I am afraid of them and afraid for them too. I don't know what I would do if any of my dear ones were seized with the wanderlust. We are meant to cherish those who through God's will are given into our hands. First of all come the members of the family, and for this it is better to live as close as possible. Maybe you would say, "Sadie is old-fashioned; she doesn't want people to live on their own." I am not old-fashioned, but I don't want any of us to turn into nomads. You don't grow rich in spirit by widening your circle but by tending your own. When you are gone, I get afraid about you. I think that you might be seized with the wanderlust and that you are not remembering the apartment very much.

Particularly this trip . . . but then I know this cannot be true and that only my nerves make me think such things. It's so hot out. This is a record-breaking summer. Remember, the apartment is not just a row of rooms. It is the material proof that our spirits are so wedded that we have but one blessed roof over our heads. There are only three of us in the apartment related by blood, but Bert Hoffer has joined the three through the normal channels of marriage, also sacred. I know that you feel this way too about it and that just nerves makes me think Camp Cataract can change anything. May I remind you also that if this family is a garland, you are the middle flower; for me you are anyway. Maybe Evy's love is now flowing more to Bert Hoffer because he's her husband, which is natural. I wish they didn't think you needed to go to Camp Cataract because of your spells. Haven't I always tended you when you had them? Bert's always taken Evy to the Hoffers and we've stayed together, just the two of us, with the door safely locked so you wouldn't in your excitement run to a neighbor's house at all hours of the morning. Evy liked going to the Hoffers because they always gave her chicken with dumplings or else goose with red cabbage. I hope you haven't got it in your head that just because you are an old maid you have to go somewhere and be by yourself. Remember, I am also an old maid. I must close now, but I am not satisfied with my letter because I have so much more to say. I know you love the apartment and feel the way I feel. You are simply getting a tourist's thrill out of being there in a cabin like all of us do. I count the days until your sweet return. Your loving sister, Sadie.' "

Harriet folded the letter. "Sister Sadie," she said to Beryl, "is a great lover of security."

"She sounds swell," said Beryl, as if Harriet were mentioning her for the first time, which was certainly not the case.

"I have no regard for it whatsoever," Harriet announced in a positive voice. *"None.* In fact, I am a great admirer of the nomad, vagabonds, gypsies, seafaring men. I tip my hat to them; the old prophets roamed the world for that matter too, and most of the visionaries." She folded her hands in her lap with an air of satisfaction. Then, clearing her throat as if for a public address, she continued. "I don't give a tinker's damn about feeling part of a community, I can assure you. . . . That's not why I stay on at the apartment . . . not for a minute, but it's a good reason why she does . . . I mean Sadie; she loves a community spirit and she loves us all to be in the apartment because the apartment is in the community. She can get an actual thrill out of knowing that. But of course I can't . . . I never could, never in a thousand years."

She tilted her head back and half closed her eyes. In the true style of a person given to interminable monologues, she was barely conscious of her audience. "Now," she said, "we can come to whether I, on the other hand, get a thrill out of Camp Cataract." She paused for a moment as if to consider this. "Actually, I don't," she pronounced sententiously, "but if you like, I will clarify my statement by calling Camp Cataract my *tree house.* You remember tree houses from your younger days. . . . You climb into them when you're a child and plan to run away from home once you are safely hidden among the leaves. They're popular with children. Suppose I tell you point-blank that I'm an extremely original woman, but also a very shallow one . . . in a sense, a *very* shallow one. I am afraid of scandal." Harriet assumed a more erect position. "I despise anything that smacks of a bohemian dash for freedom; I know that this has nothing to do with the more serious things in life . . . I'm sure there are hundreds of serious people who kick over their traces and jump into the gutter; but I'm too shallow for anything like that . . . I know it and I enjoy knowing it. Sadie on the other hand cooks and cleans all day long and yet takes her life as seriously as she would a religion . . . myself and the apartment and the Hoffers. By the Hoffers, I mean my sister Evy and her big pig of a husband Bert." She made a wry face. "I'm the only one with taste in the family but I've never even suggested a lamp for the apartment. I wouldn't lower myself by becoming involved. I do however refuse to make an unseemly dash for freedom. I refuse to be known as 'Sadie's wild sister Harriet.' There is something intensely repulsive to me about unmarried women setting out on their own . . . also a very shallow attitude. You may wonder how a woman can be shallow and know it at the same time, but then, this is precisely the tragedy of any person, if he allows himself to be griped." She paused for a moment and looked into the darkness with a fierce light in her eyes. "Now let's get back to Camp Cataract," she said with renewed vigor. "The pine groves, the canoes, the sparkling purity of the brook water and cascade . . . the cabins . . . the marshmallows, the respectable clientele."

"Did you ever think of working in a garage?" Beryl suddenly blurted out, and then she blushed again at the sound of her own voice.

"No," Harriet answered sharply. "Why should I?"

Beryl shifted her position in her chair. "Well," she said, "I think I'd like that kind of work better than waiting on tables. Especially if I could be boss and own my garage. It's hard, though, for a woman."

Harriet stared at her in silence. "Do you think Camp Cataract smacks of the gutter?" she asked a minute later.

"No, sir. . . ." Beryl shook her head with a woeful air.

"Well then, there you have it. It is, of course, the farthest point from the gutter that one could reach. Any blockhead can see that. My plan is extremely complicated and from my point of view rather brilliant. First I will come here for several years . . . I don't know yet exactly how many, but long enough to imitate roots . . . I mean to imitate the natural family roots of childhood . . . long enough so that I myself will feel: 'Camp Cataract is *habit*, Camp Cataract is life, Camp Cataract is not escape.' Escape is unladylike, habit isn't. As I remove myself gradually from within my family circle and establish myself more and more solidly into Camp Cataract, then from here at some later date I can start making my sallies into the outside world almost unnoticed. None of it will seem to the onlooker like an ugly impetuous escape. I intend to rent the same cabin every year and to stay a little longer each time. Meanwhile I'm learning a great deal about trees and flowers and bushes . . . I am interested in nature." She was quiet for a moment. "It's rather lucky too," she added, "that the doctor has approved of my separating from the family for several months out of every year. He's a blockhead and doesn't remotely suspect the extent of my scheme nor how perfectly he fits into it . . . in fact, he has even sanctioned my request that no one visit me here at the camp. I'm afraid if Sadie did, and she's the only one who would dream of it, I wouldn't be able to avoid a wrangle and then I might have a fit. The fits are unpleasant; I get much more nervous than I usually am and there's a blank moment or two." Harriet glanced sideways at Beryl to see how she was reacting to this last bit of information, but Beryl's face was impassive.

"So you see my plan," she went on, in a relaxed, offhand manner; "complicated, a bit dotty and completely original . . . but then, I *am* original . . . not like my sisters . . . oddly enough I don't even seem to belong socially to the same class as my sisters do. I am somehow"—she hesitated for a second—"more fashionable."

Harriet glanced out of the window. Night had fallen during the course of her monologue and she could see a light burning in the next cabin. "Do you think I'm a coward?" she asked Beryl.

The waitress was startled out of her torpor. Fortunately her brain registered Harriet's question as well. "No, sir," she answered. "If you were, you wouldn't go out paddling canoes solo, with all the scary shoots you run into up and down these rivers . . ."

Harriet twisted her body impatiently. She had a sudden and uncontrollable desire to be alone. "Good-by," she said rudely. "I'm not coming to supper."

Beryl rose from her chair. "I'll save something for you in case you get hungry after the dining room's closed. I'll be hanging around the lodge like I always am till bedtime." Harriet nodded and the waitress stepped out of the cabin, shutting the door carefully behind her so that it would not make any noise.

Harriet's sister Sadie was a dark woman with loose features and sad eyes. She was turning slightly too fat in her middle years and did not in any way resemble Harriet, who was only a few years her senior. Ever since she had written her last letter to Harriet about Camp Cataract and the nomads Sadie had suffered from a feeling of steadily mounting suspense—the suspense itself a curious mingling of apprehension and thrilling anticipation. Her appetite grew smaller each day and it was becoming increasingly difficult for her to accomplish her domestic tasks.

She was standing in the parlor gazing with blank eyes at her new furniture set—two enormous easy chairs with bulging arms and a sofa in the same style—when she said aloud: "I can talk to her better than I can put it in a letter." Her voice had been automatic and when she heard her own words a rush of unbounded joy flooded her heart. Thus she realized that she was going on a little journey to Camp Cataract. She often made important decisions this way, as if some prearranged plot were being suddenly revealed to her, a plot which had immediately to be concealed from the eyes of others, because for Sadie, if there was any problem implicit in making a decision, it lay, not in the difficulty of

choosing, but in the concealment of her choice. To her, secrecy was the real absolution from guilt, so automatically she protected all of her deepest feelings and compulsions from the eyes of Evy, Bert Hoffer and the other members of the family, although she had no interest in understanding or examining these herself.

The floor shook; recognizing Bert Hoffer's footsteps, she made a violent effort to control the flux of her blood so that the power of her emotion would not be reflected in her cheeks. A moment later her brother-in-law walked across the room and settled in one of the easy chairs. He sat frowning at her for quite a little while without uttering a word in greeting, but Sadie had long ago grown accustomed to his unfriendly manner; even in the beginning it had not upset her too much because she was such an obsessive that she was not very concerned with outside details.

"God-damned velours," he said finally. "It's the hottest stuff I ever sat on."

"Next summer we'll get covers," Sadie reassured him, "with a flower pattern if you like. What's your favorite flower?" she asked, just to make conversation and to distract him from looking at her face.

Bert Hoffer stared at her as if she'd quite taken leave of her senses. He was a fat man with a red face and wavy hair. Instead of answering this question, which he considered idiotic, he mopped his brow with his handkerchief.

"I'll fix you a canned pineapple salad for supper," she said to him with glowing eyes. "It will taste better than heavy meat on a night like this."

"If you're going to dish up pineapple salad for supper," Bert Hoffer answered with a dark scowl, "you can telephone some other guy to come and eat it. You'll find me over at Martie's Tavern eating meat and potatoes, if there's any messages to deliver."

"I thought because you were hot," said Sadie.

"I was talking about the velvet,

wasn't I? I didn't say anything about the meat."

He was a very trying man indeed, particularly in a small apartment, but Sadie never dwelled upon this fact at all. She was delighted to cook and clean for him and for her sister Evelyn so long as they consented to live under the same roof with her and Harriet.

Just then Evelyn walked briskly into the parlor. Like Sadie she was dark, but here the resemblance ceased, for she had a small and wiry build, with a flat chest, and her hair was as straight as an Indian's. She stared at her husband's shirt sleeves and at Sadie's apron with distaste. She was wearing a crisp summer dress with a very low neckline, an unfortunate selection for one as bony and fierce-looking as she.

"You both look ready for the dump heap, not for the dining room," she said to them. "Why do we bother to have a dining room . . . is it just a farce?"

"How was the office today?" Sadie asked her sister.

Evelyn looked at Sadie and narrowed her eyes in closer scrutiny. The muscles in her face tightened. There was a moment of dead silence, and Bert Hoffer, cocking a wary eye in his wife's direction, recognized the dangerous flush on her cheeks. Secretly he was pleased. He loved to look on when Evelyn blew up at Sadie, but he tried to conceal his enjoyment because he did not consider it a very masculine one.

"What's the matter with you?" Evelyn asked finally, drawing closer to Sadie. "There's something wrong besides your dirty apron."

Sadie colored slightly but said nothing.

"You look crazy," Evelyn yelled. "What's the matter with you? You look so crazy I'd be almost afraid to ask you to go to the store for something. Tell me what's happened!" Evelyn was very excitable; nonetheless hers was a strong and sane nature.

"I'm not crazy," Sadie mumbled. "I'll go get the dinner." She pushed slowly past Evelyn and

with her heavy step she left the parlor.

The mahogany dining table was much too wide for the small oblong-shaped room, clearing the walls comfortably only at the two ends. When many guests were present some were seated first on one side of the room and were then obliged to draw the table toward themselves, until its edge pressed painfully into their diaphragms, before the remaining guests could slide into their seats on the opposite side.

Sadie served the food, but only Bert Hoffer ate with any appetite. Evelyn jabbed at her meat once or twice, tasted it, and dropped her fork, which fell with a clatter onto her plate.

Had the food been more savory she might not have pursued her attack on Sadie until later, or very likely she would have forgotten it altogether. Unfortunately, however, Sadie, although she insisted on fulfilling the role of housewife, and never allowed the others to acquit themselves of even the smallest domestic task, was a poor cook and a careless cleaner as well. Her lumpy gravies were tasteless, and she had once or twice boiled a good cut of steak out of indifference. She was lavish, too, in spite of being indifferent, and kept her cupboards so loaded with food that a certain quantity spoiled each week and there was often an unpleasant odor about the house. Harriet, in fact, was totally unaware of Sadie's true nature and had fallen into the trap her sister had instinctively prepared for her, because beyond wearing an apron and simulating the airs of other housewives, Sadie did not possess a community spirit at all, as Harriet had stated to Beryl the waitress. Sadie certainly yearned to live in the grown-up world that her parents had established for them when they were children, but in spite of the fact that she had wanted to live in that world with Harriet, and because of Harriet, she did not understand it properly. It remained mysterious to her even though she did all the housekeeping and managed the apart-

ment entirely alone. She couldn't ever admit to herself that she lived in constant fear that Harriet would go away, but she brooded a great deal on outside dangers, and had she tried, she could not have remembered a time when this fear had not been her strongest emotion.

Sometimes an ecstatic and voracious look would come into her eyes, as if she would devour her very existence because she loved it so much. Such passionate moments of appreciation were perhaps her only reward for living a life which she knew in her heart was one of perpetual narrow escape. Although Sadie was neither sly nor tricky, but on the contrary profoundly sincere and ingenuous, she schemed unconsciously to keep the Hoffers in the apartment with them, because she did not want to reveal the true singleness of her interest either to Harriet or to herself. She sensed as well that Harriet would find it more difficult to break away from all three of them (because as a group they suggested a little society, which impressed her sister) than she would to escape from her alone. In spite of her mortal dread that Harriet might strike out on her own, she had never brooded on the possibility of her sister's marrying. Here, too, her instinct was correct: she knew that she was safe and referred often to the "normal channels of marriage," conscious all the while that such an intimate relationship with a man would be as uninteresting to Harriet as it would to herself.

From a financial point of view this communal living worked out more than satisfactorily. Each sister had inherited some real estate which yielded her a small monthly stipend; these stipends, combined with the extra money that the Hoffers contributed out of their salaries, covered their common living expenses. In return for the extra sum the Hoffers gave toward the household expenses Sadie contributed her work, thus saving them the money they would have spent hiring a servant, had they lived alone. A fourth sister, whose marriage had proved financially more successful than Evy's, contributed generously toward Harriet's support at Camp Cataract, since Harriet's stipend certainly did not yield enough to cover her share of their living expenses at the apartment and pay for a long vacation as well.

Neither Sadie nor Bert Hoffer had looked up when Evy's fork clattered onto her plate. Sadie was truly absorbed in her own thoughts, whereas Bert Hoffer was merely pretending to be, while secretly he rejoiced at the unmistakable signal that his wife was about to blow up.

"When I find out why Sadie looks like that if she isn't going to be crazy, then I'll eat," Evelyn announced flatly, and she folded her arms across her chest.

"I'm not crazy," Sadie said indistinctly, glancing toward Bert Hoffer, not in order to enlist his sympathies, but to avoid her younger sister's sharp scrutiny.

"There's a big danger of your going crazy because of Grandma and Harriet," said Evelyn crossly. "That's why I get so nervous the minute you look a little out of the way, like you do tonight. It's not that you get Harriet's expression . . . but then you might be getting a different kind of craziness . . . maybe worse. She's all right if she can go away and there's not too much excitement . . . it's only in spells anyway. But you—you might get a worse kind. Maybe it would be steadier."

"I'm not going to be crazy," Sadie murmured apologetically.

Evelyn glowered in silence and picked up her fork, but then immediately she let it fall again and turned on her sister with renewed exasperation. "Why don't you ask me why *I'm* not going to be crazy?" she demanded. "Harriet's my sister and Grandma's my grandma just as much as she is yours, isn't she?"

Sadie's eyes had a faraway look.

"If you were normal," Evelyn pursued, "you'd give me an intelligent argument instead of not paying any attention. Do you agree, Hoffer?"

"Yes, I do," he answered soberly.

Evelyn stiffened her back. "I'm too much like everybody else to be crazy," she announced with pride. "At a picture show, I feel like the norm."

The technical difficulty of disappearing without announcing her plan to Evelyn suddenly occurred to Sadie, who glanced up quite by accident at her sister. She knew, of course, that Harriet was supposed to avoid contact with her family during these vacation months, at the doctor's request and even at Harriet's own; but like some herd animal, who though threatened with the stick continues grazing, Sadie pursued her thoughts imperturbably. She did not really believe in Harriet's craziness nor in the necessity of her visits to Camp Cataract, but she was never in conscious opposition to the opinions of her sisters. Her attitude was rather like that of a child who is bored by the tedium of grown-up problems and listens to them with a vacant ear. As usual she was passionately concerned only with successfully dissimulating what she really felt, and had she been forced to admit openly that there existed such a remarkable split between her own opinions and those of her sisters, she would have suffered unbelievable torment. She was able to live among them, listening to their conferences with her dead outside ear (the more affluent sister was also present at these sessions, and her husband as well), and even to contribute a pittance toward Harriet's support at the camp, without questioning either the validity of their decisions or of her own totally divergent attitude. By a self-imposed taboo, awareness of this split was denied her, and she had never reflected upon it.

Harriet had gone to Camp Cataract for the first time a year ago, after a bad attack of nerves combined with a return of her pleurisy. It had been suggested by the doctor himself that she go with his own wife and child instead of traveling with one of her sisters. Harriet had been delighted with the suggestion and Sadie had accepted it without a murmur. It was never her habit to argue, and in fact she had thought nothing of Harriet's leaving at the time. It was only gradually that she had begun writing the letters to Harriet about Camp Cataract, the nomads and the wanderlust—for she had written others similar to her latest one, but never so eloquent or full of conviction. Previous letters had contained a hint or two here and there, but had been for the main part factual reports about her summer life in the apartment. Since writing this last letter she had not been able to forget her own wonderful and solemn words (for she was rarely eloquent), and even now at the dinner table they rose continually in her throat so that she was thrilled over and over again and could not bother her head about announcing her departure to Evelyn. "It will be easier to write a note," she said to herself. "I'll pack my valise and walk out tomorrow afternoon, while they're at business. They can get their own dinners for a few days. Maybe I'll leave a great big meat loaf." Her eyes were shining like stars.

"Take my plate and put it in the warmer, Hoffer," Evelyn was saying, "I won't eat another mouthful until Sadie tells us what we can expect. If she feels she's going off, she can at least warn us about it. I deserve to know how she feels . . . I tell every single thing I feel to her and Harriet . . . I don't sneak around the house like a thief. In the first place I don't have any time for sneaking, I'm at the office all day! Is this the latest vogue, this sneaking around and hiding everything you can from your sister? Is it?" She stared at Bert Hoffer, widening her eyes in fake astonishment. He shrugged his shoulders.

"I'm no sneak or hypocrite and neither are you, Hoffer, you're no hypocrite. You're just sore at the world, but you don't pretend you love the world, do you?"

Sadie was lightheaded with embarrassment. She had blanched at Evy's allusion to her going, which she mistook naturally for a reference to her intention of leaving for Camp Cataract.

"Only for a few days . . ." she mumbled in confusion, "and then I'll be right back here at the table."

Evelyn looked at her in consternation. "What do you mean by announcing calmly how many days it's going to be?" she shouted at her sister. "That's really sacrilegious! Did you ever hear of such a crusty sacrilegious remark in your life before?" She turned to Bert Hoffer, with a horror-stricken expression on her face. "How can I go to the office and look neat and clean and happy when this is what I hear at home . . . when my sister sits here and says she'll only go crazy for a few days? How *can* I go to the office after that? How can I look right?"

"I'm not going to be crazy," Sadie assured her again in a sorrowful tone, because although she felt relieved that Evelyn had not, after all, guessed the truth, hers was not a nature to indulge itself in trivial glee at having put someone off her track.

"You just said you were going to be crazy," Evelyn exclaimed heatedly. "Didn't she, Bert?"

"Yes," he answered, "she did say something like that . . ."

The tendons of Evelyn's neck were stretched tight as she darted her eyes from her sister's face to her husband's. "Now, tell me this much," she demanded, "do I go to the office every day looking neat and clean or do I go looking like a bum?"

"You look O.K.," Bert said.

"Then why do my sisters spit in my eye? Why do they hide everything from me if I'm so decent? I'm wide open, I'm frank, there's nothing on my mind besides what I say. Why can't they be like other sisters all over the world? One of them is so crazy that she must live in a cabin for her nerves at *my* expense, and the other one is planning to go crazy deliberately and

behind my back." She commenced to struggle out of her chair, which as usual proved to be a slow and laborious task. Exasperated, she shoved the table vehemently away from her toward the opposite wall. "Why don't we leave the space all on one side when there's no company?" she screamed at both of them, for she was now annoyed with Bert Hoffer as well as with Sadie. Fortunately they were seated at either end of the table and so did not suffer as a result of her violent gesture, but the table jammed into four chairs ranged on the opposite side, pinning three of them backward against the wall and knocking the fourth onto the floor.

"Leave it there," Evelyn shouted dramatically above the racket. "Leave it there till doomsday," and she rushed headlong out of the room.

They listened to her gallop down the hall.

"What about the dessert?" Bert Hoffer asked Sadie with a frown. He was displeased because Evelyn had spoken to him sharply.

"Leftover bread pudding without raisins." She had just gotten up to fetch the pudding when Evelyn summoned them from the parlor.

"Come in here, both of you," she hollered, "I have something to say."

They found Evelyn seated on the couch, her head tilted 'way back on a cushion, staring fixedly at the ceiling. They settled into easy chairs opposite her.

"I could be normal and light in any other family," she said, "I'm normally a gay light girl . . . not a morose one. I like all the material things."

"What do you want to do tonight?" Bert Hoffer interrupted, speaking with authority. "Do you want to be excited or do you want to go to the movies?" He was always bored by these self-appraising monologues which succeeded her explosions.

Evy looked as though she had not heard him, but after a moment or two of sitting with her

eyes shut she got up and walked briskly out of the room; her husband followed her.

Neither of them had said good-by to Sadie, who went over to the window as soon as they'd gone and looked down on the huge unsightly square below her. It was crisscrossed by trolley tracks going in every possible direction. Five pharmacies and seven cigar stores were visible from where she stood. She knew that modern industrial cities were considered ugly, but she liked them. "I'm glad Evy and Bert have gone to a picture show," Sadie remarked to herself after a while. "Evy gets high-strung from being at the office all day."

A little later she turned her back on the window and went to the dining room.

"Looks like the train went through here," she murmured, gazing quietly at the chairs tilted back against the wall and the table's unsightly angle; but the tumult in her breast had not subsided, even though she knew she was leaving for Camp Cataract. Beyond the first rush of joy she had experienced when her plan had revealed itself to her earlier, in the parlor, the feeling of suspense remained identical, a curious admixture of anxiety and anticipation, difficult to bear. Concerning the mechanics of the trip itself she was neither nervous nor foolishly excited. "I'll call up tomorrow," she said to herself, "and find out when the buses go, or maybe I'll take the train. In the morning I'll buy three different meats for the loaf, if I don't forget. It won't go rotten for a few days, and even if it does they can eat at Martie's or else Evy will make bologna and eggs . . . she knows how, and so does Bert." She was not really concentrating on these latter projects any more than she usually did on domestic details.

The lamp over the table was suspended on a heavy iron chain. She reached for the beaded string to extinguish the light. When she released it the massive lamp swung from side to side in the darkness.

"Would you like it so much by

the waterfall if you didn't know the apartment was here?" she whispered into the dark, and she was thrilled again by the beauty of her own words. "How much more I'll be able to say when I'm sitting right next to her," she murmured almost with reverence. ". . . And then we'll come back here," she added simply, not in the least startled to discover that the idea of returning with Harriet had been at the root of her plan all along.

Without bothering to clear the plates from the table, she went into the kitchen and extinguished the light there. She was suddenly overcome with fatigue.

When Sadie arrived at Camp Cataract it was raining hard.

"This shingled building is the main lodge," the hack driver said to her. "The ceiling in there is three times higher than average, if you like that style. Go up on the porch and just walk in. You'll get a kick out of it."

Sadie reached into her pocketbook for some money.

"My wife and I come here to drink beer when we're in the mood," he continued, getting out his change. "If there's nobody much inside, don't get panicky; the whole camp goes to the movies on Thursday nights. The wagon takes them and brings them back. They'll be along soon."

After thanking him she got out of the cab and climbed the wooden steps onto the porch. Without hesitating she opened the door. The driver had not exaggerated, the room was indeed so enormous that it suggested a gymnasium. Wicker chairs and settees were scattered from one end of the floor to the other and numberless sawed-off tree stumps had been set down to serve as little tables.

Sadie glanced around her and then headed automatically for a giant fireplace, difficult to reach because of the accumulation of chairs and settees that surrounded it. She threaded her way between these and stepped across the hearth into the cold vault of the chimney, high enough to shelter a person of average stature. The andirons, which reached to her waist,

had been wrought in the shape of witches. She fingered their pointed iron hats. "Novelties," she murmured to herself without enthusiasm. "They must have been especially made." Then, peering out of the fireplace, she noticed for the first time that she was not alone. Some fifty feet away a fat woman sat reading by the light of an electric bulb.

"She doesn't even know I'm in the fireplace," she said to herself. "Because the rain's so loud, she probably didn't hear me come in." She waited patiently for a while and then, suspecting that the woman might remain oblivious to her presence indefinitely, she called over to her. "Do you have anything to do with managing Camp Cataract?" she asked, speaking loudly so that she could be heard above the rain.

The woman ceased reading and switched her big light off at once, since the strong glare prevented her seeing beyond the radius of the bulb.

"No, I don't," she answered in a booming voice. "Why?"

Sadie, finding no answer to this question, remained silent.

"Do you think I look like a manager?" the woman pursued, and since Sadie had obviously no intention of answering, she continued the conversation by herself.

"I suppose you might think I was manager here, because I'm stout, and stout people have that look; also I'm about the right age for it. But I'm not the manager . . . I don't manage anything, anywhere. I have a domineering cranium all right, but I'm more the French type. I'd rather enjoy myself than give orders."

"French . . ." Sadie repeated hesitantly.

"Not French," the woman corrected her, "French *type*, with a little of the actual blood." Her voice was cold and severe.

For a while neither of them spoke, and Sadie hoped the conversation had drawn to a definite close.

"Individuality is my god," the woman announced abruptly, much to Sadie's disappointment.

"That's partly why I didn't go to the picture show tonight. I don't like doing what the groups do, and I've seen the film." She dragged her chair forward so as to be heard more clearly. "The steadies here—we call the ones who stay more than a fortnight steadies—are all crazy to get into birds-of-a-feather-flock-together arrangements. If you look around, you can see for yourself how clubby the furniture is fixed. Well, they can go in for it, if they want, but I won't. I keep my chair out in the open here, and when I feel like it I take myself over to one circle or another . . . there's about ten or twelve circles. Don't you object to the confinement of a group?"

"We haven't got a group back home," Sadie answered briefly.

"I don't go in for group worship either," the woman continued, "any more than I do for the heavy social mixing. I don't even go in for individual worship, for that matter. Most likely I was born to such a vigorous happy nature I don't feel the need to worry about what's up there over my head. I get the full flavor out of all my days whether anyone's up there or not. The groups don't allow for that kind of zip . . . never. You know what rotten apples in a barrel can do to the healthy ones."

Sadie, who had never before met an agnostic, was profoundly shocked by the woman's blasphemous attitude. "I'll bet she slept with a lot of men she wasn't married to when she was younger," she said to herself.

"Most of the humanity you bump into is unhealthy and nervous," the woman concluded, looking at Sadie with a cold eye, and then without further remarks she struggled out of her chair and began to walk toward a side door at the other end of the room. Just as she approached it the door was flung open from the other side by Beryl, whom the woman immediately warned of the new arrival. Beryl, without ceasing to spoon some beans out of a can she was holding, walked over to Sadie and offered to be of some assistance. "I can show you rooms," she suggested. "Unless you'd rather wait till the manager comes back from the movies."

When she realized, however, after a short conversation with Sadie, that she was speaking to Harriet's sister, a malevolent scowl darkened her countenance, and she spooned her beans more slowly.

"Harriet didn't tell me you were coming," she said at length; her tone was unmistakably disagreeable.

Sadie's heart commenced to beat very fast as she in turn realized that this woman in knickers was the waitress, Beryl, of whom Harriet had often spoken in her letters and at home.

"It's a surprise," Sadie told her. "I meant to come here before. I've been promising Harriet I'd visit her in camp for a long time now, but I couldn't come until I got a neighbor in to cook for Evy and Bert. They're a husband and wife . . . my sister Evy and her husband Bert."

"I know about those two," Beryl remarked sullenly. "Harriet's told me all about them."

"Will you please take me to my sister's cabin?" Sadie asked, picking up her valise and stepping forward.

Beryl continued to stir her beans around without moving.

"I thought you folks had some kind of arrangement," she said. She had recorded in her mind entire passages of Harriet's monologues out of love for her friend, although she felt no curiosity concerning the material she had gathered. "I thought you folks were supposed to stay in the apartment while she was away at camp."

"Bert Hoffer and Evy have never visited Camp Cataract," Sadie answered in a tone that was innocent of any subterfuge.

"You bet they haven't," Beryl pronounced triumphantly. "That's part of the arrangement. They're supposed to stay in the apartment while she's here at camp; the doctor said so."

"They're not coming up," Sadie repeated, and she still wore, not the foxy look that Beryl expected

would betray itself at any moment, but the look of a person who is attentive though being addressed in a foreign language. The waitress sensed that all her attempts at starting a scrap had been successfully blocked for the present and she whistled carefully, dragging some chairs into line with a rough hand. "I'll tell you what," she said, ceasing her activities as suddenly as she had begun them. "Instead of taking you down there to the Pine Cones—that's the name of the grove where her cabin is—I'll go myself and tell her to come up here to the lodge. She's got some nifty rain equipment so she won't get wet coming through the groves like you would . . . lots of pine trees out there."

Sadie nodded in silence and walked over to a fantasy chair where she sat down.

"They get a lot of fun out of that chair. When they're drunk," said Beryl, pointing to its back, made of a giant straw disc. "Well . . . so long. . . ." She strode away. "Dear Valley . . ." Sadie heard her sing as she went out the door.

Sadie lifted the top off the chair's left arm and pulled two books out of its woven hamper. The larger volume was entitled, *The Growth and Development of the Texas Oil Companies,* and the smaller, *Stories from Other Climes.* Hastily she replaced them and closed the lid.

Harriet opened the door for Beryl and quickly shut it again, but even in that instant the wooden flooring of the threshold was thoroughly soaked with rain. She was wearing a lavender kimono with a deep ruffle at the neckline; above it her face shone pale with dismay at Beryl's late and unexpected visit. She feared that perhaps the waitress was drunk. "I'm certainly not hacking out a free place for myself in this world just in order to cope with drunks," she said to herself with bitter verve. Her loose hair was hanging to her shoulders and Beryl looked at it for a moment in mute admiration before making her announcement.

"Your sister Sadie's up at the lodge," she said, recovering herself; then, feeling embarrassed, she shuffled over to her usual seat in the darkest corner of the room.

"What are you saying?" Harriet questioned her sharply.

"Your sister Sadie's up at the lodge," she repeated, not daring to look at her. "Your sister Sadie who wrote you the letter about the apartment."

"But she can't be!" Harriet screeched. "She can't be! It was all arranged that no one was to visit me here."

"That's what I told her," Beryl put in.

Harriet began pacing up and down the floor. Her pupils were dilated and she looked as if she were about to lose all control of herself. Abruptly she flopped down on the edge of the bed and began gulping in great drafts of air. She was actually practicing a system which she believed had often saved her from complete hysteria, but Beryl, who knew nothing about her method, was horrified and utterly bewildered. "Take it easy," she implored Harriet. "Take it easy!"

"Dash some water in my face," said Harriet in a strange voice, but horror and astonishment anchored Beryl securely to her chair, so that Harriet was forced to stagger over to the basin and manage by herself. After five minutes of steady dousing she wiped her face and chest with a towel and resumed her pacing. At each instant the expression on her face was more indignant and a trifle less distraught. "It's the boorishness of it that I find so appalling," she complained, a suggestion of theatricality in her tone which a moment before had not been present. "If she's determined to wreck my schemes, why doesn't she do it with some style, a little slight bit of cunning? I can't picture anything more boorish than hauling oneself onto a train and simply chugging straight up here. She has no sense of scheming, of intrigue in the grand manner . . . none whatever. Anyone meeting only Sadie would think the family raised potatoes for a living. Evy doesn't make a much better impression, I must say. If they met her they'd decide we were all clerks! But at least she goes to business. . . . She doesn't sit around thinking about how to mess my life up all day. She thinks about Bert Hoffer. Ugh!" She made a wry face.

"When did you and Sadie start fighting?" Beryl asked her.

"I don't fight with Sadie," Harriet answered, lifting her head proudly. "I wouldn't dream of fighting like a common fishwife. Everything that goes on between us goes on undercover. It's always been that way. I've always hidden everything from her ever since I was a little girl. She's perfectly aware that I know she's trying to hold me a prisoner in the apartment out of plain jealousy and she knows too that I'm afraid of being considered a bum, and that makes matters simpler for her. She pretends to be worried that I might forget myself if I left the apartment and commit a folly with some man I wasn't married to, but actually she knows perfectly well that I'm as cold as ice. I haven't the slightest interest in men . . . nor in women either for that matter; still if I stormed out of the apartment dramatically the way some do, they might think I was a bum on my way to a man . . . and I won't give Sadie that satisfaction, ever. As for marriage, of course I admit I'm peculiar and there's a bit wrong with me, but even so I shouldn't want to marry: I think the whole system of going through life with a partner is repulsive in every way." She paused, but only for a second. "Don't you imagine, however," she added severely, looking directly at Beryl, "don't you imagine that just because I'm a bit peculiar and different from the others, that I'm not fussy about my life. I *am* fussy about it, and I *hate* a scandal."

"To hell with sisters!" Beryl exclaimed happily. "Give 'em all a good swift kick in the pants." She had regained her own composure watching the color return to Harriet's cheeks and she was just be-

ginning to think with pleasure that perhaps Sadie's arrival would serve to strengthen the bond of intimacy between herself and Harriet, when this latter buried her head in her lap and burst into tears. Beryl's face fell and she blushed at her own frivolousness.

"I can't any more," Harriet sobbed in anguished tones. "I can't . . . I'm old . . . I'm much too old." Here she collapsed and sobbed so pitifully that Beryl, wringing her hands in grief, sprang to her side, for she was a most tenderhearted person toward those whom she loved. "You are not old . . . you are beautiful," she said, blushing again, and in her heart she was thankful that Providence had granted her the occasion to console her friend in a grief-stricken moment, and to compliment her at the same time.

After a bit, Harriet's sobbing subsided, and, jumping up from the bed, she grabbed the waitress. "Beryl," she gasped, "you must run back to the lodge right away." There was a beam of cunning in her tear-filled eyes.

"Sure will," Beryl answered.

"Go back to the lodge and see if there's a room left up there, and if there is, take her grip into it so that there will be no question of her staying in my cabin. I can't have her staying in my cabin. It's the only place I have in the whole wide world." The beam of cunning disappeared again and she looked at Beryl with wide, frightened eyes. ". . . And if there's no room?" she asked.

"Then I'll put her in my place," Beryl reassured her. "I've got a neat little cabin all to myself that she can have and I'll go bunk in with some dopy waitress."

"Well, then," said Harriet, "go, and hurry! Take her grip to a room in the upper lodge annex or to your own cabin before she has a chance to say anything, and then come straight back here for me. I can't get through these pine groves alone . . . now . . . I know I can't." It did not occur to her to thank Beryl for the kind offer she had made.

"All right," said the waitress, "I'll be back in a jiffy and don't you worry about a thing." A second later she was lumbering through the drenched pine groves with shining eyes.

When Beryl came into the lodge and snatched Sadie's grip up without a word of explanation, Sadie did not protest. Opposite her there was an open staircase which led to a narrow gallery hanging halfway between the ceiling and the floor. She watched the waitress climbing the stairs, but once she had passed the landing Sadie did not trouble to look up and follow her progress around the wooden balcony overhead.

A deep chill had settled into her bones and she was like a person benumbed. Exactly when this present state had succeeded the earlier one Sadie could not tell, nor did she think to ask herself such a question; but a feeling of dread now lay like a stone in her breast where before there had been stirring such powerful sensations of excitement and suspense. "I'm so low," she said to herself, "I feel like I was sitting at my own funeral." She did not say this in the spirit of hyperbolic gloom which some people nurture to work themselves out of a bad mood, but in all seriousness and with her customary attitude of passivity; in fact, she wore the humble look so often visible on the faces of sufferers who are being treated in a free clinic. It did not occur to her that a connection might exist between her present dismal state and the mission she had come to fulfill at Camp Cataract, nor did she take any notice of the fact that the words which were to enchant Harriet and accomplish her return were no longer welling up in her throat as they had done all the past week. She feared that something dreadful might happen, but whatever it was, this disaster was as remotely connected with her as a possible train wreck. "I hope nothing bad happens . . ." she thought, but she didn't have much hope in her.

Harriet slammed the front door and Sadie looked up. For the first second or two she did not recognize the woman who stood on the threshold in her dripping rubber coat and hood. Beryl was beside her; puddles were forming around the feet of the two women. Harriet had rouged her cheeks rather more highly than usual in order to hide all traces of her crying spell. Her eyes were bright and she wore a smile that was fixed and hard.

"Not a night fit for man or beast," she shouted across to Sadie, using a voice that she thought sounded hearty and yet fashionable at the same time; she did this, not in order to impress her sister, but to keep her at a safe distance.

Sadie, instead of rushing to the door, stared at her with an air of perplexity. To her Harriet appeared more robust and coarse-featured than she had five weeks ago at the apartment, and yet she knew that such a rapid change of physiognomy was scarcely possible. Recovering, she rose and went to embrace her sister. The embrace failed to reassure her because of Harriet's wet rubber coat, and her feeling of estrangement became more defined. She backed away.

Upon hearing her own voice ring out in such hearty and fashionable tones, Harriet had felt crazily confident that she might, by continuing to affect this manner, hold her sister at bay for the duration of her visit. To increase her chances of success she had determined right then not to ask Sadie why she had come, but to treat the visit in the most casual and natural way possible.

"Have you put on fat?" Sadie asked, at a loss for anything else to say.

"I'll never be fat," Harriet replied quickly, "I'm a fruit lover, not a lover of starches."

"Yes, you love fruit," Sadie said nervously. "Do you want some? I have an apple left from my lunch."

Harriet looked aghast. "Now!" she exclaimed. "Beryl can tell you that I never eat at night; in fact I never come up to the lodge at night, *never*. I stay in my cabin. I've written you all about how

early I get up . . . I don't know anything about the lodge at night," she added almost angrily, as though her sister had accused her of being festive.

"You don't?" Sadie looked at her stupidly.

"No, I don't. Are you hungry, by the way?"

"If she's hungry," put in Beryl, "we can go into the Grotto Room and I'll bring her the food there. The tables in the main dining room are all set up for tomorrow morning's breakfast."

"I despise the Grotto," said Harriet with surprising bitterness. Her voice was getting quite an edge to it, and although it still sounded fashionable it was no longer hearty.

"I'm not hungry," Sadie assured them both, "I'm sleepy."

"Well, then," Harriet replied quickly, jumping at the opportunity, "we'll sit here for a few minutes and then you must go to bed."

The three of them settled in wicker chairs close to the cold hearth. Sadie was seated opposite the other two, who both remained in their rubber coats.

"I really do despise the Grotto," Harriet went on; "actually I don't hang around the lodge at all. This is not the part of Camp Cataract that interests me. I'm interested in the pine groves, my cabin, the rocks, the streams, the bridge, and all the surrounding natural beauty . . . the sky also."

Although the rain still continued its drumming on the roof above them, to Sadie, Harriet's voice sounded intolerably loud, and she could not rid herself of the impression that her sister's face had grown fatter. "Now," she heard Harriet saying in her loud voice, "tell me about the apartment. . . . What's new, how are the dinners coming along, how are Evy and Bert?"

Fortunately, while Sadie was struggling to answer these questions, which unaccountably she found it difficult to do, the stout agnostic reappeared, and Harriet was immediately distracted.

"Rover," she called gaily across

the room, "come and sit with us. My sister Sadie's here."

The woman joined them, seating herself beside Beryl so that Sadie was now facing all three.

"It's a surprise to see you up at the lodge at night, Hermit," she remarked to Harriet without a spark of mischief in her voice.

"You see!" Harriet nodded at Sadie with immense satisfaction. "I was not fibbing, was I? How are Evy and Bert?" she asked again, her face twitching a bit. "Is the apartment hot?"

Sadie nodded.

"I don't know how long you plan to stay," Harriet rattled on, feeling increasingly powerful and therefore reckless, "but I'm going on a canoe trip the day after tomorrow for five days. We're going up the river to Pocahontas Falls. . . . I leave at four in the morning, too, which rather ruins tomorrow as well. I've been looking forward to this trip ever since last spring when I applied for my seat, back at the apartment. The canoes are limited, and the guides. . . . I'm devoted to canoe trips, as you know, and can fancy myself a redskin all the way to the Falls and back, easily."

Sadie did not answer.

"There's nothing weird about it," Harriet argued. "It's in keeping with my hatred of industrialization. In any case, you can see what a chopped-up day tomorrow's going to be. I have to make my pack in the morning and I must be in bed by eight-thirty at night, the latest, so that I can get up at four. I'll have only one real meal, at two in the afternoon. I suggest we meet at two behind the souvenir booth; you'll notice it tomorrow." Harriet waited expectantly for Sadie to answer in agreement to this suggestion, but her sister remained silent.

"Speaking of the booth," said Rover, "I'm not taking home a single souvenir this year. They're expensive and they don't last."

"You can buy salt-water taffy at Gerald's Store in town," Beryl told her. "I saw some there last week. It's a little stale but very cheap."

"Why would they sell salt-water

taffy in the mountains?" Rover asked irritably.

Sadie was half listening to the conversation; as she sat watching them, all three women were suddenly unrecognizable; it was as if she had flung open the door to some dentist's office and seen three strangers seated there. She sprang to her feet in terror.

Harriet was horrified. "What is it?" she yelled at her sister. "Why do you look like that? Are you mad?"

Sadie was pale and beads of sweat were forming under her felt hat, but the women opposite her had already regained their correct relation to herself and the present moment. Her face relaxed, and although her legs were trembling as a result of her brief but shocking experience, she felt immensely relieved that it was all over.

"Why did you jump up?" Harriet screeched at her. "Is it because you are at Camp Cataract and not at the apartment?"

"It must have been the long train trip and no food . . ." Sadie told herself, "only one sandwich."

"Is it because you are at Camp Cataract and not at the apartment?" Harriet insisted. She was really very frightened and wished to establish Sadie's fit as a purposeful one and not as an involuntary seizure similar to one of her own.

"It was a long and dirty train trip," Sadie said in a weary voice. "I had only one sandwich all day long, with no mustard or butter . . . just the processed meat. I didn't even eat my fruit."

"Beryl offered to serve you food in the Grotto!" Harriet ranted. "Do you want some now or not? For heaven's sake, speak up!"

"No . . . no." Sadie shook her head sorrowfully. "I think I'd best go to bed. Take me to your cabin. . . . I've got my slippers and my kimono and my nightgown in my satchel," she added, looking around her vaguely, for the fact that Beryl had carried her grip off had never really impressed itself upon her consciousness.

Harriet glanced at Beryl with an air of complicity and managed to give her a quick pinch. "Beryl's got you fixed up in one of the upper lodge annex rooms," she told Sadie in a false, chatterbox voice. "You'll be much more comfortable up here than you would be down in my cabin. We all use oil lamps in the grove and you know how dependent you are on electricity."

Sadie didn't know whether she was dependent on electricity or not since she had never really lived without it, but she was so tired that she said nothing.

"I get up terribly early and my cabin's drafty, besides," Harriet went on. "You'll be much more comfortable here. You'd hate the Boulder Dam wigwams as well. Anyway, the wigwams are really for boys and they're always full. There's a covered bridge leading from this building to the annex on the upper floor, so that's an advantage."

"O.K., folks," Beryl cut in, judging that she could best help Harriet by spurring them on to action. "Let's get going."

"Yes," Harriet agreed, "if we don't get out of the lodge soon the crowd will come back from the movies and we certainly want to avoid them."

They bade good night to Rover and started up the stairs.

"This balustrade is made of young birch limbs," Harriet told Sadie as they walked along the narrow gallery overhead. "I think it's very much in keeping with the lodge, don't you?"

"Yes, I do," Sadie answered.

Beryl opened the door leading from the balcony onto a covered bridge and stepped through it, motioning to the others. "Here we go onto the bridge," she said, looking over her shoulder. "You've never visited the annex, have you?" she asked Harriet.

"I've never had any reason to," Harriet answered in a huffy tone. "You know how I feel about my cabin."

They walked along the imperfectly fitted boards in the darkness. Gusts of wind blew about their ankles and they were constantly spattered with rain in spite of the wooden roofing. They reached the door at the other end very quickly, however, where they descended two steps leading into a short, brightly lit hall. Beryl closed the door to the bridge behind them. The smell of fresh plaster and cement thickened the damp air.

"This is the annex," said Beryl. "We put old ladies here mostly, because they can get back and forth to the dining room without going outdoors . . . and they've got the toilet right here, too." She flung open the door and showed it to them. "Then also," she added, "we don't like the old ladies dealing with oil lamps and here they've got electricity." She led them into a little room just at their left and switched on the light. "Pretty smart, isn't it?" she remarked, looking around her with evident satisfaction, as if she herself had designed the room; then, sauntering over to a modernistic wardrobe-bureau combination, she polished a corner of it with her pocket handkerchief. This piece was made of shiny brown wood and fitted with a rimless circular mirror. "Strong and good-looking," Beryl said, rapping on the wood with her knuckles. "Every room's got one."

Sadie sank down on the edge of the bed without removing her outer garments. Here, too, the smell of plaster and cement permeated the air, and the wind still blew about their ankles, this time from under the badly constructed doorsill.

"The cabins are much draftier than this," Harriet assured Sadie once again. "You'll be more comfortable here in the annex." She felt confident that establishing her sister in the annex would facilitate her plan, which was still to prevent her from saying whatever she had come to say.

Sadie was terribly tired. Her hat, dampened by the rain, pressed uncomfortably against her temples, but she did not attempt to remove it. "I think I've got to go to sleep," she muttered. "I can't stay awake any more."

"All right," said Harriet, "but don't forget tomorrow at two by the souvenir booth . . . you can't miss it. I don't want to see anyone in the morning because I can make my canoe pack better by myself . . . it's frightfully complicated. . . . But if I hurried I could meet you at one-thirty; would you prefer that?"

Sadie nodded.

"Then I'll do my best. . . . You see, in the morning I always practice imagination for an hour or two. It does me lots of good, but tomorrow I'll cut it short." She kissed Sadie lightly on the crown of her felt hat. "Good night," she said, "is there anything I forgot to ask you about the apartment?"

"No," Sadie assured her. "You asked everything."

"Well, good night," said Harriet once again, and, followed by Beryl, she left the room.

When Sadie awakened the next morning a feeling of dread still rested like a leaden weight on her chest. No sooner had she left the room than panic, like a small wing, started to beat under her heart. She was inordinately fearful that if she strayed any distance from the main lodge she would lose her way and so arrive late for her meeting with Harriet. This fear drove her to stand next to the souvenir booth fully an hour ahead of time. Fortunately the booth, situated on a small knoll, commanded an excellent view of the cataract, which spilled down from some high rock ledges above a deep chasm. A fancy bridge spanned this chasm only a few feet below her, so that she was able to watch the people crossing it as they walked back and forth between the camp site and the waterfall. An Indian chief in full war regalia was seated at the bridge entrance on a kitchen chair. His magnificent feather headdress curved gracefully in the breeze as he busied himself collecting the small toll that all the tourists paid on returning from the waterfall; he supplied them with change from a nickel-plated conductor's belt which he wore over his deerhide jacket, embroidered with minute beads. He was an Irishman employed by the management,

which supplied his costume. Lately he had grown careless, and often neglected to stain his freckled hands the deep brick color of his face. He divided his time between the bridge and the souvenir booth, clambering up the knoll whenever he sighted a customer.

A series of wooden arches, Gothic in conception, succeeded each other all the way across the bridge; bright banners fluttered from their rims, each one stamped with the initials of the camp, and some of them edged with a glossy fringe. Only a few feet away lay the dining terrace, a huge flagstone pavilion whose entire length skirted the chasm's edge.

Unfortunately neither the holiday crowds, nor the festooned bridge, nor even the white waters of the cataract across the way could distract Sadie from her misery. She constantly glanced behind her at the dark pine groves wherein Harriet's cabin was concealed. She dreaded to see Harriet's shape define itself between the trees, but at the same time she feared that if her sister did not arrive shortly some terrible catastrophe would befall them both before she'd had a chance to speak. In truth all desire to convince her sister that she should leave Camp Cataract and return to the apartment had miraculously shriveled away, and with the desire, the words to express it had vanished too. This did not in any way alter her intention of accomplishing her mission; on the contrary it seemed to her all the more desperately important now that she was almost certain, in her innermost heart, that her trip was already a failure. Her attitude was not an astonishing one, since like many others she conceived of her life as separate from herself; the road was laid out always a little ahead of her by sacred hands, and she walked down it without a question. This road, which was her life, would go on existing after her death, even as her death existed now while she still lived.

There were close to a hundred people dining on the terrace, and the water's roar so falsified the

clamor of voices that one minute the guests seemed to be speaking from a great distance and the next right at her elbow. Every now and then she thought she heard someone pronounce her name in a dismal tone, and however much she told herself that this was merely the waterfall playing its tricks on her ears she shuddered each time at the sound of her name. Her very position next to the booth began to embarrass her. She tucked her hands into her coat sleeves so that they would not show, and tried to keep her eyes fixed on the foaming waters across the way, but she had noticed a disapproving look in the eyes of the diners nearest her, and she could not resist glancing back at the terrace every few minutes in the hope that she had been mistaken. Each time, however, she was more convinced that she had read their expressions correctly, and that these people believed, not only that she was standing there for no good reason, but that she was a genuine vagrant who could not afford the price of a dinner. She was therefore immensely relieved when she caught sight of Harriet advancing between the tables from the far end of the dining pavilion. As she drew nearer Sadie noticed that she was wearing her black winter coat trimmed with red fur, and that her marceled hair remained neatly arranged in spite of the strong wind. Much to her relief Harriet had omitted to rouge her cheeks and her face therefore had regained its natural proportions. She saw Harriet wave at the sight of her and quicken her step. Sadie was pleased that the diners were to witness the impending meeting. "When they see us together," she thought, "they'll realize that I'm no vagrant, but a decent woman visiting her sister." She herself started down the knoll to hasten the meeting. "I thought you'd come out of the pine grove," she called out, as soon as they were within a few feet of one another. "I kept looking that way."

"I would have ordinarily," Harriet answered, reaching her side and kissing her lightly on the cheek, "but I went to the other end of the terrace first, to reserve a table for us from the waiter in charge there. That end is quieter, so it will be more suitable for a long talk."

"Good," thought Sadie as they climbed up the knoll together. "Her night's sleep has done her a world of good." She studied Harriet's face anxiously as they paused next to the souvenir booth, and discovered a sweet light reflected in her eyes. All at once she remembered their childhood together and the great tenderness Harriet had often shown toward her then.

"They have Turkish pilaff on the menu," said Harriet, "so I told the waiter to save some for you. It's such a favorite that it usually runs out at the very beginning. I know how much you love it."

Sadie, realizing that Harriet was actually eager for this dinner, the only one they would eat together at Camp Cataract, to be a success, felt the terrible leaden weight lifted from her heart; it disappeared so suddenly that for a moment or two she was like a balloon without its ballast; she could barely refrain from dancing about in delight. Harriet tugged on her arm.

"I think we'd better go now," she urged Sadie, "then after lunch we can come back here if you want to buy some souvenirs for Evy and Bert . . . and maybe for Flo and Carl and Bobby too. . . ."

Sadie bent down to adjust her cotton stockings, which were wrinkling badly at the ankles, and when she straightened up again her eyes lighted on three men dining very near the edge of the terrace; she had not noticed them before. They were all eating corn on the cob and big round hamburger sandwiches in absolute silence. To protect their clothing from spattering kernels, they had converted their napkins into bibs.

"Bert Hoffer's careful of his clothes too," Sadie reflected, and then she turned to her sister. "Don't you think men look different sitting all by themselves without women?" she asked her. She

felt an extraordinary urge to chat—an urge which she could not remember ever having experienced before.

"I think," Harriet replied, as though she had not heard Sadie's comment, "that we'd better go to our table before the waiter gives it to someone else."

"I don't like men," Sadie announced without venom, and she was about to follow Harriet when her attention was arrested by the eyes of the man nearest her. Slowly lowering his corncob to his plate, he stared across at her, his mouth twisted into a bitter smile. She stood as if rooted to the ground, and under his steady gaze all her newborn joy rapidly drained away. With desperation she realized that Harriet, darting in and out between the crowded tables, would soon be out of sight. After making what seemed to her a superhuman effort she tore herself away from the spot where she stood and lunged after Harriet, shouting her name.

Harriet was at her side again almost instantly, looking up at her with a startled expression. Together they returned to the souvenir booth, where Sadie stopped and assumed a slightly bent position as if she were suffering from an abdominal pain.

"What's the trouble?" she heard Harriet asking with concern. "Are you feeling ill?"

Instead of answering Sadie laid her hand heavily on her sister's arm and stared at her with a hunted expression in her eyes.

"Please try not to look so much like a gorilla," said Harriet in a kind voice, but Sadie, although she recognized the accuracy of this observation (for she could feel very well that she was looking like a gorilla), was powerless to change her expression, at least for a moment or two. "Come with me," she said finally, grabbing Harriet's hand and pulling her along with almost brutal force. "I've got something to tell you."

She headed down a narrow path leading into a thickly planted section of the grove, where she thought they were less likely to be

disturbed. Harriet followed with such a quick, light step that Sadie felt no pull behind her at all and her sister's hand, folded in her own thick palm, seemed as delicate as the body of a bird. Finally they entered a small clearing where they stopped. Harriet untied a handkerchief from around her neck and mopped her brow. "Gracious!" she said. "It's frightfully hot in here." She offered the kerchief to Sadie. "I suppose it's because we walked so fast and because the pine trees shut out all the wind. . . . First I'll sit down and then you must tell me what's wrong." She stepped over to a felled tree whose length blocked the clearing. Its torn roots were shockingly exposed, whereas the upper trunk and branches lay hidden in the surrounding grove. Harriet sat down; Sadie was about to sit next to her when she noticed a dense swarm of flies near the roots. Automatically she stepped toward them. "Why are they here?" she asked herself—then immediately she spotted the cause, an open can of beans some careless person had deposited inside a small hollow at the base of the trunk. She turned away in disgust and looked at Harriet. Her sister was seated on the fallen tree, her back gracefully erect and her head tilted in a listening attitude. The filtered light imparted to her face an incredibly fragile and youthful look, and Sadie gazed at her with tenderness and wonder. No sound reached them in the clearing, and she realized with a pounding heart that she could no longer postpone telling Harriet why she had come. She could not have wished for a moment more favorable to the accomplishment of her purpose. The stillness in the air, their isolation, the expectant and gentle light in Harriet's eye, all these elements should have combined to give her back her faith—faith in her own powers to persuade Harriet to come home with her and live among them once again, winter and summer alike, as she had always done before. She opened her mouth to speak and doubled over, clutching at her stomach as though an animal were devouring her. Sweat beaded her forehead and she planted her feet wide apart on the ground as if this animal would be born. Though her vision was barred with pain, she saw Harriet's tear-filled eyes, searching hers.

"Let's not go back to the apartment," Sadie said, hearing her own words as if they issued not from her mouth but from a pit in the ground. "Let's not go back there . . . let's you and me go out in the world . . . just the two of us." A second before covering her face to hide her shame Sadie glimpsed Harriet's eyes, impossibly close to her own, their pupils pointed with a hatred such as she had never seen before.

It seemed to Sadie that it was taking an eternity for her sister to leave. "Go away . . . go away . . . or I'll suffocate." She was moaning the words over and over again, her face buried deep in her hands. "Go away . . . please go away . . . I'll suffocate . . ." She could not tell, however, whether she was thinking these words or speaking them aloud.

At last she heard Harriet's footstep on the dry branches, as she started out of the clearing. Sadie listened, but although one step followed another, the cracking sound of the dry branches did not grow any fainter as Harriet penetrated farther into the grove. Sadie knew then that this agony she was suffering was itself the dreaded voyage into the world—the very voyage she had always feared Harriet would make. That she herself was making it instead of Harriet did not affect her certainty that this was it.

Sadie stood at the souvenir booth looking at some birchbark canoes. The wind was blowing colder and stronger than it had a while ago, or perhaps it only seemed this way to her, so recently returned from the airless clearing. She did not recall her trip back through the grove; she was conscious only of her haste to buy some souvenirs and to leave. Some chains of paper tacked to the side of the booth as decoration kept

flying into her face. The Indian chief was smiling at her from behind the counter of souvenirs.

"What can I do for you?" he asked.

"I'm leaving," said Sadie, "so I want souvenirs. . . ."

"Take your choice; you've got birchbark canoes with or without mailing cards attached, Mexican sombrero ash trays, exhilarating therapeutic pine cushions filled with the regional needles . . . and banners for a boy's room."

"There's no boy home," Sadie said, having caught only these last words.

"How about cushions . . . or canoes?"

She nodded.

"Which do you want?"

"Both," she answered quickly.

"How many?"

Sadie closed her eyes. Try as she would she could not count up the members of the family. She could not even reach an approximate figure. "Eleven," she blurted out finally, in desperation.

"Eleven of each?" he asked, raising his eyebrows.

"Yes . . . yes," she answered quickly, batting the paper chains out of her face, "eleven of each."

"You sure don't forget the old folks at home, do you?" he said, beginning to collect the canoes. He made an individual package of each souvenir and then wrapped them all together in coarse brown paper which he bound with thick twine.

Sadie had given him a bill and he was punching his money belt for the correct change when her eyes fell on his light, freckled hand. Startled, she shifted her glance from his hand punching the nickel belt to his brick-colored face streaked with purple and vermilion paint. For the first time she noticed his Irish blue eyes. Slowly the hot flush of shame crept along the nape of her neck. It was the same unbearable mortification that she had experienced in the clearing; it spread upward from her neck to the roots of her hair, coloring her face a dark red. That she was ashamed for the Indian this time, and not of her own

words, failed to lessen the intensity of her suffering; the boundaries of her pride had never been firmly fixed inside herself. She stared intently at his Irish blue eyes, so oddly light in his brick-colored face. What was it? She was tormented by the sight of an incongruity she couldn't name. All at once she remembered the pavilion and the people dining there; her heart started to pound. "They'll see it," she said to herself in a panic. "They'll see it and they'll know that I've seen it too." Somehow this latter possibility was the most perilous of all.

"They must never know I've seen it," she said, grinding her teeth, and she leaned over the counter, crushing some canoes under her chest. "Quickly," she whispered. "Go out your little door and meet me back of the booth. . . ."

A second later she found him there. "Listen!" She clutched his hand. "We must hurry . . . I didn't mean to see you . . . I'm sorry . . . I've been trying not to look at you for years . . . for years and years and years. . . ." She gaped at him in horror. "Why are you standing there? We've got to hurry. . . . They haven't caught me looking at you yet, but we've got to hurry." She headed for the bridge, leading the Indian behind her. He followed quickly without saying a word.

The water's roar increased in volume as they approached the opposite bank of the chasm, and Sadie found relief in the sound. Once off the bridge she ran as fast as she could along the path leading to the waterfall. The Indian followed close on her heels, his hand resting lightly in her own, as Harriet's had earlier when they'd sped together through the grove. Reaching the waterfall, she edged along the wall of rock until she stood directly behind the water's cascade. With a cry of delight she leaned back in the curve of the wall, insensible to its icy dampness, which penetrated even through the thickness of her woolen coat. She listened to the cataract's deafening roar and her heart almost burst for joy, because she had hidden the Indian safely behind the cascade where he could be neither seen nor heard. She turned around and smiled at him kindly. He too smiled, and she no longer saw in his face any trace of the incongruity that had shocked her so before.

The foaming waters were beautiful to see. Sadie stepped forward, holding her hand out to the Indian.

When Harriet awakened that morning all traces of her earlier victorious mood had vanished. She felt certain that disaster would overtake her before she could start out for Pocahontas Falls. Heavy-hearted and with fumbling hands, she set about making her pack. Luncheon with Sadie was an impossible cliff which she did not have the necessary strength to scale. When she came to three round cushions that had to be snapped into their rainproof casings she gave up with a groan and rushed headlong out of her cabin in search of Beryl.

Fortunately Beryl waited table on the second shift and so she found her reading a magazine with one leg flung over the arm of her chair.

"I can't make my pack," Harriet said hysterically, bursting into Beryl's cabin without even knocking at the door.

Beryl swung her leg around and got out of her chair. "I'll make your pack," she said in a calm voice, knocking some tobacco out of her pipe. "I would have come around this morning, but you said last night you wanted to make it alone."

"It's Sadie," Harriet complained. "It's that cursed lunch with Sadie. I can't go through with it. I know I can't. I shouldn't have to in the first place. She's not even supposed to be here. . . . I'm an ass. . . ."

"To hell with sisters," said Beryl. "Give 'em all a good swift kick in the pants."

"She's going to stop me from going on my canoe trip . . . I know she is. . . ." Harriet had adopted the whining tone of a little girl.

"No, she isn't," said Beryl, speaking with authority.

"Why not?" Harriet asked. She looked at Beryl almost wistfully.

"She'd better not try anything . . ." said Beryl. "Ever hear of ju-jitsu?" She grunted with satisfaction. "Come on, we'll go make your pack." She was so pleased with Harriet's new state of dependency that she was rapidly overcoming her original shyness. An hour later she had completed the pack, and Harriet was dressed and ready.

"Will you go with me to the souvenir booth?" she begged the waitress. "I don't want to meet her alone." She was in a worse state of nerves than ever.

"I'll go with you," said Beryl, "but let's stop at my cabin on the way so I can change into my uniform. I'm on duty soon."

They were nearly twenty minutes late arriving at the booth, and Harriet was therefore rather surprised not to see Sadie standing there. "Perhaps she's been here and gone back to the lodge for a minute," she said to Beryl. "I'll find out." She walked up to the souvenir counter and questioned the Indian, with whom she was slightly familiar. "Was there a woman waiting here a while ago, Timothy?" she asked.

"A dark, middle-aged woman?"

"That's right."

"She was here for an hour or more," he said, "never budged from this stall until about fifteen minutes ago."

"She couldn't have been here an hour!" Harriet argued. "Not my sister. . . . I told her one-thirty and it's not yet two."

"Then it wasn't your sister. The woman who was here stayed more than an hour, without moving. I noticed her because it was such a queer-looking thing. I noticed her first from my chair at the bridge and then when I came up here she was still standing by the booth. She must have stood here over an hour."

"Then it was a different middle-aged woman."

"That may be," he agreed, "but anyway, this one left about fifteen minutes ago. After standing all that time she turned around all of a sudden and bought a whole bunch of souvenirs from me . . . then just when I was punching my belt for the change she said something I couldn't understand—it sounded like Polish—and then she lit out for the bridge before I could give her a penny. That woman's got impulses," he added with a broad grin. "If she's your sister, I'll give you her change, in case she don't stop here on her way back. . . . But she sounded to me like a Polak."

"Beryl," said Harriet, "run across the bridge and see if Sadie's behind the waterfall. I'm sure this Polish woman wasn't Sadie, but they might both be back there. . . . If she's not there, we'll look in the lodge."

When Beryl returned her face was dead white; she stared at Harriet in silence, and even when Harriet finally grabbed hold of her shoulders and shook her hard, she would not say anything.

Balenciaga

For a quarter of a century Balenciaga, fashion's most pervading influence, has led the fashion world around by its elegant nose. And almost anything created during those years, give or take a hemline inch or two, looks contemporary today!

The photograph on this page shows the young designer's Valentino-type good looks, is one of the few Balenciaga ever posed for. When it was published in the 40's *Bazaar* said, "Although almost every woman, directly or indirectly, has worn a Balenciaga, it is curious to know that almost no one knows anything about the man himself. A victim of crushing shyness, he flees the press, the photographers and his admirers until they begin to wonder if there is really a Balenciaga after all."

A quarter of a century later, Balenciaga, the man, still remains a seldom photographed, illusive enigma. Nevertheless, virtually every woman *is wearing* something by Balenciaga, the designer—directly or indirectly.

LOUISE DAHL-WOLFE

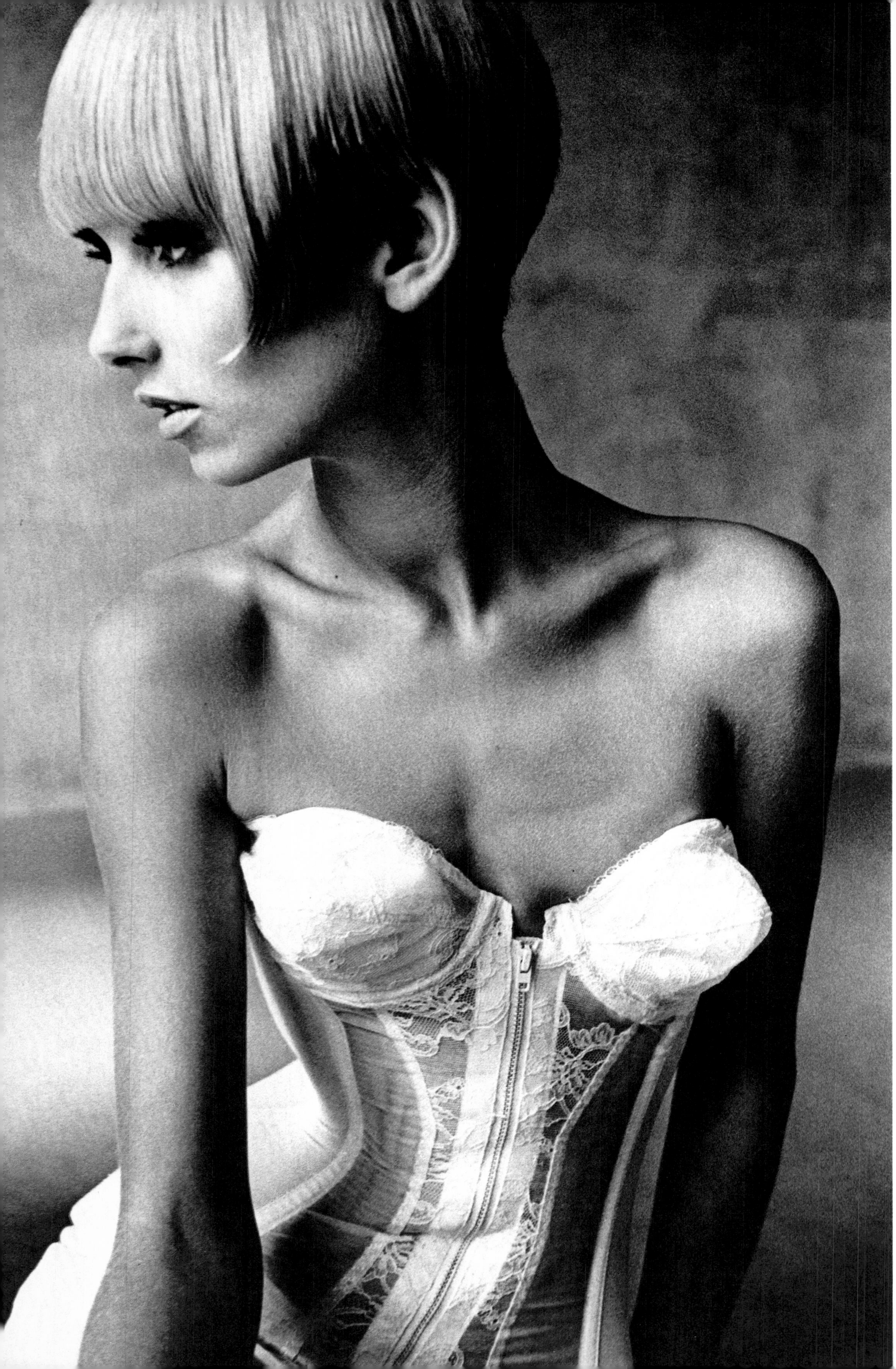

Cape Canaveral

261

GALERIE LE POULAILLER

263

264

Ballerina sheathed, shoulders on
down, in leotard forerunner of
the famous body stocking.

BAZAAR

HIRO

Magic
Moments in
BEAUTY
and
FASHION
—
GLORIA
GUINNESS:
The Chip
on the
Shoulder
—
THE
FLIRTING
GAME

A First: Black and White
Cover by Hiro

268

FONSSAGRIVES

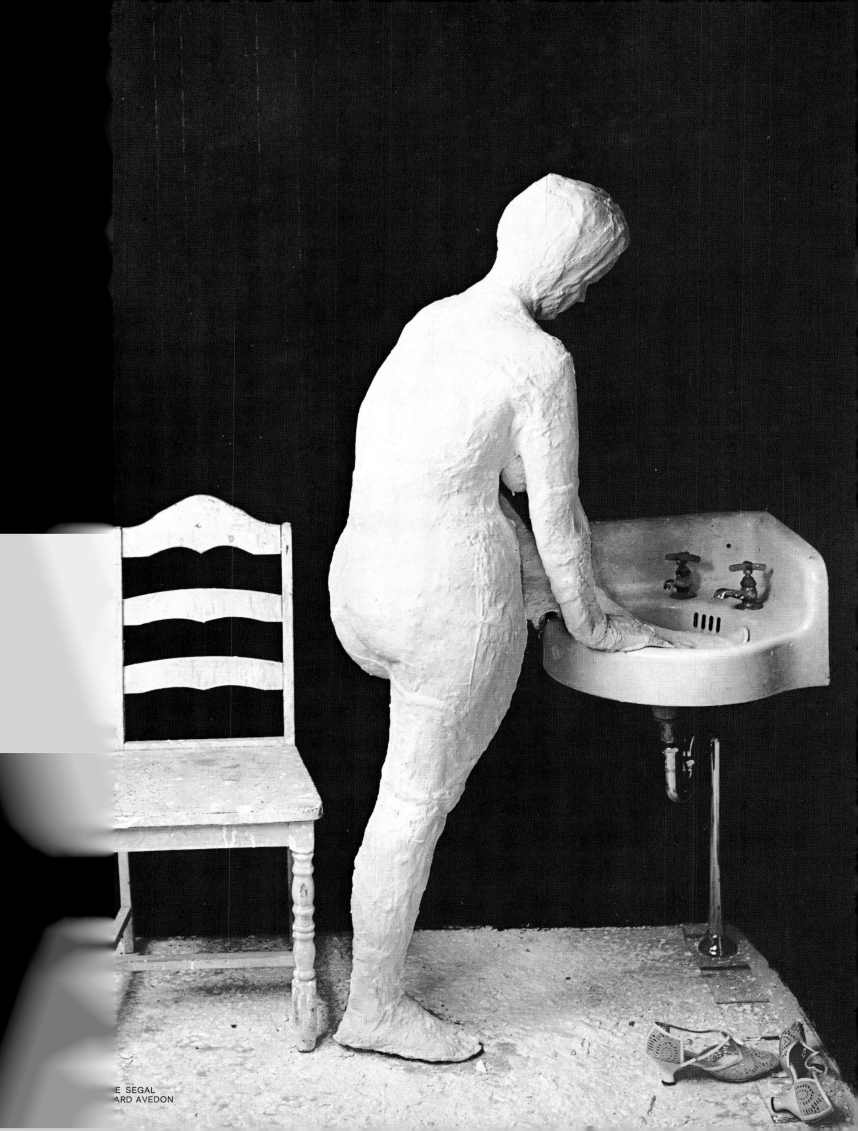

HIRO

MELVIN SOKOLSKY

The Sixties—the Decade of Hair.
Sassoon, Alexandre, Kenneth . . .
Wigs, Falls, Hairpieces.

America's Darlings

Trigère Fur Suit

Norman Norell Tunic Sweater

SCAVULLO

Mainbocher's Heart of Elegance

"Liaisons Dangereuses" by René Magritte,
a painting of 1934 in the collection of
Madame Claude Marcy, Honfleur, France.

LUCIEN CLERQUE

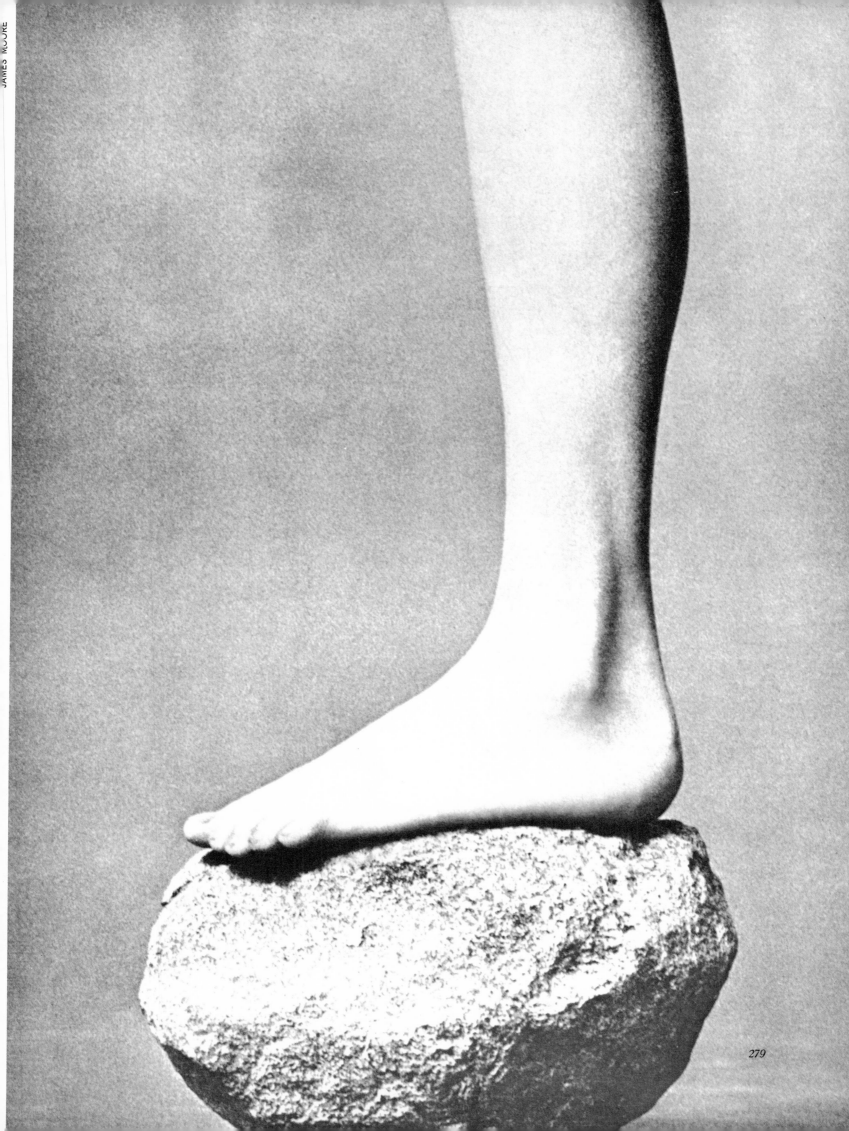

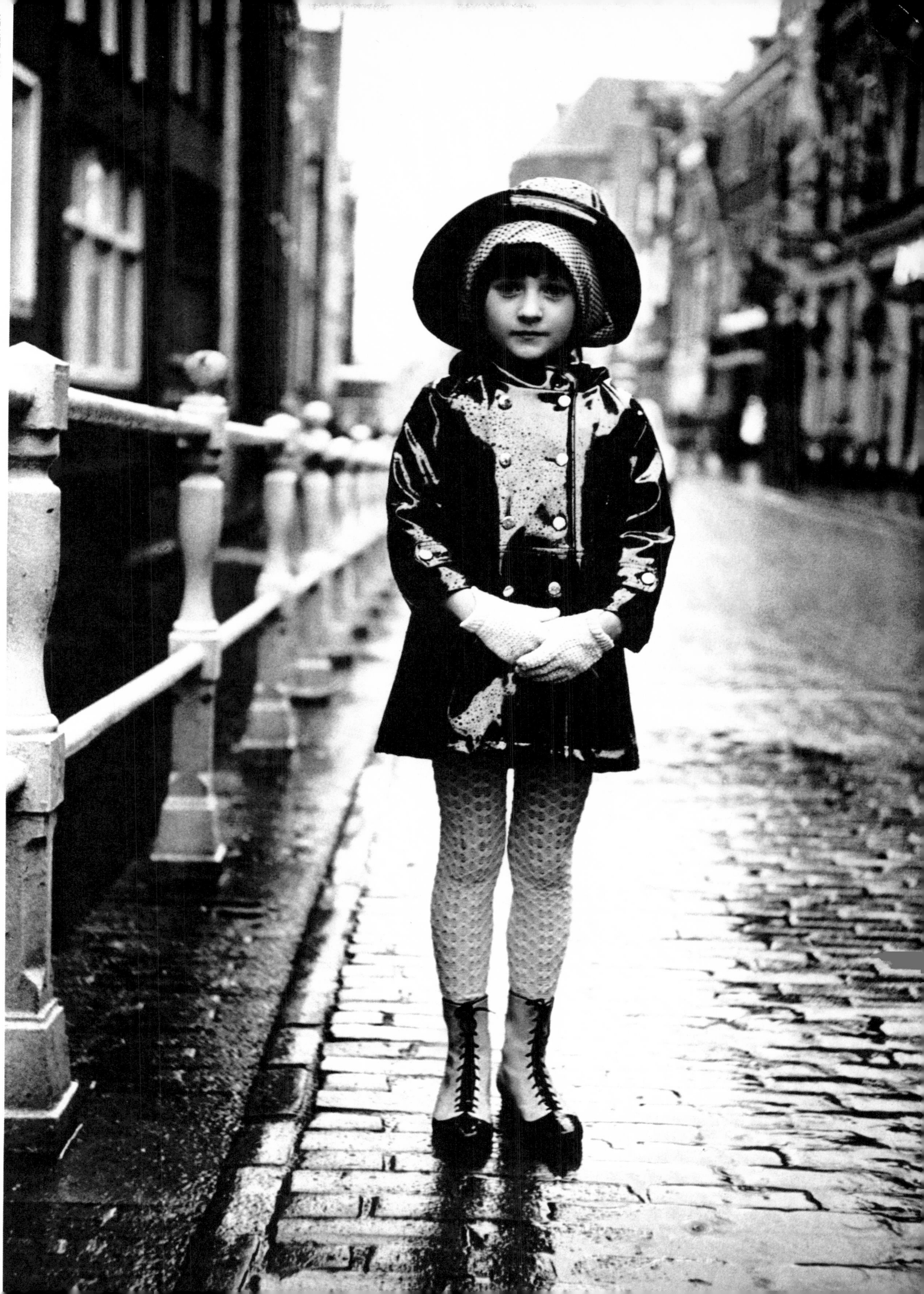

SAUL LEITER

Geraldine Chaplin

282

RICHARD AVEDON

HIRO

HIRO

286

Julie Christie

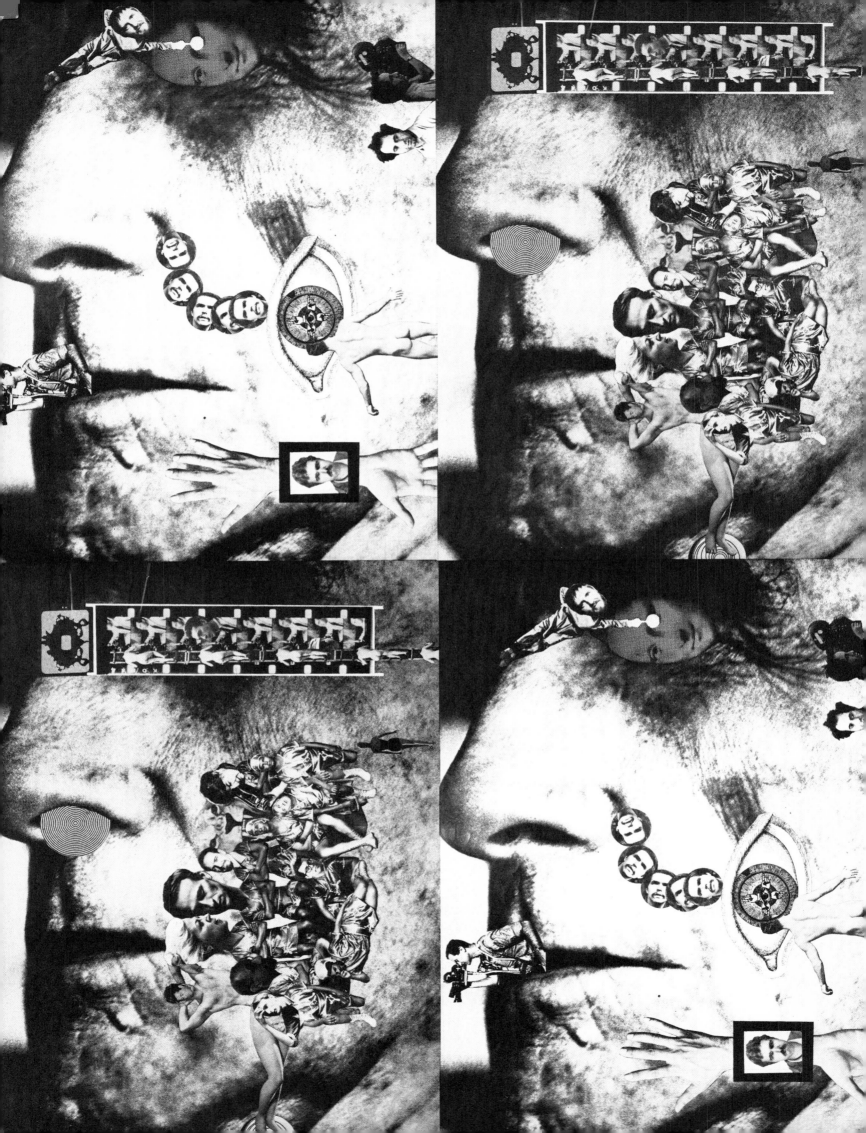

Mrs. John F. Kennedy

Courrèges

Courrèges sees a beautiful young woman no longer as a spectacle but caught up in the perpetual motion of today. The collection, his fourth, is a young one. An architect's feeling for proportion underlies its pure line, perfectly balancing the classical and the contemporary. From its look, you can infer the designer's preference for Le Corbusier and the arched lines of the Romanesque style. The clothes, shown realistically on big, healthy, handsome girls, are in the idiom of the moment—Paris present pluperfect with Castilian flavoring. Dresses have little sleeves with rolled cuffs, belts like loops of ribbon; hems barely skim the knee. The wide-shouldered, ample arch of a coat enfolds a jersey dress, but does not hug and crush. There is no pang of disappointment when the marvelous coats come off—the dresses are equal to them. Colors are full of life: vivid greens, clear pinks, strong brown and, above all, the Spanish whitewash white he loves. Boots, hats, gloves are almost all white; the blown-up Spanish-border berets explode into brilliant electric yellows, apple greens. Courrèges, who studied art before he turned to fashion and began his work in the atelier of Balenciaga, feels that the texture of a dress is like the *matière* of a sculptor. When he says modestly that he still has much to learn, he is thinking especially of the materials so rapidly evolving to meet the challenge of modern life. He chooses fabrics, resilient but not hard, that travel well. His private life centers around a collection of paintings by early Flemish and young modern artists; otherwise it is all work. When the perfection of his cut is mentioned, he says this is simply the mechanical side of his craft. What counts is the feeling behind it. He loves his work, as is truly evident in every seam.

293

Yves Saint Laurent

KUBLIN

Margot Fonteyn and Yves Saint Laurent

JEANLOUP SIEFF

This is the trend. The look. Ten of America's top designers cut it this way for mid-66, early-67. Skirts are up and going upper. They are avant-garde, drop-dead clothes.

299

100 Years of the American Female from Harper's Bazaar

Notes and Acknowledgments

When you consider how difficult it is to produce a check or a receipt for the Internal Revenue after, say, six or seven years, you can well imagine what a Sisyphean task it was to search out and track down the materials for this book after a hundred years had gone by. Many of the photos were no longer available, and we've reproduced with the families' or estates' permission directly from the bound volumes of the magazine. This, of course, didn't give our fussy art directors as clear and sharp a photo as they might have liked in a book of this sort, but we felt that even a second-impression photo of something stirring or world-shaking was better than no photo and so we used the very best reproduction we could lay our hands on. In some instances we were unable to contact either the author or the estate, and our letters were returned. Except as noted, credits, where space permitted, have been given in most instances next to the illustration.

Cecil Beaton: "Little Girl Alias Femme Fatale." Reprinted by permission of the author.

Gina Berriault: "Sublime Child." © Copyright, 1958, 1965 by Gina Berriault. Reprinted from *The Mistress and Other Stories* by Gina Berriault, by permission of E. P. Dutton & Co., Inc.

Elizabeth Bowen: "Dancing in Daylight." © Copyright, 1962 by Elizabeth Bowen. Reprinted from *Seven Winters and Afterthoughts* by Elizabeth Bowen, by permission of Alfred A. Knopf, Inc., and Curtis Brown Ltd. (London).

Jane Bowles: "Camp Cataract." Copyright 1949 by The Hearst Corporation. Reprinted by permission of the author.

Kay Boyle: "Life Sentence." © Copyright, 1938, 1966 by Kay Boyle. Reprinted from *Monday Night* by Kay Boyle, by permission of New Directions Publishing Corporation.

Colette: "The Hidden Woman," translated by George Davis. © Copyright, 1955 by The Hearst Corporation. Reprinted by permission of Farrar, Straus & Giroux, Inc., and Martin Secker & Warburg Ltd.

Maria Dermoût: "Kwan Yin's Snake," translated by James Brockway. © Copyright, 1964 by The Hearst Corporation. Reprinted by permission of the translator and Em Querido's Uitgevermij N. V. Amsterdam, Holland.

Isak Dinesen: "The Ring." © Copyright, 1958 by Isak Dinesen. Reprinted from *Anecdotes of Destiny* by Isak Dinesen, by permission of Random House, Inc.

Anita Loos: "Why Not Brunettes?" Reprinted by permission of the author.

Françoise Mallet-Joris: "The Schedule," translated by C. J. Richards. © Copyright, 1961 by Françoise Mallet-Joris. Reprinted by permission of Ann Elmo Agency, Inc.

Elsa Maxwell: "I Have Always Lived By My Wits." Reprinted by permission of Dorothy Fellowes Gordon.

Mary McCarthy: "Ghostly Father, I Confess." Copyright 1942 by Mary McCarthy. Reprinted from *The Company She Keeps* by Mary McCarthy, by permission of Brandt & Brandt.

Phyllis McGinley: "The Giveaway." Copyright 1954 by Phyllis McGinley, Reprinted from *Times Three* by Phyllis McGinley, by permission of The Viking Press, Inc.

Marianne Moore: "The Lion in Love." Copyright 1954 by Marianne Moore. Reprinted from *The Fables of Fontaine* by Marianne Moore (translated), by permission of The Viking Press, Inc.

Flannery O'Connor: "Good Country People." © Copyright, 1955 by Flannery O'Connor. Reprinted from *A Good Man Is Hard to Find and Other Stories* by Flannery O'Connor, by permission of Harcourt, Brace & World, Inc.

Susan Sontag: "The Dummy," © Copyright, 1963 by Susan Sontag. Reprinted by permission of Farrar, Straus & Giroux, Inc.

Honor Tracy: "A Blossom Viewing." Reprinted from *Kakemono* by Honor Tracy, by permission of Methuen and Co. Ltd., London.

Eudora Welty: Abridged from "The Wanderers." Copyright 1947, 1948, 1949 by Eudora Welty. Reprinted from *The Golden Apples* by Eudora Welty, by permission of Harcourt Brace & World, Inc.

Index